LYLE PRICE GUIDE
DOULTON

While every care has been taken in compiling the information contained in this volume, the publishers cannot accept any liability for loss, financial or otherwise, incurred by reliance placed on the information herein.

The publishers wish to express their sincere thanks to the following for their involvement and assistance in the production of this volume:

Editor	TONY CURTIS
Text By	LIZ TAYLOR
Editorial	EELIN McIVOR
	ANNETTE CURTIS
	DONNA RUTHERFORD
	CLAIRE COSSAR
Art Production	CATRIONA DAY
	DONNA CRUICKSHANK
	NICKY FAIRBURN
Graphics	JAMES BROWN
	MALCOLM GLASS
	DOROTHY GLASS

British Library Cataloguing-in-Publication Data.
A catalogue record for this book is available from the British Library.
ISBN 86248-152-X

The photographs on pages 3,7,10,12,13,14,15,16,17,19,20,21,23,26,27,28, 30, 31, 32, are reproduced with the kind assistance and permission of Royal Doulton Limited. Lyle Publications Limited has no connection with Royal Doulton Limited and any of its associated companies and the Royal Doulton International Collectors Club. The contents of The Lyle Price Guide to Royal Doulton have not been endorsed or approved in any way by Royal Doulton and Royal Doulton disclaims any responsibility for the book's contents.

I.S.B.N. 86248 - 152 - X

Copyright © Lyle Publications   MCMXCIV
Glenmayne, Galashiels, Scotland

Typeset by Word Power, Berwickshire
Printed and bound in Great Britain by
Butler & Tanner Ltd, Frome and London

LYLE PRICE GUIDE
DOULTON

TONY CURTIS

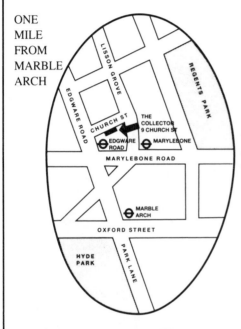

CONTENTS

ACKNOWLEDGEMENTS

MICK YEWMAN

The publishers wish to record their appreciation of the help and advice given in the preparation of this book, as on numerous previous occasions, by that acknowledged expert on Doulton, the late Mick Yewman, who died shortly before publication. His knowledge and expertise in all things Doulton will be sadly missed.

DORIS AMES
BILL & LILY BRETT
BERYL BURGESS (Toby Jug Museum, St Ives, Cornwall)
CHRISTIE'S 85 Old Brompton Road, London
DAVID COPE, Stand Even, Kidsgrove, Stoke-on-Trent
FRED DEARDEN
GILLIAN DENMARK
LEAH & GERALD FITERSTEIN
HENRY GIBBONS
DOROTHY GREEN
P. HATFIELD (Lambeth Archives Dept.)
PETER JACKMAN
PHILLIPS, Blenstock House, New Bond Street, London
TOM POWER
SOTHEBY'S, Booth Mansion, Watergate Street, Chester
PHILIP SPRINGTHORPE (Photographer)
LOUIS TAYLORS, Hanley, Stoke-on-Trent
KEN WHITBREAD (Photographer)

The author and publishers would like to express special thanks to all of the auction houses and specialist dealers and collectors who have given so generously of their time and expertise and in particular they would like to mention the help given by ROYAL DOULTON in assisting in the compilation of this book.

PRICES

The prices in this book have been carefully compiled using up to date information gleaned from both auction sales and retail outlets in the UK and abroad. Basically, they represent what the collector might fairly hope to pay if buying a piece in good condition.

When selling, depending very much on the condition and rarity of a piece, one could expect to receive about two-thirds of the prices shown, while very rare or desirable pieces might on occasion exceed them.

THE HISTORY OF DOULTON

"**B**etter to bear with singularity than crush individuality" said Henry Doulton when critics complained about the variable output of his pottery studio.

He knew that the artists and potters who worked for him were producing treasures for ordinary people at reasonable prices and also for future generations of collectors. Even though some of the hundreds of thousands of designs and individual items that were produced under the Doulton name were calculated to appeal to the bizarre and overdecorated taste of the High Victorians, there were many others of such high quality and originality that they have never lost their artistic quality and appeal.

A study of the trade catalogues of the Doulton Company gives a staggering glimpse into the enormous range of their products and the free scope which both John and Henry Doulton gave to the people who worked for them.

There never was a style 'trademark' in Doulton, each potter and artist was free to interpret influences and fashions in their own way and the result was an upsurge of creative talent which has never been equalled by any commercial enterprise in Britain.

In its Lambeth factory the company provided an opportunity for artistic creation and self expression to an army of men and women who otherwise would have lived and died in obscurity without exercising their enormous talents. Men like George Tinworth, an illiterate who became an R.A., or Frank Butler who was deaf and dumb and

whose expertise at creating beautiful pieces of pottery enthralled visitors to the Doulton works, owed everything to the liberal minded attitudes of John and particularly Henry Doulton.

The Studio also provided an outlet for the talents of artistic women and paved the way for more employment equality between the sexes. The names of Hannah and Florence Barlow, Louisa Davis and the two Elizas, Simmance and Sayers,would never be remembered today if it had not been for the fact that they were allowed and encouraged to work at Lambeth.

It is to the credit of Henry Doulton in particular that this creativity burst into life for he was the archetypal Victorian business man, forward thinking, energetic and entrepreneurial, who took over a well established business and turned it into a world famous name.

He was not however a woolly minded do-gooder, for his company first of all had to turn out a profit but still he was prepared, for the sake of an ideal, to sponsor and finance a pottery studio side by side with the money making commercial factory. In the 1860's the Lambeth Studio made a loss for several years until the public began to appreciate the quality and enormous originality of the work that was being produced there.

The Doulton story began with Henry's father John, a native of Fulham who was reputed to be the best thrower of pint pots in London. He worked as an apprentice with John Dwight, called 'the father of English

7

Terracotta panel above the entrance to Doulton House, modelled by George Tinworth, showing Sir Henry Doulton in the artists' studios.

The entrance to Doulton House on the corner of Lambeth High Street and Black Prince Road (formerly Broad St.) which housed the offices, artists' studios and showrooms.

Saltglazed stoneware jug depicting Lord Nelson by Doulton & Watts, Lambeth, circa 1830. $525 £350

pottery', who was carrying on the ancient tradition of saltglaze pottery making in Fulham. In 1815 young John, who had saved the considerable sum of £100, went into partnership in a pottery with a widow called Jones and a journeyman called Watts. They were established at Vauxhall, opposite the gate of the famous Vauxhall Pleasure Gardens, once the haunt of the fashionable beaux and belles of 18th century London.

The widow disappeared from the scene fairly quickly but Watts and Doulton continued in business. It is said that in the beginning their pottery sign board had "Watts and Doulton" on one side and "Doulton and Watts" on the other but after a short time they called themselves only Doulton and Watts until 1853 when Mr Watts retired.

By this time the firm had moved to Lambeth High Street, to a property with a large garden which was to become the nucleus of the famous Lambeth Pottery Works. It was to stay there until 1956 when it closed down because of rising transport

costs and the clean air legislation. In its 19th century heyday however it made a fine sight on the south bank of the Thames because the original works were rebuilt as an Italianate Palace, modelled on the Palazzo Vecchia of Florence on the advice of Henry Doulton's friend, John Ruskin of "The Stones of Venice" fame. The 233 foot high factory chimney was disguised as a campanile.

While John Doulton and his original partners were running the business they concentrated on making earthenware beer bottles, chimney pots, ridge tiles and garden vases. Now and again however they would produce a good selling pot 'figure'; for example the model of George IV's unfortunate Queen Caroline which they made in 1820, and also figures of contemporary heroes including Nelson and even of enemies like Napoleon, which were very much in demand with the poorer class of customers at the time.

In 1832 while the country was afire with enthusiasm for the Reform Bill which extended the male franchise, Doulton and Watts, like several other companies, brought out what are known as Reform flasks. They were really stone glazed bottles for gin but the upper half was modelled on the figure of a popular politician of the time. Because they were designed for such a utilitarian purpose few of those flasks still exist but the few that do are highly prized – and priced – by collectors.

By the time Watts left the firm and it became Doulton and Company, Henry, John's second son had joined his father in spite of his parents' wish that he become a Baptist preacher. The lure of pottery making was too much for Henry. His father proudly exhibited outside the door of their works a vast pottery urn which was Henry's handiwork. It was reputed to be the largest stoneware vessel in the world and could hold 300 gallons. However, it also seems likely that the lure of business made preaching pale into insignificance for the energetic Henry who turned out to be a prime example of Victorian enterprise and ingenuity.

No idea was too novel for him to give it serious consideration. Edwin Chadwick, the pioneer of improved sanitation, was a friend of Henry's and persuaded him that a better sewage and water supply system was the only way of freeing Britain's crowded cities of the scourge of cholera that stalked them every summer. Chadwick's theories originally must have seemed the theorising of a crank, for at the beginning of the 19th century even doctors believed that the cholera infection was spread through the air – they never guessed it was water borne. Henry Doulton however listened to Chadwick and was one of the first to start making earthenware sewage and water pipes. Many of the drainpipes and conduits made during Henry Doulton's lifetime are still in use beneath city streets today.

He designed a self-adjusting joint for water pipes and before long was extending the firm's product lines into baths, lavatories, washbasins and other sanitary fitments to cope with the new 'bathroom' craze which was to sweep the country. This branch of the business was to culminate in a magnificent order for fitting out the bathrooms of the Savoy Hotel in London with 237 specially designed baths.

At the height of their production the Doulton Works were turning out one fifth of the sewer pipes made in Britain at a rate of ten miles a week and exporting them all over the world.

Ever inventive, Henry took a chemistry course and also designed air tight jars for keeping food and a screw top bottle. He recognised the enormous potential of the new industries and inventions that were to transform Victorian Britain into the modern age and devised chemical resistant earthenware for use in telephone and electrical systems.

It was Henry's idea to install steam power in the factory to drive the potters' wheels and by doing so he put his firm in the forefront of the pottery industry because it was a good ten years before any competitor followed his example.

The development of the company into art pottery would not have been possible without the sound financial base provided by the industrial and sanitary side. By the 1860's however John and Henry Doulton were presiding over a company of enormous capacity and world fame. At the time when their finances were beginning to be established on a very stable basis, Henry was prepared to take a chance and founded a Pottery Studio in the corner of his works.

The Prince of Wales with Henry Doulton, 1885.

In doing so he was responding to a prevalent theory among the intelligentsia that art and industry should be able to co-exist. That theory was continued and fostered by the Doulton Company right till the end of the First World War and to a lesser extent after as well but by the 1930's the new generation of studio potters were rejecting the Victorian ideas of a creative collaboration between art and industry.

Henry Doulton was first approached by John Sparkes, head of the newly formed Lambeth School of Art, in the late 1850's with the proposition that some of the students should be allowed to try their hand at potting. At first the idea met with little response from John Doulton but his son was to return to it later and set aside a corner of the factory for a few Lambeth School of Art students. It is noticeable that many of them were people who would have worked at lowly or manual trades without this opportunity. Tinworth, a universally acknowledged artistic genius, was a wheelwright before Sparkes took him up and he and the famous Barlows were among the first intake to the Lambeth Studio.

Henry Doulton was ahead of his time too in his ability as a publicist for he was quick to realise the value of the exhibitions which were organised all over the world in the 19th century and, having an acute sense of what was going to be important, he never missed an opportunity to display his firm's goods. This was the medium that presented the work of his studio potters to the world.

Henry had joined his father's firm in 1835 and when the Great Exhibition was unveiled in Hyde Park in 1852, Doulton and Company exhibited but the pieces on show were all industrial items except for a figure of Old Father Time and some terracotta garden vases.

By 1862 however the Lambeth Studio had been established in a small way and in the London Exhibition of that year Doulton's exhibited their first piece of art pottery – a reproduction of a 16th century Rhenish salt cellar.

In the Paris Exhibition of 1867 however the work of George Tinworth was on the Doulton stand and it created a sensation which was followed at the London International Exhibition of 1871 where the robust and virile work of Hannah and Arthur Barlow was first displayed. Queen Victoria was so impressed by the Doulton ware in the exhibition that she ordered some to be sent to Buckingham Palace.

The Doulton name had now begun to have another meaning than just pipes and conduits. At the Vienna Exhibition of 1873 a distinctive cobalt blue glaze which the company was using was given the official name of 'Doulton blue' and in the Philadelphia Centennial Exhibition of 1876,

which perhaps marked the zenith of the Lambeth Pottery, they won five first class awards. There was such a great interest in the pieces from the American public that a cult for Doulton began which continues to this day. American collectors are among the most enthusiastic and knowledgeable in the world. Their original enthusiasm was only intensified by the Chicago International Exhibition of 1893 where the firm showed 1,500 items from its Lambeth and its recently acquired Burslem factory.

Some of the items displayed over the years were of such magnificence that they stopped the public in its tracks. For example for the Glasgow Exhibition of 1888 Doulton's made an Indian pavilion of glazed and enamelled terracotta with stained glass windows which had also been manufactured by the company. The firm's success at international exhibitions continued into the 20th century for at the Brussels Exhibition of 1958 they were the winners of the only Gold Medal awarded to a British pottery manufacturer.

They expanded rapidly throughout the 19th century and in 1877 Henry Doulton bought an earthenware factory called Pinder Bourne and Company in Burslem, Staffordshire. In spite of antagonism and opposition from rival potteries there, who regarded him as a southern incomer and upstart, he set about energising the new acquisition with his own brand of magic and in 1882 the name was changed to Doulton and Company, Burslem. His firm now had major factories in London and in Staffordshire where they were able to draw on the long established potting skills of the local population. It was in Burslem that Doulton's began to manufacture bone china in 1885 when a new wing was built onto the factory for that purpose. As in Lambeth, a Studio for creative artists and potters was established and the variety of their output was truly dazzling.

Sir Henry Doulton died in 1897, loaded with honours and success. He was given the Albert Medal by the Royal Society of Arts in 1885 and in 1887 he was knighted by

Queen Victoria, the first potter ever to be awarded the honour of a knighthood.

Part of his achievement was the creation of an artistic environment that encouraged individual creation. It must have been exhilarating to be on the staff of the Studios belonging to Doulton because their artists were given a free hand, there was no official guidelines about what sort of thing they should be turning out, no production line theories of any kind.

This manner of handling artists produced results. Not only did they create exactly the sort of thing that the mass of the public wanted to buy but they also produced in enormous volume. Hannah Barlow, at her peak, made 30 different original pieces every week and hundreds of thousands of other individual pieces were turned out by the rest of the Doulton artists. They signed their work with their initials or monograms and took a personal pride in their creations, a pride that was fostered and encouraged by their employer.

When the staff of the Lambeth Studio expanded from a handful of people to 200 by 1880 and later doubled by the end of the century, the firm enjoyed a world dominance in decorative pottery. Both factories were constantly trying to devise new ways of firing and producing exotic glazes or experimenting with new colours. C. J. Noke who joined Doulton from the Worcester Pottery in 1889 and later became the Artistic Director of Burslem, concentrated on producing a range of experimental transmutation glazed wares as good as those made by Sevres, Copenhagen or Dresden. He devised the Titanian glaze which gave a Copenhagen style look to pottery. Noke also experimented in recreating some of the Oriental techniques of the past and his work resulted in the famous Flambé, Sung, Chinese jade and Chang pottery. In the 1890's he also guided the firm into one of its most successful lines, the production of figure models. The first of these, a range of Shakespearian characters, were shown at the Chicago Exhibition in 1893.

Bone china vase featuring Pan playing his pipes, in Sung glazes by Charles Noke, 7in. high, circa 1925.   *$1,000 £650*

Bone china tobacco jar with elephant finial on cover, Sung glazes, 6in. high, circa 1936.   *$520 £325*

Doulton offices at the Albert Embankment, London, featuring a mural by GILBERT BAYES R.A.

Royal Doulton showrooms, Albert Embankment, London, circa 1900.

Eliza Simmance, 1873-1928.

death knell and though it produced the well designed range of blue plaques for the LCC which mark houses in London where famous people lived, and the Festival of Britain brought a surge of short lived energy, the Studio finally closed in 1956. That closure marked a 90 year long association between art and industry in Lambeth. Burslem however continued and carried on the success story.

Another interesting aspect of the Doulton story is the fact that while they had a famous name for producing decorative pottery they were also turning out a huge variety of other products. Not only did they continue to make sanitary and industrial goods, but they had a huge output of garden ornaments, especially in the 19th century when the age of the public park began. They made drinking fountains, garden seats, urns, edgings, pots and sundials for every sort of garden from that of a stately home to the suburban villa. After the First World War the spacious age of gardening declined but the Doulton artists then turned their

As the Lambeth Studio was getting into full swing Henry Doulton converted a group of workers' houses into individual studios where his protégès were encouraged to work without managerial interference and this policy proved to be a hothouse for talent. Creativity was allowed its head and pieces were produced with leaves or lace pressed into the glaze as the artists' fancies took them. The potters also devised new techniques like *pâte sur pâte*, as used by Florence Barlow and Eliza Simmance, and their work reflects the styles and fashions of the day. Doulton designs over the years show the influence of Japanese and Primitive art as well as the rising Art Nouveau which they were among the first to popularise, producing a range of distinctive items for Liberty's.

The First World War brought a running down to the Lambeth Studio but it survived on a reduced scale under J. H. Nott, producing some notable items including a range of Persian inspired designs. The Second World War however marked its

Linnie Watt, 1875-1890.

Doultons' premises, formerly Stiff & Sons, on the corner of Broad St. (now Black Prince Road) and the Albert Embankment, circa 1909.

attention to creating decorative things for the smaller garden including garden gnomes but some of the imaginative artefacts installed in urban housing estates of the 1920's and '30's were produced for them by academic sculptors like Gilbert Bayes.

The firm also specialised in architectural work and was particularly well known for decorative tiles which were used both to beautify the interiors and exteriors of buildings. The famous Oyster Bar in Edinburgh's Café Royal is a lovely example of Doulton tile work and many hospital wards, especially children's wards, throughout the country were decorated with tile pictures. Those that survive today are highly prized.

The great upsurge in building in the latter half of the 19th century gave the company an enormous boost and they found that terracotta was an invaluable building and decorative material. Designs made in terracotta could be easily mass reproduced and it was also longer lasting and less liable to atmospheric pollution damage than stone.

Examples of terracotta work by Doulton's can still be seen on London's Savoy Hotel and Royal Court Theatre.

Doulton's also made a huge range of advertising wares and collectors now look out for things like model feet they produced for Dr Scholl's; for ceramic pump handles; ashtrays and stoneware whisky bottles. For many years these were a profitable sideline of a multifaceted business which today continues its diversification with ceramics for the aerospace and textile industries.

Today Doulton and Co. is part of the Pearson Group and is still the largest producer of ceramic products in the U.K. with interests in glass, industrial and sanitary wares, engineering and building materials as well as producing the world famous Royal Doulton decorative pieces and tableware at Burslem. The artists in the Doulton factory continue the long artistic tradition laid down by their distinguished predecessors. They are still carrying on Henry Doulton's dream-making collectors' pieces for future generations.

15

ADVERTISING WARES

Before the advent of plastics, ceramics were used on an enormous scale for the production of advertising items.

Doultons were involved with the beer and spirit trade from the beginning of the 19th century and they produced all manner of promotional items for these industries ranging from public house tiled or terracotta frontages and ceramic beer pump handles to ashtrays and spittoons for public bars.

Some of the other advertising artefacts produced by the company included perfume bottles moulded like figures and plaques painted with portraits of Queen Victoria advertising soap or toothpaste.

One of the more unusual advertising commissions came Doulton's way in the 1950's when they were asked to make a Toby jug depicting the American industrialist Clifford Cornell, head of the Cleveland Flux Company of Ohio. He was a great fan of Winston Churchill and commissioned Doulton to make a Toby jug of him imitating the one they had recently produced of Churchill. Another oddity was a moulded white china foot which was made to advertise Dr Scholl's Zino pads.

The collecting of Doulton ceramic advertising ware is a growing field and items are eagerly sought out by enthusiasts.

'The McCallum', a large Kingsware character jug made for D. & J. McCallum Whisky Distillers, circa 1930. $1,500 £1,000

Play Goers, by George Tinworth, salt glazed stoneware, 5in. high, circa 1884.

$1,920 £1,200

ANIMAL FIGURES

Before 1912 only a few animal figures were produced by the Doulton potteries but among them were the highly successful Flambe Ware figures.

However by the time of World War One, Charles J. Noke launched a new line, very realistic figures of animals and birds which proved to be highly popular with the buying public.

In the beginning they were used to decorate ashtrays, bookends and other household objects but later they began to be produced as freestanding figures in their own right. Great care was taken to model and paint them as close to reality as possible.

In 1936 limited numbers of earthenware figures of goats, calves and deer were made by artist Raoh Schorr but one of the first series which were produced in large numbers for an eager public was the Championship Dog range, which was launched in 1939. At least 41 models were made and many of them are still in production.

The Chatcull Range of animal figures was started in 1940 with figures modelled by artist Joe Ledger who named the series after his home, Chatcull Hall. Most of these are now out of production.

In 1973 yet another artist, Robert Jefferson started animal figure modelling and his Jefferson range of limited editions still continues today.

ART POTTERY

The most astonishing aspect of Doulton Art Pottery is its range and the variety of styles and techniques introduced by the company.

These were developed in the Lambeth Studios established by Henry Doulton from 1867 onwards. The Studio was financed by the far more prosaic side of the business, sanitary and chemical ceramics.

Henry Doulton provided creative artists with the opportunity of expressing themselves in pottery and it is to his credit that he allowed their talents and eccentricities full flowering. There was never any attempt to impose a 'house style' on them.

"The personal is the true vivifying element in art," he said.

The first big name in Art Pottery was that of George Tinworth who began making little models of mice and children, mainly for his own amusement. Many of those were never exhibited.

He was followed by over 400 enthusiastic artists who worked at Lambeth over the years. They not only experimented with the sort of sculptures that could be produced in pottery but also in the intricacy of decorative painting and devised a great range of glazing and firing techniques.

One of the innovators in this respect was William Rix among whose discoveries was a way of reproducing the marbling effect found in 18th century 'agate' wares. Charles J. Noke at Burslem was to carry on the Rix tradition, producing the famous Flambe and Chang glazes among others.

Carrara Ware vase decorated with a scene of children playing, by Ada Dennis, Josephine Durtnall, Mary Denley and Katherine Smallfield, 9¾in. high, circa 1890. $880 £550

Dragon vase in Chang glazes, earthenware, 7½in. high, circa 1920. $4,480 £2,800

CARRARA WARE . . .

. . . got its name because it looks like Italian Carrara marble and is a dense off-white stoneware with a slightly transparent crystalline matt glaze which is occasionally crackled. The effect was achieved by using more Cornish china clay than usual in the mixture. It was mainly produced between 1887 and 1903 but some examples were still being made in the 1920's when it had a short lived revival.

CHANG WARE . . .

. . . was named after a Chinese master potter of the Sung Dynasty and it was an effort by Doulton to produce glazes which old Chinese potters had also tried to create. The first Chang pottery appeared in 1925 and was characterised by thick textured layers of flowing glaze in lustrous colours which gave a lava like appearance. It was used on vases, some of them festooned with dragons or lizards.

CHINESE JADE . . .

. . . In 1920, after years of experimentation, Charles J. Noke achieved his ambition of reproducing jade in ceramic. His simulated jade was used to make libation cups, figures and bowls and examples of it are now very rare because only a limited number of pieces were successfully made.

CROWN LAMBETH . . .

. . . is a fine earthenware remarkable for the richness and transparency of the decorations. It was decorated by hand painting on biscuit ware and after glazing, was re-fired and re-painted several times. Crown Lambeth was first shown in the Chicago Exhibition of 1893 and was much admired but production ceased after 1903 because heavy kiln losses meant the line was a loss maker.

Royles Patent Toilet Aquarius, earthenware, height with jug inside bowl 12in., circa 1891.

CRYSTALLINE WARE . . .

. . . the surface of the glaze sparkled because zinc oxide was mixed in the glaze compound and it was kept in a high kiln temperature for long periods. It was invented by Cuthbert Bailey who left Doulton's in 1907 but examples of crystalline ware were produced till 1914 when production ceased because of the expense caused by the high number of failures in firing.

CYPRUS WARE . . .

. . . In 1878 Cyprus was annexed to Britain by the Treaty of Berlin and Doulton's celebrated the occasion by introducing Cyprus Ware. It is recognisable by the lotus and hatched designs, based on ancient vases excavated on the island of Cyprus about the time of the Annexation. Not a great number of pieces were made and the name is mainly found on Lambeth Faience vases and bowls produced during 1879.

FLAMBE . . .

. . . the name describes the streaky, flame like effect of the deep blood red glaze which was produced by mixing copper oxide and other minerals and allowing certain amounts of oxygen to be admitted to the kiln during firing. The technique was first discovered by Bernard Moore, a chemist and innovator who worked in conjunction with Doulton at the turn of the century. After two years' experimentation the first examples of Flambe were shown at the St Louis Exhibition of 1904 and it had a huge appeal. Although it is expensive to make, Flambe is still being produced.

IMPASTO . . .

. . . the unusual effect of Impasto is achieved by fusing two harmonious pigments and firing with very little gloss. Colour was applied to raw clay and potters used a small amount of relief to add to reality. Impasto colours were browns, yellows, greens and blues and its production in the last quarter of the 19th century coincided with one of the most artistic periods of the Lambeth Pottery. The first piece was brought out of the kiln during a visit from Princess Alexandra in February 1879 and it continued in production until 1914, though the numbers produced dwindled after 1906.

Earthenware umbrella stand with Art Nouveau decoration, 24¾ins. high, circa 1895. $750 £500

Impasto Ware vase by K. Rodgers, 10in. high, circa 1885. $400 £250

MARQUETERIE WARE . . .

. . . this is the rarest of the Lambeth wares. Invented in 1886, it was patented in 1887 under the joint names of Doulton and Rix, and was a simulation of the different coloured wood inlays made by cabinetmakers. This was achieved in pottery by cutting thin slices of coloured clay in various patterns. Marqueterie Ware was produced in large quantities until 1906 when it ceased because of heavy production costs.

Bone china teapot with raised paste gilding and exotic birds painted by J. Birbeck, 5½in. high, circa 1910. $400 £250

SUNG . . .

. . . is remarkable for the mottled and veined effect of the glaze produced by high temperatures during firing. The first examples of Sung were exhibited at the British Industry Fair at the Crystal Palace in 1920 and they were of animal and figure models. One of the best known is the elephant and the lustrous green Buddha. Each piece was signed by Charles J. Noke who developed the glaze.

Luscian Ware bone china vase with blue bells painted by Louis Bilton, 5½in. high, circa 1895. $375 £250

MORRISIAN WARE . . .

. . . derives its name from the decorations of Morris dancers with which it was decorated. It was made between 1901 and 1924 at Lambeth and some items were designed by A. Pierce. Other items, not marked as Morrisian but with the same sort of decoration, were painted with figures of golfers in 17th century costume.

PERSIAN WARE . . .

. . . was based on Eastern designs with blue, green and orange colouring. Persian ware was produced between 1884 and 1912 and was influenced by the work of William de Morgan. It was used in tiles and panels for wall decoration as well as in pottery. The painting on a white slip coating was done before the glazing and firing.

Bone china Buddha decorated with Sung and lustre glazes, 4in. high, circa 1920. $1,200 £750

TITANIAN WARE . . .

. . . the name derives from titanium oxide which gives this ware its characteristic smoky blue colour. It was developed by Charles J. Noke during the early years of World War One and was often decorated with transfer printings of birds of paradise or, during the 1920's when the Tutankhamen fever was at its height, with Egyptian designs. Artists involved were Allen, Raby, Tittensor and Henri.

VELLUMA WARE . . .

. . . was only produced between 1911 and 1914 and as a consequence is extremely rare. The offwhite glaze has a parchment like texture, hence the name. The earthenware shapes were brought from Burslem and painted at Lambeth with transfers from etchings by A. E. Pearce and W. Rowe. The designs are usually landscapes or figure subjects.

Bone china vase with Japanese lady by H. Tittensor, under Titanium glazes, 14½in. high, circa 1919. $1,425 £950

CHARACTER JUGS

The first Royal Doulton Character Jug, titled 'John Barleycorn Old Lad' was produced in the early 1930's from a design and model by Charles Noke. As the popularity of the jugs grew, many new characters were introduced including 'Sairey Gamp', 'Parson Brown', 'Dick Turpin' and 'Old Charley'. Some of these jugs are still in production today but many of the earlier designs were discontinued in the sixties.

One of the first to be withdrawn was the Churchill character jug made during the Battle of Britain and designed as a Loving Cup by C. J. Noke. It is cream coloured with two black handles and bears the inscription 'Winston Churchill Prime Minister of Britain 1940'. It was withdrawn after only eighteen months however because, it is said, Churchill himself was not pleased with the likeness. Because so few were produced this jug is an extremely rare and desirable item, coveted by collectors throughout the world, and a fair estimate of its price at auction today is three thousand five hundred pounds.

Churchill character jug designed by Charles Noke, introduced 1940, D6170 bearing the inscription 'Winston Spencer Churchill Prime Minister of Britain 1940', 'this loving cup was made during the "Battle of Britain" as a tribute to a great leader'.

Old King Cole musical jug with yellow crown, D6014, issued 1939. $2,400 £1,500

The two faces of Mephistopheles D5757 designed by H. Fenton, issued 1937-1948.
$1,125 £750

Another notable jug is the 'Drake' designed by Mr H. Fenton and introduced in 1940. In the first version the rim is the character's hair but in later versions the rim is his hat. The earlier jug, known as 'The Hatless Drake', bears the inscription 'Drake He Was A Devon Man' and production was limited. Today the hatless version can sell for around £1,500 but the hatted version is less sought after and sells for only about £85

H. Fenton was also the designer of the red haired, brown haired and white haired clowns. The first two were introduced in 1937 and withdrawn in 1942. Today in auction they can sell for around £1,250. The white haired version, which was introduced in 1951 and withdrawn in 1955, sells for between £500 and £600. In the 1950's however it sold for under £5.

Other favourite jugs are the Cockney costermonger and his wife ''Arry and 'Arriet', introduced in the mid 1940's and withdrawn by 1960. The ''Arry' is usually predominantly brown in colour but if there are buttons on his hat and collar he is known as a 'Brown Pearly Boy'; a version with a blue collar and white buttons is the 'Blue Pearly Boy'. The latter is the most rare and sells for around £2,000.

''Arriet' too is predominantly brown with a green hat and handle, but if she has a blue collar and a maroon hat she is 'Blue Pearly Girl', which is extremely rare and can command a price of between £2,500 and £3,500

Small details such as the colours of buttons, triangles or hair can represent the difference between hundreds and thousands of pounds for an item. Each jug bears the Doulton backstamp and is numbered according to the firm's numbering system which greatly assists collectors.

TOBY JUGS

The name 'Toby' has long associations with conviviality and it was used by Shakespeare in his Toby Belch and by Laurence Sterne in his character Uncle Toby in 'Tristram Shandy'. Today it has come to signify a jug made like a seated male figure in a tricorn hat with a pipe or a mug of beer on his knee. This is particularly due to the creations of Doulton who took up and developed the long history of the Toby jug and made it beloved by a vast collecting public.

From 1815 when John Doulton first set up his business, the firm made Toby jugs but the earliest examples were only brown salt glazed as they had been for centuries. In 1925 however coloured Toby jugs were added to the range by Harry Simeon and their potential was immediately recognised by Charles J. Noke who made their colours even more vivid and developed them into one of the company's best selling lines.

One of the distinguishing marks of the Toby jug is that one corner of his tricorn hat is always used as a pourer for the beverage he carries.

Charlie Chaplin toby jug, 11in. high, issued 1918. $3,000 £2,000

FIGURES

The first highly skilled figure maker who worked for Doulton was George Tinworth, the Lambeth sculptor, but his figure output was small.

However in 1889 Charles J. Noke left the Royal Worcester Company where he was already showing his prodigious talent as a sculptor and went to work for Doulton's at Burslem. The son of an antique dealer who appreciated the fine vases and figures made by Derby, Bow, Chelsea, Meissen and Sevres, he was fired with the ambition of recreating the once greatly admired Staffordshire figure making industry. For the Chicago Exhibition of 1893 he made several figures including 'Jack Point' and 'Lady Jester'.

During the next five years more figures followed including Noke's 'Pierrot'; 'Geisha' and the double figures 'Oh Law!' and 'Double Jester'. The latter figure today sells for £2,000 because it was only produced in small numbers.

These figures, though finely modelled, were of dull colours and did not sell well so Noke's figure making was suspended until

Contentment designed by Leslie Harradine.

around 1912 when he re-introduced a figure range which was released to the public in 1913 after Queen Mary, on a visit to Burslem, exclaimed "What a Darling!" at the sight of a figure called 'Bedtime' modelled by Charles Vyse.

'Bedtime' was re-christened 'Darling' and proved to be one of the most popular Doulton figures ever produced. It is still in production.

The colours of the new figures were bolder and a group of very talented sculptors worked on them. One of the most notable was Harry Tittensor, (1914-21), a local art master, His 'Europa and The Bull' today sells for £2,000 and his 'Princess Badoura' for a remarkable £6,500.

The work of Leslie Harradine, who began his career at the Lambeth Studio before emigrating to Canada but returned to work at Burslem after World War One, was filled with vitality. His 'Contentment' and 'The Goose Girl' showed his ability to capture movement and he also had a great talent for picking subjects which caught the public fancy. His 'Old Balloon Seller' is still in production today and is one of the most popular Doulton figures ever.

The quality of the range which now

Darling designed by Charles Vyse.

Old Balloon Seller designed by Leslie Harradine.

studying the anatomy of animals and people, as well as ensuring that all costume details were absolutely correct. Her 'Matador and The Bull' is a good example of this and today the figure sells for £2,000 to collectors. Her group, produced in an edition of 12, entitled 'The Marriage of Art and Industry', (today's price £2,500), showing a man and a woman, the tree of knowledge and doves of peace, was centrepiece for the Doulton stand at the Brussels Exhibition of 1958. It helped them win the only Grand Prix awarded to a pottery firm at the exhibition.

Even figures which are still in production can command large prices among collectors. An example is St George by W. K. Harper. This is the third version of St George produced by Doulton and was introduced in 1978. Its price at auction is £3,000.

numbers over 2,000 is superb. Limited editions of figures and wall masks were produced by Richard Garbe, an R.A. and Professor of Sculpture at the Royal College of Art who modelled for Doulton between 1934 and 1939. His 'West Wind', which today fetches a price of £2,500, was produced in an edition of only 25 and originally sold for just over £8. Most of his wall masks, made of special porcelain with an ivory glaze, were in editions of 100.

Figure making still continues at Burslem with more than 300 still in production. The star of more recent times was Peggy Davies who was born and brought up in the pottery district of Burslem and, after studying at Burslem College of Art, began work as an assistant to Clarice Cliff. Her association with Doulton commenced in 1939 and, until her death in 1987, produced an enormous range of figures ranging from her Kate Greenaway children to period characters from English history and a modelled head of Queen Elizabeth II.

Her work is notable for meticulous research which can be clearly seen in the 'Indian Brave' (today's price £2,000). She took great care in researching her subject,

St George designed by W. K. Harper.

KINGSWARE

In 1899 a new method of stoneware production was introduced at Burslem which involved applying colour slips of subdued greens, yellows and reddish browns to the interior of plaster moulds in which a

A pair of Kingsware beakers decorated with landscape scenes, 4in. high. $70 £45

design was impressed. When another brown slip was poured in the colours fused to give a deep and soft effect to the embossed design.

Kingsware was mostly used for the production of pottery flasks to hold whisky and they were produced in enormous quantities, usually in editions of 1,000, for firms like John Dewar and Sons of Perth; Bullock Lade; Greenlees and Watson and the Hudson's Bay Company.

The glaze was most commonly a dark treacle brown but more unusual was a paler yellow called the 'Kingsware yellow glaze'.

The flasks were embossed with designs emphasising the pleasures of drinking and figures like Falstaff and the Sporting Squire were especially popular. These were often modelled by Arthur Bailey who worked between 1912 and 1932.

Some of the flasks had silver fittings and they are more likely to have survived than the everyday specimens.

Sir Francis Drake jug, designed by Noke & Fenton, issued in 1933 in a limited edition of 500, together with the original invoice for the Drake jug, dated May 14th 1932 for £1. 5 shillings.

LIMITED EDITION LOVING CUPS AND JUGS

One of Charles J. Noke's greatest talents was giving the public what it wanted and in 1930 he hit upon the idea of producing a range of limited editions of loving cups and jugs, ornately embossed and decorated to a certain theme.

They were modelled on the slip cast relief jugs which had been made in Staffordshire during Victorian times but were much more intricate and colourful.

The first one produced was 'The Master of Foxhounds Presentation Jug'. It was modelled in low relief with rich glowing colours painted by William Grace and it set the style of the lip and handle of the jug or cup continuing the theme.

The following year 'The Regency Coach Jug' appeared and it was followed by a new one each year including the 'Dickens Dream Jug'; 'The Shakespeare Jug' and 'Robin Hood and His Merry Men'. The maximum number in each edition was 1,000 and each jug or cup bore a certificate of authenticity.

Some were produced to coincide with significant dates like the one made in 1932 for George Washington's birth bicentenary which was designed for the American market. In 1953 a loving cup was issued for the coronation of Queen Elizabeth II by Cecil Noke and in 1977 another edition of only 250 was produced by Richard Johnson for her Silver Jubilee.

George Washington Bicentenary Jug, designed by C. J. Noke & H. Fenton, 10¾in. high, issued 1932 in a limited edition of 1000, colour variation on handle.

$7200 £4500

SERIES WARE

"Adorn yet serve some useful purpose" was the reasoning behind the very successful introduction of Series Ware which was the brain child of Charles J. Noke who joined Doulton's in 1889.

He realised that standard pottery shapes could be decorated with popular images and sold as 'novelty art wares' to the general public who were not able to afford the more expensive creations of individual artists.

Designs, many of them by Noke himself, were transfer printed onto plates, jugs,

Moorish Gateway, a Series Ware rack plate, designed by H. Allen, introduced 1926, withdrawn 1945, D4601, 9½in. diam. $60 £40

bowls, mugs and tea sets. Refined earthenware or bone china was used and the transfer prints were handcoloured which gave the technique the name of 'print and tint'.

The first series issued was the 'Isthmian Games' in 1889 and it was followed by a new theme almost every year till World War Two. They include Olde Worlde England, characters from legend, song or story, motoring scenes, characters from Dickens and hunting scenes. Collectors could buy everything from tooth brush holders to dinner plates with their favourite theme and the craze for collecting them continues today.

In the 1970's Doulton's revived Series Ware when they issued sets of plates for special events and anniversaries called "Collectors' International".

STONEWARE

The production of saltglazed stoneware had been carried on at Lambeth for centuries when John Doulton first went into the pottery business there in 1815.

At first his firm continued the prevalent output of cheap mass produced items like bottles, jugs and barrels and it was not until John's son Henry joined the business that more complex modelling and detail began to be introduced.

It was Henry who diversified into architectural stoneware and who started to turn his Lambeth Pottery into a centre for the production of decorative stoneware.

In 1866 he took into the company a group of students from the Lambeth School of Art and in the Paris Exhibition of 1867 their work was highly acclaimed.

The people who produced decorative stoneware at this time included the three famous Barlows, Frank Butler, George Tinworth and many others including women like Eliza Simmance. At first designs were fairly simple and incised but this led on to 'pâté sur pâté' work which involved building up a raised outline by delicate brushwork and to far more sophisticated designs of incised and carved stylised foliage which were a precursor of the Art Nouveau styles.

Stoneware manufacture ceased entirely at Lambeth in 1956 and had only been on a limited scale there since 1914 but today there is a great resurgence of interest in it among collectors.

ARTHUR BARLOW (1871-78) . . .

. . . died sadly young while his talent was in its full flowering. He was one of the first students to be accepted from the Lambeth School of Art by Henry Doulton in his Lambeth Pottery Works. Arthur Barlow's work is distinctive because of its subtle colours and his flowing use of the foliate scroll.

FLORENCE BARLOW (1873-1909) . . .

. . . was the third member of the Barlow family to work for Henry Doulton. After 1877 she made an arrangement with her more famous sister Hannah that she would only paint birds and leave the animals to Hannah. Florence was a skilled exponent of the 'pâté sur pâté' technique but throughout her career her style stayed relatively unchanged.

Florence E. Barlow, 1873-1909.

HANNAH BARLOW (1871-1913) . . .

. . . was the most famous Doulton artist who maintained an incredible level of output and variety throughout her career. Like her brother and her sister Florence she was a student at Lambeth School of Art, and when she made history by being the first female artist to be employed by Henry Doulton, she paved the way for hundreds of women who came after her. Some of her best pieces were paintings of animals for which she had a strong affection and she maintained a small private zoo at her home. Her best period was between the 1870's and the late 1880's. It is interesting to note that Hannah actually lost the use of her right hand early in her career and retrained herself to use her left.

Hannah B. Barlow, 1871-1913.

FRANK BUTLER (1872-1911) . . .

. . . became one of the best known personalities of the art world during the last quarter of the 19th century when the press discovered that he was a deaf mute who could create things of fascination and beauty from clay. He was one of the early stoneware designers working at Lambeth and often went to exhibitions where he worked in front of the public on the company's stand. His greatest talent was for folding soft clay into myriad shapes and the Indian Pavilion used as a centrepiece for Doulton's exhibit in the Glasgow Exhibition was his work. His peak was between 1872 and 1890 but when the Art Nouveau fashion developed he adopted it with enthusiasm, adapting his designs to the new styles.

LESLIE HARRADINE (1902-1915) . . .

. . . was a gifted artist with a great flair for capturing movement, who modelled at Lambeth from 1902 until 1915 when he emigrated to Canada. He returned to Britain after serving in World War One and for the rest of his life freelanced for Doulton's at Burslem producing some of their most notable figures including the Old Balloon Seller and the Beggar's Opera series. He is best known for his series of Dickens' characters, produced at a rate of about two a month for almost 40 years, and for his set of spirit flasks modelled on 20th century politicians in the same way as the Reform Flasks of 1832 were modelled on the politicians of that time.

EDITH LUPTON (1876-?) . . .

. . . her early work was incised stylised foliage but, after 1880, she turned to 'pâté sur pâté' and pierced vases. Her death is recorded in 1896 but it is not known exactly when she stopped working for Doulton though she is thought to have still been producing work in 1892.

MARK MARSHALL (1879-1912) . . .

. . . a gifted stoneware modeller who produced imaginative dragons, lizards and grotesque creatures, some of them moulded and some in limited editions. He was much influenced by the Art Nouveau movement and translated its ideas into pottery.

ELIZA SIMMANCE (1873-1928) . . .

. . . first assisted on the production of Barlow vases and silicon pieces but after 1900 her work became much more free and all her pieces thereafter were signed. Her output was enormous and her most characteristic work shows finely incised 'pâté sur pâté' decorations of flowers and blossoms.

GEORGE TINWORTH (1866-1913) . . .

. . . was the illiterate son of a Walworth wheelwright who became an artistic genius with a world famous reputation. He studied sculpture at Lambeth School of Art and was one of the first students to work for Henry Doulton who quickly recognised his talents. He produced many terracotta panels with religious themes as well as humorous figures of people and animals and incised and painted vases and jugs.

BIBELOTS . . .

. . . were small trifles which could be given as presents. They range from ring trays and inkwells to match strikers and bookends. They were produced in very large numbers and, though many of them were the work of major artists, they are nearly always unsigned.

COMMEMORATIVE WARE . . .

. . . large numbers of these were produced to mark historical events like centenaries and military actions during the 19th and early 20th centuries. Many of the designs were by John Broad and most had applied, moulded decorations.

DOULTON AND SLATER'S WARE

. . . is also known as 'Chine' and is easily recognised because it was decorated by lace pressed into the stoneware body while still soft. It was then glazed, decorated and gilded with applied motifs. The technique was the invention of John Slater who was Art Director at Burslem between 1887 and 1914.

Stoneware jug commemorating the Golden Jubilee of Queen Victoria, 9in. high, circa 1897. $240 £160

MINIATURES . . .

. . . were very popular during the last quarter of the 19th century because they made amusing gifts. They were scaled down glazed stoneware copies of popular lines of vases and jugs and great care was taken to ensure the proportions were true. Many of the miniatures were decorated by major artists.

NATURAL FOLIAGE WARE . . .

. . . was produced by pressing real leaves into soft clay and the impressions were joined by twigs which were incised before the vase was glazed. This ware was produced between 1886 and 1936.

SILICON WARE . . .

. . . is a hard, smooth, high fired stoneware with a thin glaze. It was produced in the greatest quantities between 1880 and 1912 and decorated by some of the most famous Doulton artists. Carved, pierced, gilt or lustre painted Silicon Ware can be found in considerable quantities and the predominant colours are light blue and white on buff or brown bodies.

SIMULATED WARE . . .

. . . is a type of ware in which silicon bodies have been painted to look like some other material. For example there are pottery cricket balls or cast iron weights as well as jugs that look as if they were made of copper with painted on joints and rivets and a lustre glaze. They were even given a coating of simulated verdigris. Very popular when they first appeared, were leatherwork jugs with black silicon bodies that had a dark textured surface stitched with imitation waxed threads. This range was produced from 1887, when the simulated copper first appeared, until around 1910.

SPORTING SUBJECTS . . .

. . . comprise a series of stoneware mugs and jugs decorated with relief figures of famous sportsmen. They were introduced in 1880 and the figures were the work of John Broad. One of the best examples is his W. G. Grace jug showing the famous cricketer in eight different poses.

ADVERTISING WARES

Stoneware matchstriker and holder made for Worthingtons, 4in. high, circa 1900. $150 £100

Match-holder and striker advertising 'Sir Edward Lee's Old Scotch Whisky', with the slogan 'As supplied to the House of Commons'. $150 £100

Small character jug liqueur flask made for W. Walklate Ltd. depicting 'Rip Van Winkle', 4in. high. $70 £45

Cream jug made for the Savoy Hotel, London, 3¾in. high, circa 1930, c.m.l. & c. £45 £30

Scotsman and Irishman whisky flasks in a wooden tantalus designed for Asprey & Co. of New Bond St., London. $3750 £2500

A pin tray with a map of New Zealand, circa 1928. $45 £30

Whisky flask in the form of a crow made for National Distillers of Kentucky, circa 1954. $240 £150

Dr Scholl's Zino Pads, advertising display by Doulton, 8in. high. $115 £75

News Vendor designed by W. Harper in a limited edition of 2,500 for the Newspaper Society, 1986, 7in. high. $330 £220

A Royal Doulton advertising model of a bulldog, 14.7cm. high, c.m.l. & c., Rd. no. 645658. $1125 £750

A Doulton Lambeth stoneware ashtray match holder, 'Queen Anne's Mansion'. $100 £65

Small character jug liqueur flask for W. Walklate Ltd. depicting 'Poacher', 4in. high. $70 £45

The International Collection, a set of four character liqueur flasks made for Pick-Kwik Wines and Spirits, John Bull (England), Captain Cook (Australia), Samurai Warrior (Japan) and Uncle Sam (America), 1984. $465 £310

'Cawdor Castle', a Series Ware dish made for R.G. Giles, Pool, nr. Leeds, circa 1928. $100 £65

The Major bust ashtray made for Army Club Cigarettes, 5½in. high, circa 1920. $140 £95

A Doulton & Co. Ltd. stoneware brush pot, circa 1902, 3¼in. high, c.m.l. & c. $30 £20

Small character jug liqueur flask made for W. Walklate Ltd. depicting 'Falstaff', 4in. high.
$70 £45

Doulton Lambeth Improved Foot Warmer. $70 £45

Doulton Lambeth stoneware match-holder and striker for John Dewar & Sons.
$110 £75

The Pickwick Collection, a set of four character liqueur flasks made for Jim Beam Whiskey, the handles in the form of bottle miniatures, 1983. $465 £310

An earthenware presentation beaker, 'Victoria R.I. Diamond Jubilee', made for Lewis & Hyland, Ashford, circa 1897.
$100 £65

Pip, Squeak and Wilfred, an ashtray made for The Daily Mirror, Fetter Lane, London, 4in. high, circa 1930.
$600 £400

A tea caddy made for 'Twinings of the Strand', June 1953, 7in. high. $104 £65

A miniature stoneware bottle vase for Jas. Shoolbred & Co., circa 1902, 2¹/₂in. high.
$100 £65

A stoneware match striker made for Bass, 'Bottled Bass', 3¹/₂in. high, circa 1919, c.m.l. & c.
$110 £75

A replica decanter made for Fortnum & Mason, as held in their crypt dated 1700 A.D., 7 in. high, c.m.l. & c. $75 £50

Display sign of a Beefeater for Illustrated London News, 8in. high. $1376 £850

'Worthington's' In Bottle, china jardiniere made by Royal Doulton, 20in. high.
$675 £450

Melrose Highland Whisky by Doulton, 20cm high.
$750 £500

An ashtray made for Chessington and Paignton Zoo & Circus, circa 1950, c.m.l. & c.
$40 £25

A stoneware barge made for Downey, 4 Pratt St., Lambeth, circa 1890. $340 £225

An ashtray made for Craven 'A' cigarettes, circa 1930.
$50 £35

A paperweight made for Veale Chifferiel & Co., silicon ware, circa 1890, 2³/₄in. high.
$112 £70

A small cream jug made for The Waldorf Hotel, 2¹/₂in. high, circa 1920. $50 £35

A pin tray made for the Sneyd Collieries & Brickworks Co. Ltd., Staffordshire, circa 1930, c.m.l. & c. $100 £65

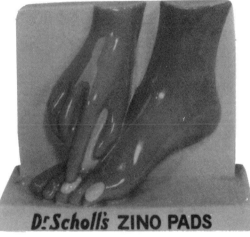

A Royal Doulton figural bottle for Sandiman's Port, 10¹/₄in. high, circa 1920-1956, c.m.l. & c.
$72 £45

Dr Scholl's Zino Pads, Counter display figure made by Doulton.
$110 £75

Display sign for 'Army Club Cigarettes' depicting the bust of a soldier. $165 £110

A pin tray made for Hughes, North St., Belfast, 'God Bless The Cat', c.m.l. & c.
$140 £95

Counter display sign for Grossmith's perfume, 'Tsang Ihang' the perfume of Thibet, circa 1923. $720 £450

A Doulton stoneware ashtray for pipes, circa 1900, DLE.
$75 £50

An ashtray for Doulton & Co. Ltd., Sanitary Dept. Showroom, Lambeth, circa 1930, c.m.l. & c. $75 £50

A Royal Doulton stoneware match striker advertising Dewar's Whisky, 2½in. high, c.m.l. & c. $100 £65

A stoneware soap dish made for Wright's Coal Tar Soap, circa 1960. $90 £60

Royal Doulton wireless loudspeaker made for Artandia Ltd. in the form of a feathered cockatoo perched on a rock, 15½in. high. $240 £150

A Doulton Lambeth stoneware sanitary fountain. $110 £75

A whisky bottle made for Bell's Old Scotch Whisky, 7¾in. high, circa 1950. $45 £30

A small 'Auld Lang Syne' whisky flagon depicting an Inn scene, 4in. high. $75 £50

A Doulton stoneware inkwell 'For Office Use Only', circa 1902. c.m.l. & c. $100 £65

Royal Doulton 'Ginger Wine' barrel made for Rawlings, complete with tap, 10in. high. $260 £175

ANIMAL FIGURES

Character Dog, head turned, HN2508, 2$\frac{1}{2}$in. high, withdrawn 1959. $190 £125

English Setter, HN1050, 3$\frac{3}{4}$in.high, c.m., withdrawn 1985. $130 £85

Irish Setter, HN1055, 5$\frac{1}{4}$in. high, withdrawn 1985. $130 £85

Persian Cat, HN999, 5in. high, c.m.l. & c., withdrawn 1985. $140 £95

Cocker Spaniel & Pheasant, HN1138, 5$\frac{1}{4}$in. high, withdrawn 1985. $165 £110

Cocker Spaniel, HN1036, 5in. high, c.m., withdrawn 1985. $130 £85

ANIMAL FIGURES

Character Dog, standing, HN2509, 2¹/₂in. high, withdrawn 1959.   **$180 £120**

Character Kitten, cleaning paw, HN2583, 2in. high, c.m., withdrawn 1985.   **$75 £50**

French Poodle, HN2631, 5¹/₂in. high, c.m.l. & c., withdrawn 1985.   **$150 £100**

Cairn, sitting, K11, 2¹/₄in. high, c.m., withdrawn 1977.   **$90 £60**

Scottish Terrier, begging, K10, 3¹/₂in. high, withdrawn 1977.   **$90 £60**

Collie, HN1059, 3¹/₂in. high, c.m.l. & c., withdrawn 1959.   **$150 £100**

Cocker Spaniel, K9, 2½in. high, c.m.l. & c., withdrawn 1977. $80 £55

Character Kitten, HN2584, 1¾in. high, c.m., withdrawn 1985. $75 £50

Three Terrier Puppies, in a basket, HN2588, 2¾in.
high, c.m.l. & c., withdrawn 1985. $90 £60

Scottish Terrier, sitting, K18, 2¼in. high, c.m.,
withdrawn 1977. $90 £60

Character Dog, bone in mouth, HN1159, 3¾in.
high, withdrawn 1985. $100 £65

A Royal Doulton figure of a bulldog draped in the
Union Jack, 7in. high, printed marks. $1040 £650

Character Dog, with plate, HN1158, 3in. high, withdrawn 1985. $100 £65

Character Dog, with brown ball, HN1103, 2¹/₂in. high, withdrawn 1985. $90 £60

Welsh Corgi, HN2559, 3¹/₂in, c.m., withdrawn 1985. $100 £65

Siamese Cat, standing, HN2660, 5¹/₄in. high, c.m., withdrawn 1985. $110 £75

Bulldog, white, small, HN1074, 3¹/₄in. high, withdrawn 1985. $130 £85

River Hog, HN2663, 3¹/₂in. high, c.m.l. & c., withdrawn 1969: $225 £150

Puppy in a basket, HN2585, 2in. high, withdrawn
1985. $100 £65

Cocker Spaniels, asleep, HN2590, 1³/₄in. high, c.m.l.
& c., withdrawn 1985. $100 £65

Labrador, HN2667, 5in. high, c.m., withdrawn
1985. $100 £65

Fox Terrier, small, HN1014, withdrawn 1985.
                                                  $61 £38

Rough Haired Terrier, HN1014, 4in. high, c.m.,
withdrawn 1985. $100 £65

Cocker Spaniel, HN1020, 5¹/₄in. high, c.m., withdrawn 1985. $100 £65

ANIMAL FIGURES

Royal Doulton 'Fox in Red Frock Coat', HN100, 16cm. high, c.m.l. & c. 1913-1942. $900 £600

Dachshund, HN1128, 3³/₄in. high, c.m., withdrawn 1985. $100 £65

The Gude Grey Mare, HN2519, 7³/₄in. high, with-drawn 1960. $410 £275

Boxer, HN2643, 6¹/₂in. high, withdrawn 1985. $100 £65

Dalmation, HN1113, 5¹/₄in. high, withdrawn 1985. $130 £85

A Royal Doulton model, 'Kingfisher', HN 131, 10.5cm. high, c.m.l. & c. $130 £85

A Royal Doulton Cairn begging, HN2589, 4in. high, withdrawn 1985. $90 £60

English Setter and Pheasant, HN2529, 8¹/₂in. high, c.m.l. & c., withdrawn 1985. $440 £295

Cocker Spaniel, in a basket, HN2586, 2³/₄in. high, c.m.l. & c., withdrawn 1985. $100 £65

Siamese Cat, sitting, HN2655, 5¹/₄in. high, withdrawn 1985. $110 £75

English Setter, HN1049, 7³/₄in. x 12¹/₄in., c.m., withdrawn 1985. $130 £85

Collie, medium, HN1058, 5¹/₄in. high, withdrawn 1985. $130 £85

Pride of the Shires, HN2528, 9in. high, withdrawn 1960. $450 £300

A Royal Doulton character kitten, curled asleep, HN2581, withdrawn 1985, 1¹/₂in. high. $75 £50

Huntsman Fox, HN6448, 4¹/₂in. high, c.m.l. & c., withdrawn 1985. $135 £90

Bulldog, with the Union Jack draped over his back, c.m.l. & c.   Large $525 £350; Med. $410 £275; Small $260 £175

Royal Doulton model of a rhinoceros, by Leslie Harradine, 6¹/₄in. high. $975 £650

Tiger on Rock, a Royal Doulton Prestige figure, HN2639, 11½ x 14in., c.m.l. & c., withdrawn 1992. $880 £550

ART POTTERY

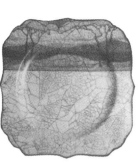

Doulton crackleglaze plate with shaped edge. **$35 £22**

Doulton crackleglaze Deadwood teapot. **$77 £48**

Doulton Burslem Royles Patent self pouring teapot, circa 1900. **$144 £90**

A Doulton Lambeth coffee pot painted with a purple iris, circa 1879. **$352 £220**

Doulton Art Pottery jardiniere with a blue ground and applied flowers, 8³/₄in. high. **$180 £120**

An oviform pate-sur-pate vase decorated with birds by Florence Barlow, 15in. high. **$560 £350**

Doulton jug of tapered cylindrical form decorated with a bird on a branch, by Florence Barlow, circa 1890. **$320 £200**

A Royal Doulton blue and white oval plaque, printed with a mother and child picking flowers, 14in. wide. **$400 £250**

A Doulton Burslem baluster vase painted with an Edwardian lady, by H.G. Theaker, 10¹/₄in. high. **$375 £250**

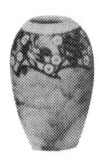

A Royal Doulton Art Pottery vase decorated with stylised flowers, 8in. high, circa 1910. **$96 £60**

A pair of Doulton Lambeth stoneware vases by Florence E. Barlow, circa 1906. **$480 £300**

Royal Doulton Art Pottery vase, 9in. high, circa 1910, **$160 £100**

Doulton Lambeth Carrara Ware vase with flared neck by Josephine Durtnall, 16in. high. **$525 £350**

Royal Doulton bowl, Japanese Fan, designed by H. Tittensor, introduced 1921, withdrawn 1938. **$480 £300**

Royal Doulton vase painted by Ethel Beard, 13in. high. **$192 £120**

One of a pair of Royal Doulton baluster shaped vases, by Francis C. Pope, 8³/₄in. high. **$224 £140**

Pair of Royal Doulton cylindrical vases painted by L. Johnson, 30cm. high. **$600 £400**

Doulton Lambeth ewer by Hannah Barlow, decorated with a pate-sur-pate frieze of dogs, 11in. high. **$480 £300**

Royal Doulton pottery jardiniere, cobalt blue glazed, 9in. diam. **$136 £85**

A Doulton Lambeth Silicon Ware oviform vase, by Edith D. Lupton and Ada Dennis, 20.5cm. high, dated 1885. **$260 £175**

A Royal Doulton earthenware globular vase, 21.8cm. high, c.m.l. & c. **$180 £120**

Doulton Lambeth vase by Florence Barlow, decorated in pate-sur-pate with an owl, 12½in. high. **$464 £290**

Pair of Doulton saltglazed stoneware baluster vases, circa 1906/7, 12½in. high. **$300 £200**

A Doulton Crown Lambeth two-handled vase and cover decorated with panels of wild flowers by Emma Harrison, circa 1889. **$480 £300**

A large Doulton Burslem vase and cover, painted by G. White, signed, circa 1910, 20¾in. high. **$1360 £850**

A Royal Doulton jug decorated with a maiden wearing a flowing dress, 10½in. high. **$240 £150**

A fine hand painted vase with bird and flower decoration, 11in. high. **$450 £300**

CHANG

A Chang bowl by Noke and Nixon, 8in. diam. $675 £450

A Royal Doulton Chang vase by Nixon and Noke, 9¼in. high, circa 1925. $1920 £1200

Royal Doulton Chang bowl by Nixon and Noke, circa 1930. $900 £600

Royal Doulton Chang vase by Noke and Moore, 7½in. high, circa 1935. $880 £550

A Chang vase by Noke and Nixon, 10in. high. $2400 £1600

A Chang vase by Noke and Nixon, 10in. high. $1350 £900

Royal Doulton Chang vase by Noke and Nixon, 8¾in. high. $1050 £700

A Chang vase by Noke and Nixon, 7in. high. $1280 £800

Royal Doulton Chang vase by Nixon and Noke, 5¾in. high, circa 1920. $800 £500

CHANG

A Chang bowl by Noke and Nixon, 5in. high. $1360 £850

A Chang vase by Noke and Nixon, 5in. high. $1280 £800

A Chang bowl by Noke and Nixon, 8in, diam. $1840 £1150

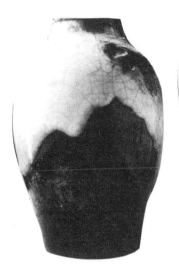

A Chang vase by Noke and Nixon, 10in. high. $1350 £900

A Chang vase by Noke and Nixon, 8in. high. $1400 £900

The Chang Potter lamp base by Noke and Nixon, 10½in. high.
$3000 £2000

Royal Doulton Chang vase by Noke and Nixon, 10¼in. high.
$1360 £850

Royal Doulton Chang vase by C.J. Noke and Harry Nixon, 7½in. high, circa 1930.
$1425 £950

A Chang vase by Noke and Nixon, 5in. high. $750 £500

CHANG

A Chang vase by Noke and Nixon, 8in. high. **$1200 £800**

A Royal Doulton 'Chang' jar and cover, by Harry Nixon, 8in. high. **$1120 £700**

A Chang vase by Noke and Nixon, 9in. high. **$1350 £900**

CHINESE JADE

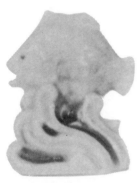

A Chinese jade model of a fish in white and green by Noke, 3¼in. high. **$750 £500**

Royal Doulton Chinese jade two-handled bowl in white and green, 3½in. high. **$512 £320**

'Leaping Salmon', a large Chinese jade figure, signed Noke and Nixon, 11½in. high, circa 1930. **$1050 £700**

FAIENCE

Royal Doulton faience vase by John H. McLennan, decorated with panels representing Earth and Water, 13½in. high. **$368 £230**

A pair of Doulton Lambeth faience oil lamp bases decorated by Esther Lewis, 10¼in. high. **$720 £450**

A Doulton Lambeth faience vase painted with stylised flowers, by Emily Gillman, 9¼in. high. **$176 £110**

FAIENCE

A Doulton Lambeth faience
wall plaque decorated with
fruit and foliage, 13¾in. diam.
$192 £120

Doulton Lambeth faience vase
decorated with daffodils and
narcissi, 10½in. high.
$176 £110

Doulton Lambeth faience vase
with the artist's monogram for
Mary Butterton, circa 1880.
$288 £180

Doulton Lambeth faience vase
by Mary Capes, decorated with
flowers, circa 1878. $165 £110

A Doulton Lambeth faience
coffee service painted with
azaleas, dahlias and dog roses,
circa 1879. $352 £220

One of a pair of Doulton faience
vases decorated by Katherine
Smallfield, 12½in. high.
$330 £220

A large Doulton Lambeth
faience plaque by Florence E.
Lewis, 15½in. diam., circa 1880.
$288 £180

Pair of Doulton Lambeth faience
vases decorated with sprays of
leaves and flowers by Mary M.
Arding, 14¾in. high, circa 1880.
$512 £320

Doulton faience moonflask
decorated with leaves and wild
flowers, 14¼in. high.
$330 £220

FAIENCE

A Doulton Lambeth stoneware vase, signed initials of Florence E. Barlow, impressed date for 1880, 10in. high.　**$264 £165**

A Doulton Lambeth faience wall plaque, painted by L. Watt, 51cm. diam.　**$400 £250**

A faience vase decorated with leaves and flowers, by Josephine A. Durtnall, 5in. high, circa 1876.　**$104 £65**

A Doulton Lambeth vase by Kate Rogers, decorated with wild flowers, 8in. high.　**$240 £150**

A pair of Doulton faience vases by Fanny Stable, decorated with dragons amongst clouds, 11½in. high, circa 1879.　**$525 £350**

A faience vase decorated with panels of flowers, by Alberta L. Green, 9¼in. high, circa 1882.　**$225 £150**

A Doulton Lambeth faience moonflask, decorated by H. Barlow.　**$608 £380**

Doulton Lambeth faience two-handled vase decorated with a band of wild flowers by Margaret M. Challis, 7½in. high, circa 1880.　**$176 £110**

Doulton Lambeth faience wall plaque, 'Old Cottage, Bromley, Kent', by Esther Lewis, 14¾in. diam., circa 1882.　**$336 £210**

FAIENCE

A faience vase decorated with entwined leaves and fruit, 8^1/$_2$in. high, circa 1877.   **$160 £100**

A faience teapot decorated with flowers, by Gertrude Smith, 6in. high, circa 1889.   **$160 £100**

A faience vase decorated with flowers and birds, by Josephine A. Durtnall, 10^1/$_2$in. high, circa 1887.   **$224 £140**

Royal Doulton faience vase and cover, by Ada Dennis, Esther Lewis and Mary Denley, 24in. high, circa 1885. **$3000 £2000**

A Doulton Lambeth faience tile panel, 61.5 x 20.6cm., printed c.m. on reverse of each.   **$600 £400**

Doulton Lambeth faience water jug decorated with flowers, 7^1/$_2$in. high.   **$110 £75**

A large Doulton faience moon-fask decorated with flowers and fruit, 14^1/$_4$in. high. **$410 £275**

Pair of Doulton Lambeth faience vases decorated with sprays of leaves, by Mary M. Arding, 14^1/$_4$in. high, circa 1880.   **$512 £320**

Doulton Lambeth faience wall plaque by Helen A. Arding, circa 1880.   **$224 £140**

FLAMBE

A Doulton Lambeth flambe ashtray with elephant heads on the corners, by Moore, 3½in. wide.
$240 £160

A Royal Doulton flambe figure of a crab, 4½in. wide.
$400 £250

The Dragon, a Royal Doulton flambe figure, 2085, introduced 1973, 7½in. high.   Rec. Retail Price

Royal Doulton flambe jardiniere decorated with a desert scene. $375 £250

Royal Doulton flambe model of a collie dog, 7¾in. high, circa 1926. $480 £300

A Royal Doulton flambe figure modelled as a seated Buddha, 6¾in. high, possibly by C.J. Noke.
$2250 £1500

Rhinoceros, a Royal Doulton flambe figure, 615, introduced 1973, 9½in. long.   Rec. Retail Price

Royal Doulton flambe model of a terrier, 5¼in. high, circa 1930. $272 £170

FLAMBE

Pig Dish, 2¹/₂in. high x 4¹/₂in. long, silver mounted, circa 1927.   **$480 £300**

Tiger, snarling, HN225, 2¹/₂in. high x 9in. long, circa 1930.   **$400 £250**

Guinea Fowl, Model 69, 3in. high.   **$260 £175**

Pomegranate, 2³/₄in. high.   **$240 £150**

Monkeys, embracing, Model 486, 5¹/₂in. high.   **$224 £140**

Fox, sitting, head up, Model 102, 9¹/₂in. high, designed by Noke, introduced 1962, withdrawn 1965.   **$340 £225**

'The Cat' sitting, a Royal Doulton flambe model 2259, 11¹/₂in. high.   **Rec. Retail Price**

A Royal Doulton flambe model of a pair of penguins, 15cm. high, c.m.l. & c.   **$300 £200**

FLAMBE

Mallard, Model 654, 4in. high, designed by Noke, introduced 1920, withdrawn 1961. $312 £195

Fox, slinking, full length, Model 29, 2¹/₂in. high x 12in. long. $375 £250

Leaping Salmon, Model 666, 12in. high, designed by Noke, introduced 1940, withdrawn 1950.
$480 £300

Elephant, a Royal Doulton flambe model 489A, 5¹/₂in. high.   Rec. Retail Price

Monkey, dunce's cap, HN972, 5¹/₂in. high.
$1125 £750

Penguin, double, Model 103, HN133, 6in. high, circa 1929. $300 £200

Pigeons, two fantail, Model 46, 3³/₄in. high.
$450 £300

A Royal Doulton flambe model of a bulldog, 14.2cm. high, c.m.l. & c., impressed date 10.26, no. 135.
$1125 £750

FLAMBE

Tiger, Model 1809, 5½in. long.   Rec. Retail Price

Two foxes, curled asleep, Model 15, 4in. long.
$340 £225

Royal Doulton flambe Buddha, signed Noke, 8in.
high.   **$1500 £1000**

Fish, group of, Model 682, 6½in. high, circa 1921.
$432 £270

Dobermann Pinscher, a Royal Doulton
figure, HN2645, 6in. high, withdrawn 1985, c.m.
                                        $300 £200

Mouse, on cube, Model 1164, HN255, 2½in. high,
circa 1908.   **$320 £200**

A Royal Doulton flambe model of an elephant,
16.8cm. high, c.m.l. & c., signed Noke. **$410 £275**

Elephant, trunk down, 12in. high, circa 1930.
                                        $1125 £750

ART POTTERY

HOLBEIN WARE

A Royal Doulton Holbein Ware plaque, by Walter Nunn, 11.4 x 18.3cm. image area, c.m.l. & c.
$640 £400

A Holbein Ware vase with silver rim, 9in. high. $320 £200

A large Royal Doulton Burslem Holbein Ware jardiniere decorated with four cavaliers playing cards, 13¼in. high, signed W. Nunn. $720 £450

IMPASTO

A Doulton Lambeth Impasto jardiniere decorated with wild flowers by Rosa Keen. 10½in. high. $288 £180

A Doulton Lambeth Impasto vase decorated with chrysanthemums, by Rosa Keen, 11in. high. $264 £165

A Doulton Lambeth Impasto wall plaque decorated with chrysanthemums, by Frances Linnell, 14½in. diam., circa 1882. $225 £150

MORRISIAN WARE

Doulton Burslem Morrisian Ware teapot with a frieze of girls dancing, 8in. high. $225 £150

Doulton Burslem Morrisian Ware tobacco jar and cover decorated with a band of dancing girls, 5½in. high. $225 £150

A Doulton Burslem Morrisian Ware teapot decorated with a band of dancing maidens, 7¾in. high, circa 1899 $225 £150

A Royal Doulton 'Tango' pattern porcelain part coffee set, coffee pot, 20.75cm. high, c.m.l. & c., impressed dates 1.1.35 and 2.1.35. $675 £450

A Doulton Burslem porcelain fruit set, by Walter Slater, each piece painted in natural colours with dandelion buds and clocks, flowers and leaves, b.r.m. & c., England Rd. no. 72067. $410 £275

A Royal Doulton 'Aubrey' shape toilet set comprising a large bowl, jug, chamber pot, soap dish and toothbrush holder, decorated with Art Nouveau floral motifs in sepia, rust, blue and yellow colours.
$480 £300

SUNG

Royal Doulton Sung model of a rabbit, 4in. long, circa 1928.
$480 £300

Royal Doulton Sung vase decorated with a leopard in a mountainous landscape, 6³/₄in. high.
$200 £125

Royal Doulton Sung bowl decorated with stylised flowers, 9in. diam., circa 1920. $375 £250

Royal Doulton Sung vase by Noke, decorated with a peacock painted by A. Eaton, 10¹/₂in. high.
$480 £300

A large Royal Doulton Sung vase by Arthur Eaton, decorated with dragons amongst clouds, 13in. high, circa 1930.
$1280 £800

Royal Doulton Sung vase decorated by A. Eaton, 14¹/₂in. high.
$675 £450

A Royal Doulton Sung vase and cover, circa 1926, 13in. high.
$675 £450

A Royal Doulton Sung vase by Noke, 6³/₄in. high, circa 1928.
$640 £400

Royal Doulton Sung vase by Charles Noke and Fred Moore, 10¹/₄in. high, circa 1930.
$450 £300

SUNG

Royal Doulton Sung vase
painted with fish swimming
among weeds, 6¹/₄in. high, circa
1930. **$240 £150**

A Royal Doulton Sung ashtray
by Charles Noke and Fred
Moore, 3³/₄in. square.
$420 £280

A Royal Doulton Sung vase by
Charles Noke and Fred Moore,
7in. high, circa 1930.
$825 £550

A tall Royal Doulton Sung vase
by Charles Noke and F. Allen,
11¹/₂in. high, circa 1930.
$525 £350

Royal Doulton Sung vase signed
by A. Eaton, 5³/₄in. high.
$975 £650

Royal Doulton Sung vase decorated with a peacock by Arthur
Eaton, 8¹/₂in. high, circa 1925.
$450 £300

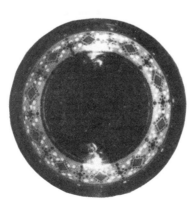

Royal Doulton Sung vase by
Noke, decorated with flying
birds, 8³/₄in. high. **$525 £350**

Royal Doulton Sung bowl decorated with a band of geometric
ornament, 8in. diam., circa
1925. **$400 £250**

Royal Doulton Sung tobacco jar
and cover of hexagonal form,
6¹/₄in. high, circa 1930.
$525 £350

TITANIAN WARE

A Royal Doulton Titanian Ware teapot, 6¹/₂in. high, circa 1920. $180 £120

A Royal Doulton Titanian Ware vase by F. Henri, decorated with a cat seated beneath a crescent moon. $375 £250

Royal Doulton Titanian Ware sugar bowl and cover, 4¹/₄in. high, circa 1922. $110 £75

Royal Doulton Titanian figure, 'The Smiling Buddha', by Noke, issued in 1921, withdrawn 1938. $960 £600

A pair of Royal Doulton Cecil Aldin Titanian glazed Series ware vases, 15.5cm. high, D4525. $560 £350

Royal Doulton Titanian figure of 'Blighty', 11¹/₂in. high, circa 1919. $975 £650

A Royal Doulton Titanian bowl decorated with a dragon, 14¹/₂in. diam. $160 £100

Royal Doulton Titanian vase by Harry Allen decorated with a long eared owl, 13in. high. $560 £350

A Royal Doulton Titanian Ware teapot, 6¹/₂in. high, circa 1922. $180 £120

CHARACTER JUGS

AIRMAN (THE) D6870
Designer: W. K. Harper
Height: Small
Issued: 1991
Price: R.R.P.

ANGLER (THE) D6866
Designer: S. Taylor
Height: Small
Issued: 1990
Price: R.R.P.

ANNE BOLEYN D6644
Designer: D. Tootle
Height: Large
Issued: 1975–1990
Price: $110 £75

ANNE BOLEYN D6650
Designer: D. Tootle
Height: Small
Issued: 1980–1990
Price: $70 £45

ANNE BOLEYN D6651
Designer: D. Tootle
Height: Mini
Issued: 1980–1990
Price: $50 £35

ANNE OF CLEVES D6753
Designer: M. Abberley
Height: Small
Issued: 1987–1990
Price: $70 £45

ANNE OF CLEVES D6754
Designer: M. Abberley
Height: Mini
Issued: 1987–1990
Price: $50 £35

ANNE OF CLEVES D6653
Designer: M. Abberley
Height: Large
Issued: 1980
Price: $190 £125 (Ears Up)

ANNE OF CLEVES D6653
Designer: M. Abberley
Height: Large
Issued: 1980–1990
Price: $110 £75

ANNIE OAKLEY D6732
Designer: S. Taylor
Height: Medium
Issued: 1985–1988
Price: $70 £45

ANTIQUE DEALER
(Kevin Francis) D6809
Limited edition of 5000
Designer: G. Blower
Height: Large
Issued: 1988–1992
Price: $110 £75

ANTONY AND CLEOPATRA
D6728 Limited edition of 9500
Designer: M. Abberley
Height: Large
Issued: 1985–1992
Price: $130 £85

ANNE OF CLEVES D6653   ANTONY AND CLEOPATRA D6728

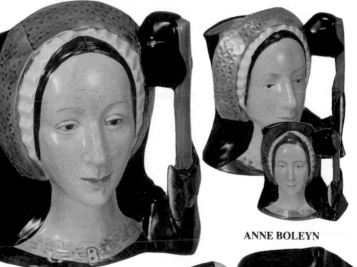

ANNE BOLEYN

ANNIE OAKLEY D6732   ANTIQUE DEALER   D6809

CHARACTER JUGS

APOTHECARY D6567
Designer: M. Henk
Height: Large
Issued: 1963–1983
Price: $110 £75

APOTHECARY D6574
Designer: M. Henk
Height: Small
Issued: 1963–1983
Price: $70 £45

APOTHECARY D6581
Designer: M. Henk
Height: Mini
Issued: 1963–1983
Price: $60 £40

ARAMIS D6441
Designer: M. Henk
Height: Large
Issued: 1956–1991
Price: $90 £60

ARAMIS D6454
Designer: M. Henk
Height: Small
Issued: 1956–1991
Price: $50 £35

ARAMIS D6508
Designer: M. Henk
Height: Mini
Issued: 1960–1991
Price: $50 £35

ARAMIS D6828
(Peter Jones) New colourway
Limited edition of 1000
Designer: M. Henk
Height: Large
Issued: 1988–1992
Price: $100 £65

'ARD OF 'EARING D6588
Designer: D. Biggs
Height: Large
Issued: 1964–1967
Price: $975 £650

'ARD OF 'EARING D6591
Designer: D. Biggs
Height: Small
Issued: 1964–1967
Price: $675 £450

'ARD OF 'EARING D6594
Designer: D. Biggs
Height: Mini
Issued: 1964–1967
Price: $675 £450

'ARRIET D6208
Designer: H. Fenton
Height: Large
Issued: 1947–1960
Price: $190 £125

'ARRIET D6236
Designer: H. Fenton
Height: Small
Issued: 1947–1960
Price: $90 £60

APOTHECARY D6567

'ARD OF 'EARING D6588

AULD MAC D6253

'ARRIET D6250
Designer: H. Fenton
Height: Mini
Issued: 1947–1960
Price: $70 £45

'ARRIET D6256
Designer: H. Fenton
Height: Tiny
Issued: 1947–1960
Price: $140 £95

'ARRY D6207
Designer: H. Fenton
Height: Large
Issued: 1947–1960
Price: $190 £125

'ARRY D6235
Designer: H. Fenton
Height: Small
Issued: 1947–1960
Price: $90 £60

'ARRY D6249
Designer: H. Fenton
Height: Mini
Issued: 1947–1960
Price: $70 £45

'ARRY D6255
Designer: H. Fenton
Height: Tiny
Issued: 1947–1960
Price: $140 £95

ATHOS D6439
Designer: M. Henk
Height: Large
Issued: 1956–1991
Price: $90 £60

ATHOS D6452
Designer: M. Henk
Height: Small
Issued: 1956–1991
Price: $50 £35

ATHOS D6509
Designer: M. Henk
Height: Mini
Issued: 1960–1991
Price: $50 £35

ATHOS D6827
(Peter Jones) New colourway
Limited edition of 1000
Designer: M. Henk
Height: Large
Issued: 1988
Price: $100 £65

AUCTIONEER (Kevin Francis)
D6838 Limited edition of 5000
Designer: G. Blower
Height: Large
Issued: 1988–1992
Price: $130 £85

AULD MAC D5823
Designer: H. Fenton
Height: Large
Issued: 1937–1985
Price: $100 £65

AULD MAC D5824
Designer: H. Fenton
Height: Small
Issued: 1937–1985
Price: $50 £35

AULD MAC D6253
Designer: H. Fenton
Height: Mini
Issued: 1937–1985
Price: $45 £30

AULD MAC D6257
Designer: H. Fenton
Height: Tiny
Issued: 1946–1960
Price: $165 £110

BACCHUS D6499
Designer: M. Henk
Height: Large
Issued: 1959–1991
Price: $75 £50

BACCHUS D6505
Designer: M. Henk
Height: Small
Issued: 1959–1991
Price: $50 £35

BACCHUS D6521
Designer: M. Henk
Height: Mini
Issued: 1960–1991
Price: $45 £30

BEEFEATER D6206
Designer: H. Fenton
Height: Large
Issued: 1947–
Price: R.R.P.

BEEFEATER D6233
Designer: H. Fenton
Height: Small
Issued: 1947–
Price: R.R.P.

BEEFEATER D6251
Designer: H. Fenton
Height: Mini
Issued: 1947–1991
Price: $50 £35

BEEFEATER (GR on handle) D6206
Designer: H. Fenton
Height: Large
Issued: 1947–1953
Price: $110 £75

BEEFEATER (GR on yellow handle) D6206
Designer: H. Fenton
Height: Large
Issued: 1947–1953
Price: $975 £650

BEEFEATER (GR on yellow handle) D6206
Designer: H. Fenton
Height: Small
Issued: 1947–1953
Price: $750 £500

AUCTIONEER (Kevin Francis) D6838

ARAMIS D6828

ATHOS D6827 (Peter Jones)

'ARRY D6207

'ARRIET D6208

BACCHUS D6499

CHARACTER JUGS

BEEFEATER (GR on handle)
D6233
Designer: H. Fenton
Height: Small
Issued: 1947–1953
Price: $70 £45

BEEFEATER (GR on handle)
D6251
Designer: H. Fenton
Height: Mini
Issued: 1947–1953
Price: $70 £45

BEEFEATER D6806
(Collectors' Club)
Designer: R. Tabbenor
Height: Tiny
Issued: 1988
Price: $75 £50

BENJAMIN FRANKLIN D6695
Designer: E. Griffiths
Height: Small
Issued: 1982–1988
Price: $60 £40

BLACKSMITH D6571
Designer: D. Biggs
Height: Large
Issued: 1963–1983
Price: $100 £65

BLACKSMITH D6578
Designer: D. Biggs
Height: Small
Issued: 1963–1983
Price: $70 £45

BLACKSMITH D6585
Designer: D. Biggs
Height: Mini
Issued: 1963–1983
Price: $60 £40

BONNIE PRINCE CHARLIE
D6858
Designer: W. K. Harper
Height: Large
Issued: 1990
Price: R.R.P.

BOOTMAKER D6572
Designer: D. Biggs
Height: Large
Issued: 1963–1983
Price: $100 £65

BOOTMAKER D6579
Designer: D. Biggs
Height: Small
Issued: 1963–1983
Price: $70 £45

BOOTMAKER D6586
Designer: D. Biggs
Height: Mini
Issued: 1963–1983
Price: $60 £40

BOWLS PLAYER D6896
Designer: S. Taylor
Height: Small
Issued: 1991
Price: R.R.P.

BEEFEATER D6206

BENJAMIN FRANKLIN D6695

BLACKSMITH D6571

BUFFALO BILL D6735
Designer: S. Taylor
Height: Medium
Issued: 1985–1988
Price: $70 £45

BUSKER D6775
Designer: S. Taylor
Height: Large
Issued: 1988–1991
Price: $80 £55

BUZ FUZ D5838
Designer: L. Harradine &
         H. Fenton
Height: Intermediate
Issued: 1938–1948
Price: $165 £110

BUZ FUZ D5838
Designer: L. Harradine &
         H. Fenton
Height: Small
Issued: 1948–1960
Price: $100 £65

CAPTAIN AHAB D6500
Designer: G. Sharpe
Height: Large
Issued: 1959–1985
Price: $100 £65

CAPTAIN AHAB D6506
Designer: G. Sharpe
Height: Small
Issued: 1959–1985
Price: $60 £40

CAPTAIN AHAB D6522
Designer: G. Sharpe
Height: Mini
Issued: 1960–1985
Price: $50 £35

CAP'N CUTTLE D5842
Designer: L. Harradine
Height: Intermediate
Issued: 1938–1945
Price: $165 £110

CAP'N CUTTLE D5842
Designer: L. Harradine
Height: Small
Issued: 1948–1960
Price: $100 £65

CAPTAIN HENRY MORGAN
D6467
Designer: G. Sharpe
Height: Large
Issued: 1958–1982
Price: $100 £65

CAPTAIN HENRY MORGAN
D6469
Designer: G. Sharpe
Height: Small
Issued: 1958–1982
Price: $70 £45

BUSKER D6775

BUFFALO BILL D6735

CAPTAIN AHAB D6500

CAP'N CUTTLE D5842

BUZ FUZ D5838

BOOTMAKER D6572

CHARACTER JUGS

CAPTAIN HENRY MORGAN
D6510
Designer: G. Sharpe
Height: Mini
Issued: 1960–1982
Price: $50 £35

CAPTAIN HOOK D6597
Designer: M. Henk & D. Biggs
Height: Large
Issued: 1965–1971
Price: $440 £295

CAPTAIN HOOK D6601
Designer: M. Henk & D. Biggs
Height: Small
Issued: 1965–1971
Price: $384 £240

CAPTAIN HOOK D6605
Designer: M. Henk & D. Biggs
Height: Mini
Issued: 1965–1971
Price: $290 £195

CAPTAIN HOOK D6947
Designer: Martyn Alcock
Height: Large
Issued: 1994
Price: R.R.P.

CARDINAL D5614
Designer: C. Noke
Height: Large
Issued: 1936–1960
Price: $130 £85

CARDINAL D6033
Designer: C. Noke
Height: Small
Issued: 1939–1960
Price: $75 £50

CARDINAL D6129
Designer: C. Noke
Height: Mini
Issued: 1940–1960
Price: $70 £45

CARDINAL D6258
Designer: C. Noke
Height: Tiny
Issued: 1947–1960
Price: $165 £110

CATHERINE HOWARD D6645
Designer: P. Gee
Height: Large
Issued: 1978–1989
Price: $110 £75

CATHERINE HOWARD D6692
Designer: P. Gee
Height: Small
Issued: 1984–1989
Price: $70 £45

CATHERINE HOWARD D6693
Designer: P. Gee
Height: Mini
Issued: 1984–1989
Price: $50 £35

CATHERINE PARR D6664

CARDINAL D6129

CAPTAIN HOOK D6597

CATHERINE OF ARAGON
D6643
Designer: A. Maslankowski
Height: Large
Issued: 1975–1989
Price: $110 £75

CATHERINE OF ARAGON
D6657
Designer: A. Maslankowski
Height: Small
Issued: 1981–1989
Price: $70 £45

CATHERINE OF ARAGON
D6658
Designer: A. Maslankowski
Height: Mini
Issued: 1981–1989
Price: $50 £35

CATHERINE PARR D6664
Designer: M. Abberley
Height: Large
Issued: 1981–1989
Price: $110 £75

CATHERINE PARR D6752
Designer: M. Abberley
Height: Mini
Issued: 1987–1989
Price: $100 £65

CATHERINE PARR D6751
Designer: M. Abberley
Height: Small
Issued: 1987–1989
Price: $70 £45

CAVALIER D6114
Designer: H. Fenton
Height: Large
Issued: 1940–1960
Price: $130 £85

CAVALIER D6173
Designer: H. Fenton
Height: Small
Issued: 1941–1960
Price: $70 £45

CAVALIER D6114
Designer: H. Fenton
Height: Large (with goatee beard)
Issued: 1940–1942
Price: $2475 £1650

CHELSEA PENSIONER D6817
Designer: S. Taylor
Height: Large
Issued: 1989–1992
Price: $100 £65

CHIEF SITTING BULL AND GEORGE ARMSTRONG CUSTER D6712
Limited edition of 9500
Designer: M. Abberley
Height: Large
Issued: 1984–
Price: $180 £120

CATHERINE HOWARD D6645

CAVALIER D6114

CHIEF SITTING BULL AND GEORGE ARMSTRONG CUSTER D6712

CAPTAIN HENRY MORGAN D6467

CHELSEA PENSIONER D6817

CATHERINE OF ARAGON D6643

CHURCHILL (Natural) D6170
Two handled Loving Cup, very
rare
Designer: C. Noke
Height: Large
Issued: 1940–1941
Price: $18750 £12500

CHURCHILL (White) D6170
Two handled Loving Cup, rare
Designer: C. Noke
Height: Large
Issued: 1940–1941
Price: $5600 £3500

CHURCHILL (White) D6849
(Lawleys)
Designer: S. Taylor
Height: Small
Issued: 1989–1992
Price: $80 £50

CHURCHILL – JUG OF THE
YEAR 1992 D6907
Designer: C. Noke & S. Taylor
Height: Large
Issued: 1992–1994
Price: R.R.P.

CITY GENT D6815
Designer: S. Taylor
Height: Large
Issued: 1988–1991
Price: $90 £60

CLARK GABLE D6709
Designer: S. Taylor
Height: Large
Issued: 1984–
Price: $3000 £2000

CLOWN D5610
Designer: H. Fenton
Height: Large
(Red Haired)
Issued: 1937–1942
Price: $2000 £1250

CLOWN D5610
Designer: H. Fenton
Height: Large
(Brown Haired)
Issued: 1937–1942
Price: $2000 £1250

CLOWN D6322
Designer: H. Fenton
Height: Large
(White Haired)
Issued: 1951–1955
Price: $880 £550

CLOWN D5610
Designer: H. Fenton
Height: Large
(Black Haired)
Issued: 1937–1942
Price: $12000 £7500

CLOWN D6834
Designer: S. Taylor
Height: Large
Issued: 1989
Price: R.R.P.

CHURCHILL (Natural) D6170

CHURCHILL (White) D6170

CITY GENT D6815

COLLECTOR D6796 (Kevin
Francis) Limited edition of 5000
Designer: S. Taylor
Height: Large
Issued: 1988–1992
Price: $130 £85

COLUMBUS D6891
Designer: S. Taylor
Height: Large
Issued: 1991
Price: R.R.P.

COOK and CHESHIRE CAT
D6842
Designer: W. K. Harper
Height: Large
Issued: 1990–1991
Price: $130 £85

D'ARTAGNAN D6691
Designer: S. Taylor
Height: Large
Issued: 1982–
Price: R.R.P.

D'ARTAGNAN D6764
Designer: S. Taylor
Height: Small
Issued: 1988
Price: R.R.P.

D'ARTAGNAN D6765
Designer: S. Taylor
Height: Mini
Issued: 1988–1991
Price: $50 £35

DAVY CROCKETT/SANTA
ANNA D6729
Designer: M. Abberley
Height: Large
Issued: 1985–1991
Price: $130 £85

DICK TURPIN (First version)
D5485
Designer: C. Noke & H. Fenton
Height: Large
Issued: 1935–1960
Price: $130 £85

DICK TURPIN (First version)
D5618
Designer: C. Noke & H. Fenton
Height: Small
Issued: 1936–1960
Price: $70 £45

DICK TURPIN (First version)
D6128
Designer: C. Noke & H. Fenton
Height: Mini
Issued: 1940–1960
Price: $70 £45

DICK TURPIN (Second version)
D6528
Designer: D. Biggs
Height: Large
Issued: 1960–1981
Price: $100 £65

CLARK GABLE D6709

CLOWN D5610

COLLECTOR D6796 (Kevin Francis)

DAVY CROCKETT/SANTA ANNA D6729

D'ARTAGNAN D6691

DICK TURPIN (First version) D5485

DICK TURPIN (Second version)
D6535
Designer: D. Biggs
Height: Small
Issued: 1960–1981
Price: $70 £45

DICK TURPIN (Second version)
D6542
Designer: D. Biggs
Height: Mini
Issued: 1960–1981
Price: $50 £35

DICK TURPIN (DIAMOND ANNIVERSARY) D6951
Designer: C. Noke
Height: Tiny
Issued: 1994
Price: R.R.P.

DICK WHITTINGTON D6375
Designer: G. Blower
Height: Large
Issued: 1953–1960
Price: $340 £225

DICK WHITTINGTON D6846
(China Guild)
Limited edition of 6000
Designer: W. K. Harper
Height: Large
Issued: 1989
Price: $104 £65

DOC HOLLIDAY D6731
Designer: S. Taylor
Height: Medium
Issued: 1985–1988
Price: $70 £45

DON QUIXOTE D6455
Designer: G. Blower
Height: Large
Issued: 1960–1991
Price: $90 £55

DON QUIXOTE D6460
Designer: G. Blower
Height: Small
Issued: 1960–
Price: $50 £35

DON QUIXOTE D6511
Designer: G. Blower
Height: Mini
Issued: 1960–1991
Price: $50 £35

DRAKE D6115
Designer: H. Fenton
Height: Large (Hatless)
Issued: 1940–1941
Price: $2250 £1500

DRAKE D6115
Designer: H. Fenton
Height: Large
Issued: 1940–1960
Price: $130 £85

DRAKE D6174
Designer: H. Fenton
Height: Small
Issued: 1941–1960
Price: $70 £45

DICK WHITTINGTON D6375

DICK WHITTINGTON D6846

DOC HOLLIDAY D6731

DUKE OF WELLINGTON
D6848 (U.K. Ceramics)
Limited edition of 5000
Designer: W. K. Harper
Height: Large
Issued: 1989
Price: $150 £95

EARL MOUNTBATTEN OF BURMA D6851 (Lawleys)
Limited edition of 9500
Designer: S. Taylor
Height: Small
Issued: 1989
Price: $80 £50

EARL MOUNTBATTEN OF BURMA D6944
Limited edition of 5000
Designer: S. Taylor
Height: Large
Issued: 1993
Price: R.R.P.

ELEPHANT TRAINER D6841
Designer: S. Taylor
Height: Large
Issued: 1990–1992
Price: $90 £60

ENGINE DRIVER D6823
(Lawleys)
Limited edition of 5000
Designer: S. Taylor
Height: Small
Issued: 1987
Price: $50 £35

FALCONER D6533
Designer: M. Henk
Height: Large
Issued: 1960–1991
Price: $75 £50

FALCONER D6540
Designer: M. Henk
Height: Small
Issued: 1960–
Price: $50 £35

FALCONER D6547
Designer: M. Henk
Height: Mini
Issued: 1960–1992
Price: $48 £30

FALCONER D6800 (Peter Jones) Limited edition of 1000
Designer: M. Henk
Height: Large
Issued: 1987–1991
Price: $110 £75

FALSTAFF D6287
Designer: H. Fenton
Height: Large
Issued: 1950–
Price: R.R.P.

FALSTAFF D6385
Designer: H. Fenton
Height: Small
Issued: 1950–
Price: R.R.P.

ENGINE DRIVER D6823

DRAKE D6115

DON QUIXOTE D6455

DUKE OF WELLINGTON D6848

DRAKE D6115

FALCONER D6800

FALSTAFF D6519
Designer: H. Fenton
Height: Mini
Issued: 1960–1992
Price: $75 £50

FALSTAFF D6795 (U.K. Fairs)
Limited edition of 1500
Designer: H. Fenton
Height: Large
Issued: 1987
Price: $110 £75

FARMER JOHN D5788
Designer: C. Noke
Height: Large
Issued: 1938–1960
Price: $130 £85

FARMER JOHN D5789
Designer: C. Noke
Height: Small
Issued: 1938–1960
Price: $80 £55

FAT BOY D5840
Designer: L. Harradine &
H. Fenton
Height: Intermediate
Issued: 1938–1948
Price: $180 £120

FAT BOY D5840
Designer: L. Harradine &
H. Fenton
Height: Small
Issued: 1948–1960
Price: $90 £55

FAT BOY D6139
Designer: L. Harradine &
H. Fenton
Height: Mini
Issued: 1940–1960
Price: $60 £40

FAT BOY D6142
Designer: L. Harradine &
H. Fenton
Height: Tiny
Issued: 1940–1960
Price: $100 £65

FIREMAN D6697
Designer: R. Tabbenor
Height: Large
Issued: 1984–1991
Price: $90 £60

FIREMAN D6839 (Lawleys)
Limited edition of 5000
Designer: S. Taylor
Height: Small
Issued: 1987
Price: $50 £35

FORTUNE TELLER D6497
Designer: G. Sharpe
Height: Large
Issued: 1959–1967
Price: $440 £295

FORTUNE TELLER D6503
Designer: G. Sharpe
Height: Small
Issued: 1959–1967
Price: $290 £195

FALSTAFF D6795

FARMER JOHN D5788

FAT BOY D5840

FORTUNE TELLER D6523
Designer: G. Sharpe
Height: Mini
Issued: 1960–1967
Price: $288 £180

FRIAR TUCK D6321
Designer: H. Fenton
Height: Large
Issued: 1951–1960
Price: $300 £200

GAOLER D6570
Designer: D. Biggs
Height: Large
Issued: 1963–1983
Price: $100 £65

GAOLER D6577
Designer: D. Biggs
Height: Small
Issued: 1963–1983
Price: $70 £45

GAOLER D6584
Designer: D. Biggs
Height: Mini
Issued: 1963–1983
Price: $50 £35

GARDENER D6630
Designer: D. Biggs
Height: Large
Issued: 1973–1981
Price: $180 £120

GARDENER D6634
Designer: D. Biggs
Height: Small
Issued: 1973–1981
Price: $130 £85

GARDENER D6638
Designer: D. Biggs
Height: Mini
Issued: 1973–1981
Price: $100 £65

GARDENER D6868
Designer: S. Taylor
Height: Small
Issued: 1990
Price: R.R.P.

GEORGE HARRISON D6727
Designer: S. Taylor
Height: Medium
Issued: 1984–1991
Price: $75 £50

GEORGE WASHINGTON
D6669
Designer: S. Taylor
Height: Large
Issued: 1982–
Price: R.R.P.

GEORGE WASHINGTON/
KING GEORGE III D6749
Limited edition of 9500
Designer: M. Abberley
Height: Large
Issued: 1986
Price: $130 £85

FIREMAN D6697

FORTUNE TELLER
D6497

FRIAR TUCK D6321

GAOLER D6570

GEORGE HARRISON D6727

GEORGE WASHINGTON D6669

GERONIMO D6733
Designer: S. Taylor
Height: Medium
Issued: 1985–1988
Price: $90 £60

GLADIATOR D6550
Designer: M. Henk
Height: Large
Issued: 1961–1967
Price: $440 £295

GLADIATOR D6553
Designer: M. Henk
Height: Small
Issued: 1961–1967
Price: $290 £195

GLADIATOR D6556
Designer: M. Henk
Height: Mini
Issued: 1961–1967
Price: $290 £195

GOLFER D6623
Designer: D. Biggs
Height: Large
Issued: 1971–
Price: R.R.P.

GOLFER D6756
Designer: D. Biggs
Height: Small
Issued: 1987–1992
Price: $50 £35

GOLFER D6757
Designer: D. Biggs
Height: Mini
Issued: 1987–1991
Price: $50 £35

GOLFER D6784 (John Sinclair)
Limited edition of 1000
Designer: D. Biggs
Height: Large
Issued: 1987–
Price: $100 £65

GOLFER D6865
Designer: S. Taylor
Height: Small
Issued: 1990
Price: R.R.P.

GONDOLIER D6589
Designer: D. Biggs
Height: Large
Issued: 1964–1969
Price: $440 £295

GONDOLIER D6592
Designer: D. Biggs
Height: Small
Issued: 1964–1969
Price: $290 £195

GONDOLIER D6595
Designer: D. Biggs
Height: Mini
Issued: 1964–1969
Price: $290 £195

**GEORGE WASHINGTON/
KING GEORGE III D6749**

GERONIMO D6733

GOLFER D6784

GONE AWAY D6531
Designer: G. Sharpe
Height: Large
Issued: 1960–1982
Price: $100 £65

GONE AWAY D6538
Designer: G. Sharpe
Height: Small
Issued: 1960–1982
Price: $72 £45

GONE AWAY D6545
Designer: G. Sharpe
Height: Mini
Issued: 1960–1982
Price: $50 £35

GRADUATE (THE) D6916
Designer: S. Taylor
Height: Small
Issued: 1993
Price: R.R.P.

GRANNY D5521
Designer: H. Fenton &
        M. Henk
Height: Large
Issued: 1935–1983
Price: $110 £75

**GRANNY (Toothless version)
D5521**
Designer: H. Fenton &
        M. Henk
Height: Large
Issued: 1935
Price: $720 £450

GRANNY D6384
Designer: H. Fenton &
        M. Henk
Height: Small
Issued: 1953–1983
Price: $70 £45

GRANNY D6520
Designer: H. Fenton &
        M. Henk
Height: Mini
Issued: 1960–1983
Price: $50 £35

**GRANNY (DIAMOND
ANNIVERSARY) D6954**
Designer: H. Fenton
Height: Tiny
Issued: 1994
Price: R.R.P.

GROUCHO MARX D6710
Designer: S. Taylor
Height: Large
Issued: 1984–1987
Price: $110 £75

GUARDSMAN D6568
Designer: M. Henk
Height: Large
Issued: 1963–1983
Price: $100 £65

GRANNY D5521

GONDOLIER D6589

GUARDSMAN D6568

GLADIATOR D6550

GONE AWAY D6531

GROUCHO MARX D6710

CHARACTER JUGS

GUARDSMAN D6755
Designer: S. Taylor
Height: Large
Issued: 1986
Price: R.R.P.

GUARDSMAN D6575
Designer: M. Henk
Height: Small
Issued: 1963–1983
Price: $60 £40

GUARDSMAN D6582
Designer: M. Henk
Height: Mini
Issued: 1963–1983
Price: $40 £25

GUARDSMEN D6771
Designer: S. Taylor
Height: Small
Issued: 1986
Price: R.R.P.

GUARDSMEN D6772
Designer: S. Taylor
Height: Mini
Issued: 1986–1992
Price: $45 £30

GULLIVER D6560
Designer: D. Biggs
Height: Large
Issued: 1962–1967
Price: $490 £325

GULLIVER D6563
Designer: D. Biggs
Height: Small
Issued: 1962–1967
Price: $340 £225

GULLIVER D6566
Designer: D. Biggs
Height: Mini
Issued: 1962–1967
Price: $340 £225

GUNSMITH D6573
Designer: D. Biggs
Height: Large
Issued: 1963–1983
Price: $100 £65

GUNSMITH D6580
Designer: D. Biggs
Height: Small
Issued: 1963–1983
Price: $70 £45

GUNSMITH D6587
Designer: D. Biggs
Height: Mini
Issued: 1963–1983
Price: $50 £35

GUY FAWKES D6861
Designer: W. K. Harper
Height: Large
Issued: 1990
Price: R.R.P.

HAMLET D6672
Designer: M. Abberley
Height: Large
Issued: 1982–1988
Price: $110 £75

HAMPSHIRE CRICKETER D6739

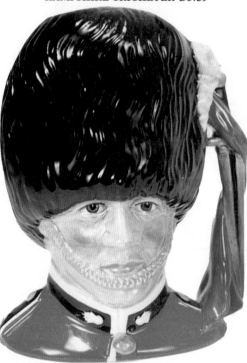

GUARDSMAN D6755

JANE SEYMOUR D6746

**HAMPSHIRE CRICKETER
D6739 (H.C.C. Club)**
Limited edition of 5000
Designer: H. Sales
Height: Medium
Issued: 1985
Price: $90 £60

HENRY V D6671
Designer: R. Tabbenor
Height: Large
Issued: 1982–1988
Price: $110 £75

HENRY VIII D6642
Designer: E. Griffiths
Height: Large
Issued: 1979–
Price: R.R.P.

HENRY VIII D6647
Designer: E. Griffiths
Height: Small
Issued: 1979–
Price: R.R.P.

HENRY VIII D6648
Designer: E. Griffiths
Height: Mini
Issued: 1979–1989
Price: $110 £75

IZAAC WALTON D6404
Designer: G. Blower
Height: Large
Issued: 1953–1982
Price: $110 £75

JANE SEYMOUR D6646
Designer: M. Abberley
Height: Large
Issued: 1979–1990
Price: $110 £75

JANE SEYMOUR D6747
Designer: M. Abberley
Height: Mini
Issued: 1986–1990
Price: $60 £40

JANE SEYMOUR D6746
Designer: M. Abberley
Height: Small
Issued: 1986–1990
Price: $70 £45

JARGE D6288
Designer: H. Fenton
Height: Large
Issued: 1950–1960
Price: $340 £225

JARGE D6295
Designer: H. Fenton
Height: Small
Issued: 1950–1960
Price: $165 £110

JESTER D5556
Designer: C. Noke
Height: Small
Issued: 1936–1960
Price: $80 £55

GULLIVER D6560

HAMLET D6672

JESTER D5556

JARGE D6295

HENRY VIII D6647

HENRY V D6671

IZAAC WALTON D6404

GUNSMITH D6573

JESTER (DIAMOND ANNIVERSARY) D6953
Designer: C. Noke
Height: Tiny
Issued: 1994
Price: R.R.P.

JIMMY DURANTE D6708
Designer: D. Biggs
Height: Large
Issued: 1985–1986
Price: $110 £75

JOCKEY D6625
Designer: D. Biggs
Height: Large
Issued: 1971–1975
Price: $340 £225

JOCKEY D6877
Designer: S. Taylor
Height: Small
Issued: 1991
Price: R.R.P.

JOHN BARLEYCORN D5327
Designer: C. Noke
Height: Large
Issued: 1934–1960
Price: $130 £85

JOHN BARLEYCORN D5735
Designer: C. Noke
Height: Small
Issued: 1937–1960
Price: $80 £55

JOHN BARLEYCORN D6041
Designer: C. Noke
Height: Mini
Issued: 1939–1960
Price: $70 £45

JOHN BARLEYCORN (DIAMOND ANNIVERSARY) D6952
Designer: C. Noke & H. Fenton
Height: Tiny
Issued: 1994
Price: R.R.P.

JOHN DOULTON D6656 (Collectors' Club)
Designer: E. Griffiths
Height: Small
Issued: 1980
Price: $40 £25
Showing 2pm.
$100 £65
Showing 8pm.

JOHN LENNON D6725
Designer: S. Taylor
Height: Medium
Issued: 1984–1991
Price: $75 £50

JOHN LENNON D6797 (John Sinclair) New colourway
Limited edition of 1000
Designer: S. Taylor
Height: Medium
Issued: 1987–
Price: $110 £75

JIMMY DURANTE D6708

JOCKEY D6625

KING PHILIP II of SPAIN D6822

JOHN PEEL D5612
Designer: H. Fenton
Height: Large
Issued: 1936–1960
Price: $130 £85

JOHN PEEL D5731
Designer: H. Fenton
Height: Small
Issued: 1937–1960
Price: $70 £45

JOHN PEEL D6130
Designer: H. Fenton
Height: Mini
Issued: 1940–1960
Price: $60 £40

JOHN PEEL D6259
Designer: H. Fenton
Height: Tiny
Issued: 1947–1960
Price: $165 £110

JOHNNY APPLESEED D6372
Designer: H. Fenton
Height: Large
Issued: 1953–1969
Price: $340 £225

JUGGLER D6835
Designer: S. Taylor
Height: Large
Issued: 1989–1991
Price: $100 £65

KING ARTHUR and GUINEVERE D6836
Limited edition of 9500
Designer: S. Taylor
Height: Large
Issued: 1989–1992
Price: $130 £85

KING CHARLES D6917
Limited edition of 2500
Designer: W. K. Harper
Height: Large
Issued: 1992
Price: R.R.P.

KING PHILIP II of SPAIN D6822 (Lawleys)
Limited edition of 9500
Designer: W. K. Harper
Height: Small
Issued: 1988–1992
Price: $80 £55

LAWYER D6498
Designer: M. Henk
Height: Large
Issued: 1959–
Price: R.R.P.

LAWYER D6504
Designer: M. Henk
Height: Small
Issued: 1959–
Price: R.R.P.

LAWYER D6524
Designer: M. Henk
Height: Mini
Issued: 1960–1991
Price: $45 £30

JOHN LENNON D6725

JOHN PEEL D6130

LAWYER D6498

KING ARTHUR and
GUINEVERE D6836

JOHN BARLEYCORN D5327

JOHNNY APPLESEED D6372

LEPRECHAUN D6847
Designer: W. K. Harper
Height: Large
Issued: 1990
Price: R.R.P.

LEPRECHAUN D6909
Designer: W. K. Harper
Height: Small
Issued: 1990
Price: R.R.P.

LITTLE MESTER D6819 (John Sinclair) Limited edition of 3500
Designer: S. Taylor
Height: Large
Issued: 1988–
Price: $104 £65

LOBSTER MAN D6617
Designer: D. Biggs
Height: Large
Issued: 1968–1991
Price: $75 £50

LOBSTER MAN D6620
Designer: D. Biggs
Height: Small
Issued: 1968–1991
Price: $50 £35

LOBSTER MAN D6652
Designer: D. Biggs
Height: Mini
Issued: 1980–1991
Price: $45 £30

LOBSTER MAN D6783
New colourway
Designer: D. Biggs
Height: Large
Issued: 1987–1989
Price: $100 £65

LONDON BOBBY D6744
Designer: S. Taylor
Height: Large
Issued: 1986
Price: R.R.P.

LONDON BOBBY D6762
Designer: S. Taylor
Height: Small
Issued: 1986
Price: R.R.P.

LONDON BOBBY D6763
Designer: S. Taylor
Height: Mini
Issued: 1986–1991
Price: $45 £30

LONG JOHN SILVER D6335
Designer: M. Henk
Height: Large
Issued: 1960–
Price: R.R.P.

LITTLE MESTER D6819

LOBSTER MAN D6617

LONG JOHN SILVER D6335

LONG JOHN SILVER D6386
Designer: M. Henk
Height: Small
Issued: 1960–
Price: R.R.P.

LONG JOHN SILVER D6512
Designer: M. Henk
Height: Mini
Issued: 1960–1992
Price: $45 £30

LORD NELSON D6336
Designer: G. Blower
Height: Large
Issued: 1952–1969
Price: $300 £200

LOUIS ARMSTRONG D6707
Designer: D. Biggs
Height: Large
Issued: 1984–1987
Price: $110 £75

LUMBERJACK D6610
Designer: M. Henk
Height: Large
Issued: 1967–1983
Price: $100 £65

LUMBERJACK D6613
Designer: M. Henk
Height: Small
Issued: 1967–1983
Price: $70 £45

MACBETH D6667
Designer: M. Abberley
Height: Large
Issued: 1982–1988
Price: $110 £75

MAD HATTER D6598
Designer: M. Henk
Height: Large
Issued: 1965–1983
Price: $130 £85

MAD HATTER D6602
Designer: M. Henk
Height: Small
Issued: 1965–1983
Price: $70 £45

MAD HATTER D6606
Designer: M. Henk
Height: Mini
Issued: 1965–1983
Price: $70 £45

MAE WEST D6688
Designer: C. Davidson
Height: Large
Issued: 1983–1985
Price: $110 £75

LORD NELSON D6336

LOUIS ARMSTRONG D6707

LUMBERJACK D6610

MACBETH D6667

MAD HATTER D6598

MAE WEST D6688

CHARACTER JUGS

MAORI
Designer: Unknown
Height: Large
Issued: c.1939
Price: $12000 £7500

MARCH HARE D6776
Designer: W. K. Harper
Height: Large
Issued: 1989
Price: R.R.P.

MARK TWAIN D6654
Designer: E. Griffiths
Height: Large
Issued: 1980–1990
Price: $75 £50

MARK TWAIN D6694
Designer: E. Griffiths
Height: Small
Issued: 1983–1990
Price: $60 £40

MARK TWAIN D6758
Designer: E. Griffiths
Height: Mini
Issued: 1987–1990
Price: $50 £35

MASTER (THE) D6898
Designer: S. Taylor
Height: Small
Issued: 1991
Price: R.R.P.

MEPHISTOPHELES D5757
Designer: H. Fenton
Height: Large
Issued: 1937–1948
Price: $1125 £750

MEPHISTOPHELES D5758
Designer: H. Fenton
Height: Small
Issued: 1937–1948
Price: $880 £550

MERLIN D6529
Designer: G. Sharpe
Height: Large
Issued: 1960–
Price: R.R.P.

MERLIN D6536
Designer: G. Sharpe
Height: Small
Issued: 1960–
Price: R.R.P.

MERLIN D6543
Designer: G. Sharpe
Height: Mini
Issued: 1960–1992
Price: R.R.P.

MICHAEL DOULTON D6808
Designer: W. K. Harper
Height: Small
Issued: 1988–1989
Price: $56 £35

MIKADO D6501
Designer: M. Henk
Height: Large
Issued: 1959–1969
Price: $410 £275

MARK TWAIN D6654

MEPHISTOPHELES D5757

MERLIN D6529

MIKADO D6507
Designer: M. Henk
Height: Small
Issued: 1959–1969
Price: $260 £175

MIKADO D6525
Designer: M. Henk
Height: Mini
Issued: 1960–1969
Price: $280 £175

MINE HOST D6468
Designer: M. Henk
Height: Large
Issued: 1958–1982
Price: $100 £65

MINE HOST D6470
Designer: M. Henk
Height: Small
Issued: 1958–1982
Price: $70 £45

MINE HOST D6513
Designer: M. Henk
Height: Mini
Issued: 1960–1982
Price: $48 £30

MONTGOMERY D6908
Limited edition of 2500
Designer: H. Fenton & S. Taylor
Height: Large
Issued: 1992
Price: $147 £99

MONTY D6202
Designer: H. Fenton
Height: Large
Issued: 1946–1991
Price: $75 £50

MR MICAWBER D5843
Designer: L. Harradine and
         H. Fenton
Height: Intermediate
Issued: 1938–1948
Price: $165 £110

MR MICAWBER D5843
Designer: L. Harradine and
         H. Fenton
Height: Small
Issued: 1948–1960
Price: $70 £45

MR MICAWBER D6138
Designer: L. Harradine and
         H. Fenton
Height: Mini
Issued: 1940–1960
Price: $56 £35

MR MICAWBER D6143
Designer: L. Harradine and
         H. Fenton
Height: Tiny
Issued: 1940–1960
Price: $96 £60

MR PICKWICK D6060
Designer: L. Harradine and
         H. Fenton
Height: Large
Issued: 1940–1960
Price: $165 £110

MR PICKWICK D5839
Designer: L. Harradine and
          H. Fenton
Height: Intermediate
Issued: 1938–1948
Price: $165 £110

MR PICKWICK D5839
Designer: L. Harradine and
          H. Fenton
Height: Small
Issued: 1948–1960
Price: $75 £50

MR PICKWICK D6245
Designer: L. Harradine and
          H. Fenton
Height: Mini
Issued: 1947–1960
Price: $56 £35

MR PICKWICK D6260
Designer: L. Harradine and
          H. Fenton
Height: Tiny
Issued: 1947–1960
Price: $165 £110

MR QUAKER D6738 (Quaker
Oats) Limited edition of 3500
Designer: H. Sales
Height: Large
Issued: 1985
Price: $360 £225

NAPOLEON D6908
Limited edition of 2500
Designer: S. Taylor
Height: Large
Issued: 1993
Price: R.R.P.

**NAPOLEON AND JOSEPHINE
D6750**
Designer: M. Abberley
Height: Large
Issued: 1986 Limited edition
Price: $130 £85

NEPTUNE D6548
Designer: M. Henk
Height: Large
Issued: 1961–1991
Price: $75 £50

NEPTUNE D6552
Designer: M. Henk
Height: Small
Issued: 1961–1991
Price: $50 £35

NEPTUNE D6555
Designer: M. Henk
Height: Mini
Issued: 1961–1991
Price: $45 £30

NIGHT WATCHMAN D6569
Designer: M. Henk
Height: Large
Issued: 1963–1983
Price: $100 £65

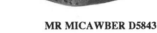

MR MICAWBER D5843

MICHAEL DOULTON D6808
(Collectors' Club)

MR PICKWICK D6060

MONTY D6202

NEPTUNE D6548

MR QUAKER D6738

CHARACTER JUGS

NIGHT WATCHMAN D6576
Designer: M. Henk
Height: Small
Issued: 1963–1983
Price: $70 £45

NIGHT WATCHMAN D6583
Designer: M. Henk
Height: Mini
Issued: 1963–1983
Price: $50 £35

NORTH AMERICAN INDIAN D6611
Designer: M. Henk
Height: Large
Issued: 1967–1991
Price: $75 £50

NORTH AMERICAN INDIAN D6611
Designer: M. Henk
Height: Large
Issued: 1967
Price: $180 £120
(Special Back Stamp Canadian Centennial)

NORTH AMERICAN INDIAN D6614
Designer: M. Henk
Height: Small
Issued: 1967–1991
Price: $50 £35

NORTH AMERICAN INDIAN D6665
Designer: M. Henk
Height: Mini
Issued: 1967–1992
Price: $45 £30

NORTH AMERICAN INDIAN D6786 (John Sinclair)
Limited edition of 1000
Designer: M. Henk
Height: Large
Issued: 1987–1991
Price: $100 £65

OLD CHARLEY D5420
Designer: C. Noke
Height: Large
Issued: 1934–1983
Price: $100 £65

OLD CHARLEY D5527
Designer: C. Noke
Height: Small
Issued: 1935–1983
Price: $60 £40

OLD CHARLEY D6046
Designer: C. Noke
Height: Mini
Issued: 1939–1982
Price: $45 £30

OLD CHARLEY D6144
Designer: C. Noke
Height: Tiny
Issued: 1940–1960
Price: $100 £65

NIGHT WATCHMAN D6569

NORTH AMERICAN INDIAN D6786

OLD CHARLEY D5420

OLD KING COLE D6036
Designer: H. Fenton
Height: Large
Issued: 1939–1960
Price: $190 £125

OLD KING COLE D6037
Designer: H. Fenton
Height: Small
Issued: 1939–1960
Price: $165 £110

OLD KING COLE (Yellow Crown) D6036
Designer: H. Fenton
Height: Large
Issued: 1939–1940
Price: $2250 £1500

OLD KING COLE (Yellow Crown) D6037
Designer: H. Fenton
Height: Small
Issued: 1939–1940
Price: $1425 £950

OLD SALT D6551
Designer: G. Sharpe
Height: Large
Issued: 1961–
Price: R.R.P.

OLD SALT D6554
Designer: G. Sharpe
Height: Small
Issued: 1961–
Price: R.R.P.

OLD SALT D6557
Designer: P. Gee
Height: Large
Issued: 1984–1992
Price: R.R.P.

OLD SALT D6782
New colourway
Designer: G. Sharpe
Height: Large
Issued: 1987–1991
Price: $100 £65

OTHELLO D6673
Designer: M. Abberley
Height: Large
Issued: 1982–1988
Price: $110 £75

PADDY D5753
Designer: H. Fenton
Height: Large
Issued: 1937–1960
Price: $110 £75

PADDY D5768
Designer: H. Fenton
Height: Small
Issued: 1937–1960
Price: $70 £45

PADDY D6042
Designer: H. Fenton
Height: Mini
Issued: 1939–1960
Price: $50 £35

OLD KING COLE (Yellow Crown) D6036

OLD KING COLE D6036

OTHELLO D6673

OLD SALT D6551

NORTH AMERICAN INDIAN D6611

PADDY D5753

CHARACTER JUGS

PADDY D6145
Designer: H. Fenton
Height: Tiny
Issued: 1940–1960
Price: $100 £65

PARSON BROWN D5486
Designer: C. Noke
Height: Large
Issued: 1935–1960
Price: $130 £85

PARSON BROWN D5529
Designer: C. Noke
Height: Small
Issued: 1935–1960
Price: $70 £45

PARSON BROWN (DIAMOND ANNIVERSARY) D6955
Designer: C. Noke
Height: Tiny
Issued: 1994
Price: R.R.P.

PAUL McCARTNEY D6724
Designer: S. Taylor
Height: Medium
Issued: 1984–1991
Price: $75 £50

PEARLY BOY (Blue)
Designer: H. Fenton
Height: Large
Issued: 1947–
Price: $3600 £2250

PEARLY BOY (Blue)
Designer: H. Fenton
Height: Small
Issued: 1947–
Price: $1920 £1200

PEARLY BOY (Blue)
Designer: H. Fenton
Height: Mini
Issued: 1947–1992
Price: $3000 £2000

PEARLY BOY (Brown buttons)
An early version of 'ARRY'
Designer: H. Fenton
Height: Large
Issued: 1947–
Price: $1125 £750

PEARLY BOY (Brown buttons)
An early version of 'ARRY'
Designer: H. Fenton
Height: Small
Issued: 1947–
Price: $720 £450

PEARLY BOY (Brown buttons)
An early version of 'ARRY'
Designer: H. Fenton
Height: Mini
Issued: 1947–1992
Price: $448 £280

PEARLY GIRL (Blue)
A very rare version of 'ARRIET'
Designer: H. Fenton
Height: Large
Issued: 1947–
Price: $4500 £3000

PEARLY GIRL (Blue)
A very rare version of 'ARRIET'
Designer: H. Fenton
Height: Small
Issued: 1947–
Price: $3000 £2000

PEARLY KING D6760
Designer: S. Taylor
Height: Large
Issued: 1987–1991
Price: $90 £60

PEARLY KING D6844
Designer: S. Taylor
Height: Small
Issued: 1990–1991
Price: $50 £35

PEARLY QUEEN D6759
Designer: S. Taylor
Height: Large
Issued: 1987–1991
Price: $90 £60

PEARLY QUEEN D6843
Designer: S. Taylor
Height: Small
Issued: 1990–1991
Price: $50 £35

PENDLE WITCH D6826 (Kevin Francis) Limited edition of 5000
Designer: G. Blower
Height: Large
Issued: 1988–1992
Price: $130 £85

PIED PIPER D6403
Designer: G. Blower
Height: Large
Issued: 1954–1981
Price: $110 £75

PIED PIPER D6462
Designer: G. Blower
Height: Small
Issued: 1957–1981
Price: $70 £45

PIED PIPER D6514
Designer: G. Blower
Height: Mini
Issued: 1960–1981
Price: $60 £40

PIPER THE D6918
Designer: S. Taylor
Height: Large
Issued: 1992–1994
Price: $200 £135

POACHER D6429
Designer: M. Henk
Height: Large
Issued: 1955–
Price: R.R.P.

POACHER D6464
Designer: M. Henk
Height: Small
Issued: 1957–
Price: R.R.P.

PARSON BROWN D5486

PAUL McCARTNEY D6724

PEARLY BOY (Blue)

PEARLY BOY (Blue)

PEARLY KING D6760

POACHER D6429

PENDLE WITCH D6826

PEARLY QUEEN D6759

PIED PIPER D6403

CHARACTER JUGS

POACHER D6515
Designer: M. Henk
Height: Mini
Issued: 1960–1991
Price: $45 £30

POACHER D6781
New colourway
Designer: M. Henk
Height: Large
Issued: 1987–1989
Price: $100 £65

POLICEMAN D6852 (Lawleys)
Limited edition of 5000
Designer: S. Taylor
Height: Small
Issued: 1990
Price: $50 £35

PORTHOS D6440
Designer: M. Henk
Height: Large
Issued: 1956–1991
Price: $100 £65

PORTHOS D6453
Designer: M. Henk
Height: Small
Issued: 1956–1991
Price: $50 £35

PORTHOS D6516
Designer: M. Henk
Height: Mini
Issued: 1960–1991
Price: $45 £30

PORTHOS D6828 (Peter Jones)
New colourway
Limited edition of 1000
Designer: M. Henk
Height: Large
Issued: 1988
Price: $110 £75

POSTMAN D6801 (Lawleys)
Limited edition of 5000
Designer: S. Taylor
Height: Small
Issued: 1987–1988
Price: $180 £120

PUNCH AND JUDY MAN D6590
Designer: D. Biggs
Height: Large
Issued: 1964–1969
Price: $440 £295

PUNCH AND JUDY MAN D6593
Designer: D. Biggs
Height: Small
Issued: 1964–1969
Price: $340 £225

PUNCH AND JUDY MAN D6596
Designer: D. Biggs
Height: Mini
Issued: 1964–1969
Price: $340 £225

PORTHOS D6828 (Peter Jones)

POSTMAN D6801 (Lawleys)

PORTHOS D6440

PUNCH AND JUDY MAN D6946
Limited edition of 2500
Designer: S. Taylor
Height: Large
Issued: 1993
Price: R.R.P.

QUEEN ELIZABETH I of ENGLAND D6821 (Lawleys)
Limited edition of 5000
Designer: W. K. Harper
Height: Small
Issued: 1988–1992
Price: $80 £55

QUEEN VICTORIA D6816
Designer: S. Taylor
Height: Large
Issued: 1988–1991
Price: $90 £60

QUEEN VICTORIA D6788 (China Guild)
Limited edition of 3000
Designer: S. Taylor
Height: Large
Issued: 1988
Price: $104 £65

RED QUEEN D6777
Designer: W. K. Harper
Height: Large
Issued: 1987–1991
Price: $90 £60

RED QUEEN D6859
Designer: W. K. Harper
Height: Small
Issued: 1990–1991
Price: $50 £35

RED QUEEN D6860
Designer: W. K. Harper
Height: Mini
Issued: 1990–1991
Price: $45 £30

REGENCY BEAU D6559
Designer: D. Biggs
Height: Large
Issued: 1962–1967
Price: $720 £450

REGENCY BEAU D6562
Designer: D. Biggs
Height: Small
Issued: 1962–1967
Price: $490 £325

REGENCY BEAU D6565
Designer: D. Biggs
Height: Mini
Issued: 1962–1967
Price: $490 £325

RINGO STARR D6726
Designer: S. Taylor
Height: Medium
Issued: 1984–1991
Price: $75 £50

RIP VAN WINKLE D6438
Designer: G. Blower
Height: Large
Issued: 1955–
Price: R.R.P.

CHARACTER JUGS

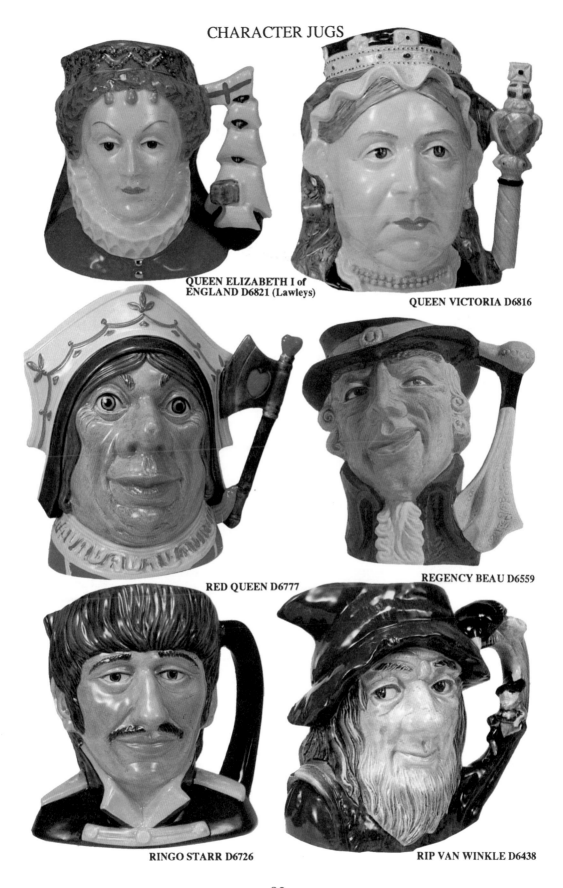

QUEEN ELIZABETH I of
ENGLAND D6821 (Lawleys)

QUEEN VICTORIA D6816

RED QUEEN D6777

REGENCY BEAU D6559

RINGO STARR D6726

RIP VAN WINKLE D6438

RIP VAN WINKLE D6463
Designer: G. Blower
Height: Small
Issued: 1957–
Price: R.R.P.

RIP VAN WINKLE D6517
Designer: G. Blower
Height: Mini
Issued: 1960–1991
Price: $45 £30

RIP VAN WINKLE D6788
(John Sinclair) New colourway
Limited edition of 1000
Designer: G. Blower
Height: Large
Issued: 1987–1991
Price: $100 £65

RIP VAN WINKLE D6788

ROBIN HOOD (First version)
D6205
Designer: H. Fenton
Height: Large
Issued: 1947–1960
Price: $130 £85

ROBIN HOOD (First version)
D6234
Designer: H. Fenton
Height: Small
Issued: 1947–1960
Price: $70 £45

ROBIN HOOD (First version)
D6252
Designer: H. Fenton
Height: Mini
Issued: 1947–1960
Price: $50 £35

ROBIN HOOD (Second version)
D6527
Designer: M. Henk
Height: Large
Issued: 1960–1992
Price: $75 £50

ROBIN HOOD (First version)
D6205

ROBIN HOOD (Second version)
D6534
Designer: M. Henk
Height: Small
Issued: 1960–1992
Price: $50 £35

ROBIN HOOD (Second version)
D6541
Designer: M. Henk
Height: Mini
Issued: 1960–1991
Price: $45 £30

ROBINSON CRUSOE D6532
Designer: M. Henk
Height: Large
Issued: 1960–1983
Price: $100 £65

ROBINSON CRUSOE D6539
Designer: M. Henk
Height: Small
Issued: 1960–1983
Price: $50 £35

ROBIN HOOD (Second version)
D6527

ROBINSON CRUSOE D6546
Designer: M. Henk
Height: Mini
Issued: 1960–1983
Price: $45 £30

ROMEO D6670
Designer: D. Biggs
Height: Large
Issued: 1983–1988
Price: $110 £75

RONALD REAGAN D6718
(Republic Committee)
Limited edition of 5000
Designer: E. Griffiths
Height: Large
Issued: 1984
Price: $400 £250

SAILOR (THE) D6875
Designer: W. K. Harper
Height: Small
Issued: 1991
Price: R.R.P.

ST. GEORGE D6618
Designer: M. Henk
Height: Large
Issued: 1968–1975
Price: $260 £175

ST. GEORGE D6621
Designer: M. Henk
Height: Small
Issued: 1968–1975
Price: $165 £110

SAIREY GAMP D5451
Designer: L. Harradine and
H. Fenton
Height: Large
Issued: 1935–1986
Price: $100 £65

SAIREY GAMP D5528
Designer: L. Harradine and
H. Fenton
Height: Small
Issued: 1935–1986
Price: $50 £35

SAIREY GAMP D6045
Designer: L. Harradine and
H. Fenton
Height: Mini
Issued: 1939–1986
Price: $45 £30

SAIREY GAMP D6146
Designer: L. Harradine and
H. Fenton
Height: Tiny
Issued: 1940–1960
Price: $100 £65

SAM WELLER D6140
Designer: L. Harradine and
H. Fenton
Height: Mini
Issued: 1940–1960
Price: $60 £40

SAM WELLER D6140

SAIREY GAMP D5451

RONALD REAGAN D6718

ST. GEORGE D6618

ROBINSON CRUSOE D6532

ROMEO D6670

SAM WELLER D6064
Designer: L. Harradine and
H. Fenton
Height: Large
Issued: 1940–1960
Price: $120 £80

SAM WELLER D5841
Designer: L. Harradine
H. Fenton
Height: Intermediate
Issued: 1938–1948
Price: $180 £120

SAM WELLER D5841
Designer: L. Harradine and
H. Fenton
Height: Small
Issued: 1948–1960
Price: $60 £40

SAM WELLER D6147
Designer: L. Harradine and
H. Fenton
Height: Tiny
Issued: 1940–1960
Price: $104 £65

SAMSON and DELILAH D6787
Limited edition of 9500
Designer: S. Taylor
Height: Large
Issued: 1988–1991
Price: $110 £75

SAMUEL JOHNSON D6289
Designer: H. Fenton
Height: Large
Issued: 1950–1960
Price: $330 £220

SAMUEL JOHNSON D6296
Designer: H. Fenton
Height: Small
Issued: 1950–1960
Price: $180 £120

SANCHO PANZA D6456
Designer: G. Blower
Height: Large
Issued: 1957–1983
Price: $100 £65

SANCHO PANZA D6461
Designer: G. Blower
Height: Small
Issued: 1957–1983
Price: $50 £35

SANCHO PANZA D6518
Designer: G. Blower
Height: Mini
Issued: 1960–1983
Price: $45 £30

SANTA ANNA/DAVY CROCKETT D6729
Limited edition of 9500
Designer: M. Abberley
Height: Large
Issued: 1985–1991
Price: $130 £85

SAMSON and DELILAH D6787

SAMUEL JOHNSON D6289

SANCHO PANZA D6456

SANTA CLAUS D6668
Designer: M. Abberley
Height: Large with Peg Doll
Handle
Issued: 1981
Price: $110 £75

SANTA CLAUS D6675
Designer: M. Abberley
Height: Large with Reindeer
Handle
Issued: 1982
Price: $110 £75

SANTA CLAUS D6690
Designer: M. Abberley
Height: Large with Sack of
Toys Handle
Issued: 1983
Price: $140 £95

SANTA CLAUS D6704
Designer: M. Abberley
Height: Large
Issued: 1984–
Price: R.R.P.

SANTA CLAUS D6705
Designer: M. Abberley
Height: Small
Issued: 1984–
Price: R.R.P.

SANTA CLAUS D6706
Designer: M. Abberley
Height: Mini
Issued: 1984–1991
Price: $45 £30

SCARAMOUCHE D6558
Designer: M. Henk
Height: Large
Issued: 1962–1967
Price: $640 £400

SCARAMOUCHE D6561
Designer: M. Henk
Height: Small
Issued: 1962–1967
Price: $410 £275

SCARAMOUCHE D6564
Designer: M. Henk
Height: Mini
Issued: 1962–1967
Price: $448 £280

SCARAMOUCHE D6774
(China Guild)
Limited edition of 1500
Designer: S. Taylor
Height: Large
Issued: 1987
Price: $165 £110

SCARAMOUCHE D6814
Designer: S. Taylor
Height: Large
Issued: 1988–1991
Price: $90 £60

SHAKESPEARE D6938
Designer: W. K. Harper
Height: Small
Issued: 1993
Price: R.R.P.

SIMON THE CELLARER
D5504
Designer: C. Noke and
         H. Fenton
Height: Large
Issued: 1935–1960
Price: $130 £85

SIMON THE CELLARER
D5616
Designer: C. Noke and
         H. Fenton
Height: Small
Issued: 1936–1960
Price: $64 £40

SIMON THE CELLARER
(DIAMOND ANNIVERSARY)
D6956
Designer: C. Noke and
         H. Fenton
Height: Tiny
Issued: 1994
Price: R.R.P.

SANTA CLAUS D6690

SIMPLE SIMON D6374
Designer: G. Blower
Height: Large
Issued: 1953–1960
Price: $416 £260

SIR FRANCIS DRAKE D6805
(China Guild)
Limited edition of 6000
Designer: P. Gee
Height: Large
Issued: 1988–1991
Price: $100 £65

SIR HENRY DOULTON D6703
Designer: E. Griffiths
Height: Small
Issued: 1984
Price: $140 £95

SIR THOMAS MORE D6792
Designer: S. Taylor
Height: Large
Issued: 1988–1991
Price: $90 £60

SITTING BULL/GEORGE
ARMSTRONG CUSTER D6712
Limited edition of 9500
Designer: M. Abberley
Height: Large
Issued: 1984
Price: $120 £75

SLEUTH D6631
Designer: A. Moore
Height: Large
Issued: 1973–
Price: R.R.P.

SLEUTH D6635
Designer: A. Moore
Height: Small
Issued: 1973–
Price: R.R.P

SLEUTH D6639
Designer: A. Moore
Height: Mini
Issued: 1973–1992
Price: R.R.P.

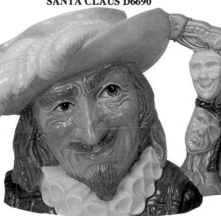

SCARAMOUCHE D6814

SMUTS D6198

SLEUTH D6773 (Lawleys)
Limited edition of 5000
Designer: S. Taylor
Height: Small
Issued: 1988–1991
Price: $70 £45

SMUGGLER D6616
Designer: D. Biggs
Height: Large
Issued: 1968–1981
Price: $100 £65

SMUGGLER D6619
Designer: D. Biggs
Height: Small
Issued: 1968–1981
Price: $70 £45

SMUTS D6198
Designer: H. Fenton
Height: Large
Issued: 1946–c.1948
Price: $1275 £850

SNOOKER PLAYER (THE)
D6879
Designer: S. Taylor
Height: Small
Issued: 1991
Price: R.R.P.

SOLDIER (THE) D6816
Designer: W. K. Harper
Height: Small
Issued: 1991
Price: R.R.P.

TAM O'SHANTER D6632
Designer: M. Henk
Height: Large
Issued: 1973–1980
Price: $135 £85

TAM O'SHANTER D6636
Designer: M. Henk
Height: Small
Issued: 1973–1980
Price: $135 £85

TAM O'SHANTER D6640
Designer: M. Henk
Height: Mini
Issued: 1973–1980
Price: $70 £45

TOBY GILLETTE D6717
Limited edition of three
Two owned by an American
Collector and the other in the
Sir Henry Doulton Museum
Stoke-on-Trent
Designer: E. Griffiths
Height: Large
Issued: 1984
Price: $25600 £16000

TOBY PHILPOTS D5736
Designer: C. Noke
Height: Large
Issued: 1937–1969
Price: $130 £85

CHARACTER JUGS

TOBY PHILPOTS D5737
Designer: C. Noke
Height: Small
Issued: 1937–1969
Price: $70 £45

TOBY PHILPOTS D6043
Designer: C. Noke
Height: Mini
Issued: 1939–1969
Price: $50 £35

TONY WELLER D5531
Designer: L. Harradine and
　　　　　H. Fenton
Height: Extra Large
Issued: c.1936
Price: $250 £165

TONY WELLER D5531
Designer: L. Harradine and
　　　　　H. Fenton
Height: Large
Issued: c.1936–1960
Price: $130 £85

TONY WELLER D5530
Designer: L. Harradine and
　　　　　H. Fenton
Height: Small
Issued: 1936–1960
Price: $70 £45

TONY WELLER D6044
Designer: L. Harradine and
　　　　　H. Fenton
Height: Mini
Issued: 1939–1960
Price: $50 £35

TOUCHSTONE D5613
Designer: C. Noke
Height: Large
Issued: 1936–1960
Price: $230 £145

TOWN CRIER D6530
Designer: D. Biggs
Height: Large
Issued: 1960–1973
Price: $220 £145

TOWN CRIER D6537
Designer: D. Biggs
Height: Small
Issued: 1960–1973
Price: $135 £90

TOWN CRIER D6544
Designer: D. Biggs
Height: Mini
Issued: 1960–1973
Price: $150 £100

TOWN CRIER D6895
Designer: S. Taylor
Height: Large
Issued: 1991
Price: R.R.P.

TRAPPER D6609
Designer: M. Henk and D. Biggs
Height: Large
Issued: 1967–1983
Price: $100 £65

TOBY PHILPOTS D5736

TONY WELLER D5531

TOUCHSTONE D5613

TRAPPER D6609
Designer: M. Henk and D. Biggs
Height: Large (Centennial
　　　　　Back Stamp)
Price: $180 £120

TRAPPER D6612
Designer: M. Henk and D. Biggs
Height: Small
Issued: 1967–1983
Price: $70 £45

UGLY DUCHESS D6599
Designer: M. Henk
Height: Large
Issued: 1965–1973
Price: $440 £295

UGLY DUCHESS D6603
Designer: M. Henk
Height: Small
Issued: 1965–1973
Price: $340 £225

UGLY DUCHESS D6607
Designer: M. Henk
Height: Mini
Issued: 1965–1973
Price: $300 £200

**ULYSSES S. GRANT and
ROBERT E. LEE D6698**
Designer: M. Abberley
Height: Large
Issued: 1983–1986
Price: $250 £165

**UNCLE TOM COBBLEIGH
D6337**
Designer: M. Henk
Height: Large
Issued: 1952–1960
Price: $300 £200

VETERAN MOTORIST D6633
Designer: D. Biggs
Height: Large
Issued: 1973–1983
Price: $130 £85

VETERAN MOTORIST D6637
Designer: D. Biggs
Height: Small
Issued: 1973–1983
Price: $80 £55

VETERAN MOTORIST D6641
Designer: D. Biggs
Height: Mini
Issued: 1973–1983
Price: $70 £45

VICAR OF BRAY D5615
Designer: C. Noke and
　　　　　H. Fenton
Height: Large
Issued: 1936–1960
Price: $180 £120

VIKING D6496
Designer: M. Henk
Height: Large
Issued: 1959–1975
Price: $190 £125

TOWN CRIER D6530

ULYSSES S. GRANT and ROBERT E. LEE D6698

TRAPPER D6609

UNCLE TOM COBBLEIGH D6337

UGLY DUCHESS D6599

VETERAN MOTORIST D6633

VIKING D6502
Designer: M. Henk
Height: Small
Issued: 1959–1975
Price: $130 £85

VIKING D6526
Designer: M. Henk
Height: Mini
Issued: 1959–1975
Price: $150 £100

VISCOUNT MONTGOMERY of ALAMEIN D6850 (Lawleys)
Limited edition of 9500
Designer: S. Taylor
Height: Small
Issued: 1989–1992
Price: $80 £50

W. C. FIELDS D6674
Designer: D. Biggs
Height: Large
Issued: 1983–1985
Price: $130 £85

W. G. GRACE D6845 (Lawleys)
Limited edition of 9500
Designer: S. Taylor
Height: Small
Issued: 1989
Price: R.R.P.

WALRUS AND CARPENTER D6600
Designer: M. Henk
Height: Large
Issued: 1965–1980
Price: $130 £85

WALRUS AND CARPENTER D6604
Designer: M. Henk
Height: Small
Issued: 1965–1980
Price: $80 £55

WALRUS AND CARPENTER D6608
Designer: M. Henk
Height: Mini
Issued: 1965–1980
Price: $70 £45

WILD BILL HICKOCK D6736
Designer: M. Abberley
Height: Medium
Issued: 1985–1988
Price: $70 £45

WILLIAM SHAKESPEARE D6689
Designer: M. Abberley
Height: Large
Issued: 1983–1991
Price: $100 £65

WINSTON CHURCHILL D6934
Designer: S. Taylor
Height: Small
Issued: 1993
Price: R.R.P.

WIZARD (THE) D6862
Designer: S. Taylor
Height: Large
Issued: 1990
Price: R.R.P.

WIZARD (THE) D6909
Designer: S. Taylor
Height: Small
Issued: 1990
Price: R.R.P.

WYATT EARP D6711
Designer: S. Taylor
Height: Medium
Issued: 1985–1988
Price: $70 £45

YACHTSMAN D6622
Designer: D. Biggs
Height: Large
Issued: 1971–1980
Price: $140 £95

YACHTSMAN D6820
Designer: S. Taylor
Height: Large
Issued: 1989–1991
Price: $90 £60

YEOMAN OF THE GUARD D6873
Designer: S. Taylor
Height: Large
Issued: 1991
Price: R.R.P.

WALRUS AND CARPENTER D6600

W. C. FIELDS D6674

W. G. GRACE D6845

WILD BILL HICKOCK D6736

FIGURES

A LA MODE HN2544
Designer: E.J. Griffiths
Height: 12¼in., 31.1cm.
Issued: 1974–1977
Price: $340 £225

A PENNY'S WORTH HN2408
Designer: M. Nicoll
Height: 7in., 20cm.
Issued: 1986–1990
Price: $190 £125

ABDULLAH HN1410
Designer: L. Harradine
Height: 5¾in., 14.6cm.
Issued: 1930–1938
Price: $675 £450

ABDULLAH HN2104
Designer: L. Harradine
Height: 6in., 15.2cm.
Issued: 1953–1962
Colour variation
Price: $375 £250

ACE, THE HN3398
Designer: Robert Tabbenor
Height: 10in., 25.5cm.
Issued: 1991
Price: R.R.P.

A-COURTING HN2004
Designer: L. Harradine
Height: 7¼in., 18.4cm.
Issued: 1947–1953
Price: $340 £225

ADELE HN2480
Designer: P. Davies
Height: 8in., 20cm.
Issued: 1987–1992
Price: $165 £110

ADORNMENT HN3015
Designer: P. Parsons
Height: 9½in., 24cm.
Issued: 1989 in a limited
edition of 750
Price: $825 £550

ADRIENNE HN2152
Designer: P. Davies
Height: 7½in., 19.1cm.
Issued: 1964–1976
Price: $220 £145

ADRIENNE HN2304
Designer: P. Davies
Height: 7½in., 19.1cm.
Issued: 1964–1991
Colour variation
Price: $165 £110

AFFECTION HN2236
Designer: P. Davies
Height: 4½in., 11.4cm.
Issued: 1962–
Price: R.R.P.

AFTERNOON TEA HN1747
Designer: P. Railston
Height: 5¾in., 14.6cm.
Issued: 1935–1981
Price: $445 £295

ABDULLAH HN2104

A LA MODE HN2544

THE ACE HN3398

ADRIENNE HN2152

ADRIENNE HN2304

AFTERNOON TEA HN1748
Designer: P. Railston
Height: 5¼in., 13.3cm.
Issued: 1935–1949
           Colour variation
Price: $675 £450

AILEEN HN1645
Designer: L. Harradine
Height: 6in., 15.2cm.
Issued: 1934–1938
Price: $675 £450

AILEEN HN1664
Designer: L. Harradine
Height: 6in., 15.2cm.
Issued: 1934–1938
           Colour variation
Price: $675 £450

AILEEN HN1803
Designer: L. Harradine
Height: 6in., 15.2cm.
Issued: 1937–1949
           Colour variation
Price: $675 £450

AJAX HN2908
Designer: S. Keenan
Height: 9¾in., 24.8cm.
Issued: 1980 in a limited
           edition of 950
Price: $375 £250

ALCHEMIST HN1259
Designer: L. Harradine
Height: 11½in., 29.2cm.
Issued: 1927–1938
Price: $975 £650

ALCHEMIST HN1282
Designer: L. Harradine
Height: 11¼in., 28.5cm.
Issued: 1928–1938
           Colour variation
Price: $975 £650

ALEXANDRA HN2398
Designer: P. Davies
Height: 7¾in., 19.7cm.
Issued: 1970–1976
Price: $250 £165

ALEXANDRA HN3286
Designer: D. V. Tootle
Height: 7¾in., 19.5cm.
Issued: 1990
Price: R.R.P.

ALFRED JINGLE HN541
Designer: L. Harradine
Height: 3¾in., 9.5cm.
Issued: 1922–1932
Price: $70 £45

ALFRED JINGLE M52
Designer: L. Harradine
Height: 3¾in., 9.5cm.
Issued: 1932–1982
Price: $60 £40

ALICE HN2158
Designer: P. Davies
Height: 5in., 12.7cm.
Issued: 1960–1980
Price: $180 £120

ALCHEMIST HN1259   AILEEN HN1645

AFTERNOON TEA HN1747

ALICE HN3368
Designer: Nada Pedley
Height: 8¼in., 21cm.
Issued: 1991
Price: R.R.P.

ALISON HN2336
Designer: P. Davies
Height: 7½in., 19.1cm.
Issued: 1966–1992
Price: $190 £125

ALISON HN3264
Designer: P. Davies
Height: 7½in., 19.1cm.
Issued: 1989–1993
Price: $150 £100

ALL-A-BLOOMING HN1457
Designer: L. Harradine
Height: 6½in., 16.5cm.
Issued: 1931–not known
Price: $600 £400

ALL-A-BLOOMING HN1466
Designer: L. Harradine
Height: 6½in., 16.5cm.
Issued: 1931–1938
Price: $600 £400

ALL ABOARD HN2940
Designer: R. Tabbenor
Height: 9¼in., 23.5cm.
Issued: 1982–1986
Price: $250 £165

ALLURE HN3080
Designer: E. Griffiths
Height: 12¼in., 31cm.
Issued: 1987–1989
Price: $150 £100

ALMOST GROWN HN3425
Designer: Nada Pedley
Height: 4½in., 11.5cm.
Issued: 1993
Price: R.R.P.

**ALWAYS & FOREVER
HN3550**
Designer: Adrian Hughes
Height: 4½in., 11.5cm.
Issued: 1993
Price: R.R.P.

AMANDA HN2996
Designer: R. Tabbenor
Height: 5¼in., 13.5cm.
Issued: 1986
Price: R.R.P.

AMANDA HN3406
Designer: R. Tabbenor
Height: 5¼in., 13.5cm.
Issued: 1993
Colour variation
Price: R.R.P.

AMANDA HN3632
Designer: R. Tabbenor
Height: 5¼in., 13.5cm.
Issued: 1994
Colour variation
Price: R.R.P.

ALMOST GROWN HN3425

ALEXANDRA HN2398

ALICE HN3368

ALL ABOARD HN2940

AMANDA HN3406

103

FIGURES

AMY HN2958
Designer: Pauline Parsons
Height: 6in., 15cm.
Issued: 1982–1987
Price: $190 £125

AMY HN3316

AMY HN3316
Designer: Peter Gee
Height: 8in., 20.3cm.
Issued: 1991
Price: $450 £300

AMY'S SISTER HN3445
Designer: Peter Gee
Height: 8in., 20cm.
Issued: 1993
Price: R.R.P.

AND ONE FOR YOU HN2970
Designer: A. Hughes
Height: 6½in., 16.5cm.
Issued: 1982–1985
Price: $120 £75

AND SO TO BED HN2966
Designer: P. Parsons
Height: 7½in., 19cm.
Issued: 1982–1985
Price: $220 £145

ANDREA HN3058
Designer: A. Hughes
Height: 5¼in., 13cm.
Issued: 1985–
Price: R.R.P.

ANGELA (Style one) HN1204
Designer: L. Harradine
Height: 7¼in., 18.4cm.
Issued: 1926–1938
Price: $975 £650

ANGELA (Style one) HN1303
Designer: L. Harradine
Height: 7¼in., 18.4cm.
Issued: 1928–1938
Colour variation
Price: $975 £650

ANGELA (Style two) HN2389
Designer: P. Davies
Height: 7½in., 19cm.
Issued: 1983–1986
Price: $220 £145

ANGELINA HN2013
Designer: L. Harradine
Height: 6¾in., 17.1cm.
Issued: 1948–1951
Price: $560 £375

ANN HN3259

ANN HN2739
Designer: D. Tootle
Height: 7¾in., 19.5cm.
Issued: 1983–1986
Price: $190 £125

ANN HN3259
Designer: D. V. Tootle
Height: 8in., 20cm.
Issued: 1990
Price: R.R.P.

AMY'S SISTER HN3445

ANNA HN2802
Designer: P. Davies
Height: 5¾in., 14.6cm.
Issued: 1976–1982
Price: $140 £95

ANNABEL HN3273
Designer: R. Tabbenor
Height: 5½in., 14cm.
Issued: 1989–1992
Price: $250 £165

ANNABELLA HN1871
Designer: L. Harradine
Height: 5¼in., 13.3cm.
Issued: 1938–1949
Price: $525 £350

ANNABELLA HN1872
Designer: L. Harradine
Height: 5¼in., 13.3cm.
Issued: 1938–1949
Colour variation
Price: $525 £350

ANNABELLA HN1875
Designer: L. Harradine
Height: 4¾in., 12cm.
Issued: 1938–1949
Colour variation
Price: $525 £350

ANNE BOLEYN HN3232
Designer: Pauline Parsons
Height: 8¼in., 21cm.
Issued: 1993
Price: R.R.P.

ANNE OF CLEVES HN3356
Designer: Pauline Parsons
Height: 6½in., 16.5cm.
Issued: 1993
Price: R.R.P.

ANNETTE HN1471
Designer: L. Harradine
Height: 6¼in., 15.9cm.
Issued: 1931–1938
Price: $420 £275

ANNETTE HN1472
Designer: L. Harradine
Height: 6in., 15.2cm.
Issued: 1931–1949
Colour variation
Price: $340 £225

ANNETTE HN1550
Designer: L. Harradine
Height: 6¼in., 15.9cm.
Issued: 1933–1949
Price: $290 £195

ANNETTE HN3495
Designer: P. Davies
Height: 7¾in., 19.7cm.
Issued: 1993
Colour variation
Price: $150 £100

ANTHEA HN1526
Designer: L. Harradine
Height: 6½in., 16.5cm.
Issued: 1932–1938
Price: $675 £450

FIGURES

ANTHEA HN1527
Designer: L. Harradine
Height: 6½in., 16.5cm.
Issued: 1932–1949
Colour variation
Price: $675 £450

ANTHEA HN1669
Designer: L. Harradine
Height: 6½in., 16.5cm.
Issued: 1934–1938
Colour variation
Price: $675 £450

ANTOINETTE (Style one) HN1850
Designer: L. Harradine
Height: 8¼in., 21cm.
Issued: 1938–1949
Price: $750 £500

ANTOINETTE (Style one) HN1851
Designer: L. Harradine
Height: 8¼in., 21cm.
Issued: 1938–1949
Colour variation
Price: $750 £500

ANTOINETTE (Style two) HN2326
Designer: P. Davies
Height: 6¼in., 15.9cm.
Issued: 1967–1978
Price: $220 £145

ANTHONY & CLEOPATRA HN3114
Designer: Robert Jefferson
Height: 12in., 30.5cm.
Issued: 1995 in a limited edition of 150
Price: R.R.P.

APPLE MAID HN2160
Designer: L. Harradine
Height: 6½in., 16.5cm.
Issued: 1957–1962
Price: $340 £225

APRIL HN2708
Designer: P. Davies
Height: 7¾in., 19.7cm.
Issued: 1987
Price: $165 £110

APRIL HN3333
Designer: P. Davies
Height: 7½in., 19cm.
Issued: 1991
Price: $165 £110

APRIL HN3344
Designer: P. Davies
Height: 7½in., 19cm.
Issued: 1991
Price: $165 £110

APRIL SHOWER HN3024
Designer: R. Jefferson
Height: 4¾in., 12cm.
Issued: 1983–1986
Price: $56 £35

ANNE OF CLEVES HN3356

ANNE BOLEYN HN3232

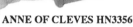

APPLE MAID HN2160

ANNETTE HN3495

APRIL HN3333

APRIL SHOWER HN3024

ARAB HN33
Designer: C. J. Noke
Height: 15³/₄in., 40cm.
Issued: 1913–1938
Price: $1275 £850

ARAB HN343
Designer: C. J. Noke
Height: 16¹/₂in., 41.9cm.
Issued: 1919–1938
Colour variation
Price: $1275 £850

ARAB HN378
Designer: C. J. Noke
Height: 16¹/₂in., 41.9cm.
Issued: 1920–1938
Colour variation
Price: $1275 £850

ARAGORN HN2916
Designer: H. Sales
Height: 6¹/₄in., 15.9cm.
Issued: 1979–1984
Price: $120 £75

ARTFUL DODGER HN546
Designer: L. Harradine
Height: 3³/₄in., 9.5cm.
Issued: 1922–1932
Price: $70 £45

ARTFUL DODGER M55
Designer: L. Harradine
Height: 4¹/₄in., 10.8cm.
Issued: 1932–1983
Price: $60 £40

AS GOOD AS NEW HN2971
Designer: A. Hughes
Height: 6¹/₂in., 16.5cm.
Issued: 1982–1985
Price: $120 £75

ASCOT HN2356
Designer: P. Davies
Height: 5³/₄in., 14.6cm.
Issued: 1968–
Price: R.R.P.

ASCOT HN3471
Designer: Valerie Annand
Height: 8¹/₂in., 21.5cm.
Issued: 1994 in a limited
edition of 5000
Price: R.R.P.

ASHLEY HN3420
Designer: Nada Pedley
Height: 8in., 20cm.
Issued: 1992
Price: R.R.P.

AT EASE HN2473
Designer: P. Davies
Height: 6in., 15.2cm.
Issued: 1973–1978
Price: $340 £225

AUCTIONEER HN2988
Designer: R. Tabbenor
Height: 8in., 20.3cm.
Issued: 1986
Price: $260 £175

AS GOOD AS NEW HN2971

ARAGORN HN2916

AUCTIONEER HN2988

ASCOT HN3471

FIGURES

AUGUST HN3325
Designer: P. Davies
Height: 7½in., 19cm.
Issued: 1991
Price: $165 £110

AUGUST HN3165
Designer: P. Davies
Height: 7¾in., 19.7cm.
Issued: 1987
Price: $165 £110

AUGUST HN3408
Designer: P. Davies
Height: 7½in., 19cm.
Issued: 1991
Price: $165 £110

L'AUTOMNE HN3068
Designer: R. Jefferson
Height: 11½in., 29cm.
Issued: 1987 in a limited
          edition of 300
Price: $1125 £750

AUTUMN (Style one) HN314
Designer: Unknown
Height: 7¼in., 18.4cm.
Issued: 1918–1938
Price: $975 £650

AUTUMN (Style one) HN474
Designer: Unknown
Height: 7½in., 19.1cm.
Issued: 1921–1938
          Colour variation
Price: $975 £650

AUTUMN (Style two) HN2087
Designer: P. Davies
Height: 7¼in., 18.4cm.
Issued: 1952–1959
Price: $410 £275

**AUTUMN ATTRACTION
HN3612**
Designer: P. Davies
Height: 7in., 17.8cm.
Issued: 1993
Price: R.R.P.

AUTUMN BREEZES HN2131
(Red/orange/black)
Designer: Leslie Harradine
Height: 7½in., 19cm.
Issued: 1990
Price: R.R.P.

AUTUMN BREEZES HN2176
Designer: Leslie Harradine
Height: 4in., 10cm.
Issued: 1991
Price: R.R.P.

AUTUMN BREEZES HN2147
Designer: L. Harradine
Height: 7½in., 19.1cm.
Issued: 1955–1971
          Colour variation
Price: $250 £165

AUTUMN BREEZES HN1934
Designer: L. Harradine
Height: 7½in., 19.1cm.
Issued: 1940–
          Colour variation
Price: R.R.P.

AUGUST HN3325

AUGUST HN3165

AUTUMN ATTRACTION
HN3612

AUGUST HN3408

AUTUMN BREEZES HN2176   AUTUMN BREEZES HN2131

107

AUTUMN BREEZES HN1911
Designer: L. Harradine
Height: 7¹/₂in., 19.1cm.
Issued: 1939–1976
Price: $250 £165

AUTUMN BREEZES HN1913
Designer: L. Harradine
Height: 7¹/₂in., 19.1cm.
Issued: 1939–1971
Colour variation
Price: $250 £165

AUTUMN TIME HN3231
Designer: C. Parsons
Height: 8in., 20.3cm.
Issued: 1989
Price: $290 £195

AWAKENING HN1927
Designer: L. Harradine
Height: Unknown
Issued: 1940–1949
Price: $1425 £950

AWAKENING HN2838 (Black)
Designer: P. Davies
Height: 8¹/₂in., 22cm.
Issued: 1981–
Price: R.R.P.

AWAKENING HN2875 (White)
Designer: P. Davies
Height: 8¹/₂in., 22cm.
Issued: 1981–
Price: R.R.P.

B

BABA HN1230
Designer: L. Harradine
Height: 3¹/₄in., 8.3cm.
Issued: 1927–1938
Price: $490 £325

BABA HN1243
Designer: L. Harradine
Height: 3¹/₄in., 8.3cm.
Issued: 1927–1938
Colour variation
Price: $490 £325

BABA HN1244
Designer: L. Harradine
Height: 3¹/₄in., 8.3cm.
Issued: 1927–1938
Colour variation
Price: $490 £325

BABA HN1245
Designer: L. Harradine
Height: 3¹/₄in., 8.3cm.
Issued: 1927–1938
Colour variation
Price: $490 £325

BABA HN1246
Designer: L. Harradine
Height: 3¹/₄in., 8.3cm.
Issued: 1927–1938
Colour variation
Price: $490 £325

AUTUMN BREEZES HN1913

BALINESE DANCER HN2808

BABA HN1247
Designer: L. Harradine
Height: 3¹/₄in., 8.3cm.
Issued: 1927–1938
Colour variation
Price: $490 £325

BABA HN1248
Designer: L. Harradine
Height: 3¹/₄in., 8.3cm.
Issued: 1927–1938
Colour variation
Price: $490 £325

BABETTE HN1423
Designer: L. Harradine
Height: 5in., 12.7cm.
Issued: 1930–1938
Price: $490 £350

BABETTE HN1424
Designer: L. Harradine
Height: 5in., 12.7cm.
Issued: 1930–1938
Colour variation
Price: $490 £350

BABIE HN1679
Designer: L. Harradine
Height: 4³/₄in., 12cm.
Issued: 1935–
Price: $100 £65

BABIE HN1842
Designer: L. Harradine
Height: 4³/₄in., 12cm.
Issued: 1938–1949
Colour variation
Price: $190 £125

BABIE HN2121
Designer: L. Harradine
Height: 4³/₄in., 12cm.
Issued: 1983–
Price: $90 £60

BABY HN12
Designer: C. J. Noke
Height: Unknown
Issued: 1913–1938
Price: $2250 £1500

BABY BUNTING HN2108
Designer: P. Davies
Height: 5¹/₄in., 13.3cm.
Issued: 1953–1959
Price: $290 £195

BACHELOR HN2319
Designer: M. Nicholl
Height: 7in., 17.8cm.
Issued: 1964–1975
Price: $340 £225

BALINESE DANCER HN2808
Designer: P. Davies
Height: 8³/₄in., 22.2cm.
Issued: 1982 in a limited
edition of 750
Price: $675 £450

BALLAD SELLER HN2266
Designer: P. Davies
Height: 7¹/₂in., 19.1cm.
Issued: 1968–1973
Price: $340 £225

FIGURES

BALLERINA HN2116
Designer: P. Davies
Height: 7¼in., 18.4cm.
Issued: 1953–1973
Price: $340 £225

BALLET CLASS HN3134
Designer: P. Parsons
Height: 6in., 15.5cm.
Issued: 1987
Price: R.R.P.

BALLET SHOES HN3434
Designer: Alan Maslankowski
Height: 3¼in., 8cm.
Issued: 1993
Price: R.R.P.

BALLOON BOY HN2934
Designer: P. Gee
Height: 7½in., 19cm.
Issued: 1984–
Price: R.R.P.

BALLOON CLOWN HN2894
Designer: W. K. Harper
Height: 9¼in., 23cm.
Issued: 1986–1992
Price: $180 £120

BALLOON GIRL HN2818
Designer: W. K. Harper
Height: 6½in., 16.5cm.
Issued: 1982–
Price: R.R.P.

BALLOON LADY HN2935
Designer: P. Gee
Height: 8¼in., 21cm.
Issued: 1984–
Price: R.R.P.

BALLOON MAN HN1954
Designer: L. Harradine
Height: 7¼in., 18.4cm.
Issued: 1940–
Price: R.R.P.

BALLOON SELLER HN479
Designer: L. Harradine
Height: 9in., 22.9cm.
Issued: 1921–1938
Price: $825 £550

BALLOON SELLER HN486
Designer: L. Harradine
Height: 9in., 22.9cm.
Issued: 1921–1938
Price: $675 £450

BALLOON SELLER HN548
Designer: L. Harradine
Height: 9in., 22.9cm.
Issued: 1922–1938
          Colour variation
Price: $675 £450

BALLOON SELLER HN583
Designer: L. Harradine
Height: 9in., 22.9cm.
Issued: 1923–1949
          Colour variation
Price: $450 £300

BACHELOR
HN2319

BALLOON GIRL
HN2818

BALLET SHOES
HN3434

BALLERINA
HN2116

BABETTE HN1423

BALLOON MAN HN1954

BALLOON SELLER HN697
Designer: L. Harradine
Height: 9in., 22.9cm.
Issued: 1925–1938
　　　　Colour variation
Price: $825 £550

BALLOON SELLER HN2130
Designer: L. Harradine
Height: 4in., 10cm.
Issued: 1989–1992
Price: $100 £65

BARBARA HN1421
Designer: L. Harradine
Height: 7³/₄in., 19.7cm.
Issued: 1930–1938
Price: $600 £400

BARBARA HN1432
Designer: L. Harradine
Height: 7³/₄in., 19.7cm.
Issued: 1930–1938
Price: $600 £400

BARBARA HN1461
Designer: L. Harradine
Height: 7³/₄in., 19.7cm.
Issued: 1931–1938
　　　　Colour variation
Price: $600 £400

BARBARA HN2962
Designer: P. Parsons
Height: 8in., 20cm.
Issued: 1982–1984
Price: $250 £165

BARBARA HN3441
Designer: P. Gee
Height: 8in., 20cm.
Issued: 1992 in a special
　　　　edition of 9500
Price: R.R.P.

**BARLIMAN BUTTERBUR
HN2923**
Designer: D. Lyttleton
Height: 5¹/₄in., 13cm.
Issued: 1982–1984
Price: $340 £225

BASKET WEAVER HN2245
Designer: M. Nicholl
Height: 5³/₄in., 14.6cm.
Issued: 1959–1962
Price: $400 £275

BATHER (Style one) HN597
Designer: L. Harradine
Height: 7³/₄in., 19.7cm.
Issued: 1924–1938
Price: $825 £550

BATHER (Style one) HN687
Designer: L. Harradine
Height: 7³/₄in., 19.7cm.
Issued: 1924–1949
　　　　Colour variation
Price: $825 £550

BATHER (Style one) HN781
Designer: L. Harradine
Height: 7³/₄in., 19.7cm.
Issued: 1926–1938
　　　　Colour variation
Price: $975 £650

BARBARA HN3441

BATHER (Style two) HN773

BARLIMAN BUTTERBUR
HN2923

BARBARA HN2962

BATHER (Style one) HN782
Designer: L. Harradine
Height: 7³/₄in., 19.7cm.
Issued: 1926–1938
Colour variation
Price: $975 £650

BATHER (Style one) HN1238
Designer: L. Harradine
Height: 7³/₄in., 19.7cm.
Issued: 1927–1938
Colour variation
Price: $975 £650

BATHER (Style one) HN1708
Designer: L. Harradine
Height: 7³/₄in., 19.7cm.
Issued: 1935–1938
Colour variation
Price: $975 £650

BATHER (Style two) HN773
Designer: L. Harradine
Height: 7¹/₂in., 19.1cm.
Issued: 1925–1938
Price: $975 £650

BATHER (Style two) HN774
Designer: L. Harradine
Height: 7³/₄in., 19.7cm.
Issued: 1925–1938
Price: $975 £650

BATHER (Style two) HN1227
Designer: L. Harradine
Height: 7¹/₂in., 19.1cm.
Issued: 1927–1938
Colour variation
Price: $975 £650

BATHING BEAUTY HN3156
Designer: A. Hughes
Height: 9¹/₂in., 26cm.
Issued: 1988–1989
Price: $250 £165

BEACHCOMBER HN2487
Designer: M. Nicholl
Height: 6¹/₄in., 15.9cm.
Issued: 1973–1976
Price: $220 £145

BEAT YOU TO IT HN2871
Designer: P. Davies
Height: 6¹/₂in., 16.5cm.
Issued: 1980–1987
Price: $340 £225

BEATRICE HN3263
Designer: P. Davies
Height: 7in., 17.8cm.
Issued: 1989
Price: R.R.P.

BEATRICE HN3631
U.S.A. edition
Price: R.R.P.

BECKY HN2740
Designer: D. Tootle
Height: 8in., 20cm.
Issued: 1987–1992
Price: $165 £110

BEACHCOMBER HN2487

BEATRICE HN3631

BEAT YOU TO IT HN2871

111

FIGURES

BEDTIME HN1978
Designer: L. Harradine
Height: 5³/₄in., 14.6cm.
Issued: 1945–
Price: R.R.P.

BEDTIME HN2219
Designer: P. Gee
Height: 5¹/₃in., 13.3cm.
Issued: 1992
Price: Colour variation
R.R.P.

BEDTIME HN3418
Designer: N. Pedley
Height: 7¹/₄in., 18.4cm.
Issued: 1992 in a limited
edition of 9500
Price: $204 £136

BEDTIME STORY HN2059
Designer: L. Harradine
Height: 4³/₄in., 12cm.
Issued: 1950–
Price: R.R.P.

BEETHOVEN HN1778
Designer: R. Garbe
Height: 22in., 55.8cm.
Issued: 1933 in a limited
edition of 25
Price: $3200 £2000

BEGGAR (Style one) HN526
Designer: L. Harradine
Height: 6¹/₂in., 16.5cm.
Issued: 1921–1949
Price: $375 £250

BEGGAR (Style one) HN591
Designer: L. Harradine
Height: 6³/₄in., 17.2cm.
Issued: 1924–1949
Price: $375 £250

BEGGAR (Style two) HN2175
Designer: L. Harradine
Height: 6³/₄in., 17.2cm.
Issued: 1956–1972
Price: $300 £200

BELLE HN754
Designer: L. Harradine
Height: 6¹/₂in., 16.5cm.
Issued: 1925–1938
Price: $675 £450

BELLE HN776
Designer: L. Harradine
Height: 6¹/₂in., 16.5cm.
Issued: 1925–1938
Price: $675 £450

BELLE HN2340
Designer: P. Davies
Height: 4¹/₂in., 11.4cm.
Issued: 1968–1988
Price: $110 £75

BELLE O' THE BALL HN1997
Designer: L. Harradine
Height: 6in., 15.2cm.
Issued: 1947–1978
Price: $340 £225

BEDTIME STORY HN2059

BEDTIME HN2219

BEDTIME HN3418

BEDTIME HN1978

BENMORE HN2909
Designer: S. Keenan
Height: 9¼in., 23.5cm.
Issued: 1980 in a limited
    edition of 950
Price: $440 £295

BERNICE HN2071
Designer: P. Davies
Height: 7¾in., 19.7cm.
Issued: 1951–1953
Price: $750 £500

BESS HN2002
Designer: L. Harradine
Height: 7¼in., 18.4cm.
Issued: 1947–1969
Price: $370 £245

BESS HN2003
Designer: L. Harradine
Height: 7¼in., 18.4cm.
Issued: 1947–1950
    Colour variation
Price: $525 £350

BEST WISHES HN3426
Designer: Nada Pedley
Height: ·6in., 15cm.
Issued: 1993
Price: R.R.P.

BETH HN2870
Designer: P. Davies
Height: 5¾in., 14.6cm.
Issued: 1980–1983
Price: $180 £120

BETSY HN2111
Designer: L. Harradine
Height: 7in., 17.8cm.
Issued: 1953–1959
Price: $410 £275

BETTY (Style one) HN402
Designer: L. Harradine
Height: 7½in., 19cm.
Issued: 1920–1938
Price: $2250 £1500

BETTY (Style one) HN403
Designer: L. Harradine
Height: 7½in., 19cm.
Issued: 1920–1938
    Colour variation
Price: $2250 £1500

BETTY (Style one) HN435
Designer: L. Harradine
Height: 7½in., 19cm.
Issued: 1921–1938
    Colour variation
Price: $2250 £1500

BETTY (Style one) HN438
Designer: L. Harradine
Height: 7½in., 19cm.
Issued: 1921–1938
    Colour variation
Price: $2250 £1500

BETTY (Style one) HN477
Designer: L. Harradine
Height: 7½in., 19cm.
Issued: 1921–1938
    Colour variation
Price: $2250 £1500

BEST WISHES HN3426

BEGGAR (Style one) HN526

BESS HN2002

BELLE O' THE BALL HN1997

FIGURES

BETTY (Style one) HN478
Designer: L. Harradine
Height: 7¹/₂in., 19cm.
Issued: 1921–1938
Colour variation
Price: $2250 £1500

BETTY (Style two) HN1404
Designer: L. Harradine
Height: 4¹/₂in., 11.4cm.
Issued: 1930–1938
Price: $975 £650

BETTY (Style two) HN1405
Designer: L. Harradine
Height: 4¹/₂in., 11.4cm.
Issued: 1930–1938
Colour variation
Price: $975 £650

BETTY (Style two) HN1435
Designer: L. Harradine
Height: 4¹/₂in., 11.4cm.
Issued: 1930–1938
Colour variation
Price: $975 £650

BETTY (Style two) HN1436
Designer: L. Harradine
Height: 4¹/₂in., 11.4cm.
Issued: 1930–1938
Colour variation
Price: $975 £650

BIDDY HN1445
Designer: L. Harradine
Height: 5¹/₂in., 14cm.
Issued: 1931–1938
Price: $292 £195

BIDDY HN1500
Designer: L. Harradine
Height: 5¹/₂in., 14cm.
Issued: 1932–1938
Price: $260 £175

BIDDY HN1513
Designer: L. Harradine
Height: 5¹/₂in., 14cm.
Issued: 1932–1951
Colour variation
Price: $225 £150

BIDDY PENNY FARTHING
HN1843
Designer: L. Harradine
Height: 9in., 22.9cm.
Issued: 1938–
Price: R.R.P.

BILBO HN2914
Designer: Harry Sales
Height: 4¹/₂in., 11.4cm.
Issued: 1979–1984
Price: $120 £80

BILL SYKES HN537
Designer: L. Harradine
Height: 3³/₄in., 9.5cm.
Issued: 1922–1932
Price: $70 £45

BILL SYKES M54
Designer: L. Harradine
Height: 4¹/₄in., 10.8cm.
Issued: 1932–1982
Price: $60 £40

BIDDY HN1445

BIDDY PENNY FARTHING
HN1843

BLITHE MORNING HN2021

BIRTHDAY GIRL HN3423
Designer: Nada Pedley
Height: 6in., 15cm.
Issued: 1993
Price: R.R.P.

BLACKSMITH HN2782
Designer: W. K. Harper
Height: 9in., 22.5cm.
Issued: 1987–1991
Price: $225 £150

BLACKSMITH OF
WILLIAMSBURG HN2240
Designer: P. Davies
Height: 6³/₄in., 17.2cm.
Issued: 1960–1983
Price: $250 £165

BLIGHTY HN323
Designer: E. W. Light
Height: 11¹/₄in., 28.5cm.
Issued: 1918–1938
Price: $975 £650

BLITHE MORNING HN2021
Designer: L. Harradine
Height: 7¹/₄in., 18.4cm.
Issued: 1949–1971
Price: $250 £165

BLITHE MORNING HN2065
Designer: L. Harradine
Height: 7¹/₄in., 18.4cm.
Issued: 1950–1973
Colour variation
Price: $250 £165

BLOSSOM HN1667
Designer: L. Harradine
Height: 6³/₄in., 17.2cm.
Issued: 1934–1949
Price: $750 £500

BLUE BEARD (Style one) HN75
Designer: E. W. Light
Height: Unknown
Issued: 1917–1938
Price: $2250 £1500

BLUE BEARD (Style one)
HN410
Designer: E. W. Light
Height: Unknown
Issued: 1920–1938
Colour variation
Price: $2250 £1500

BLUE BEARD (Style two)
HN1528
Designer: L. Harradine
Height: 11¹/₂in., 29.2cm.
Issued: 1932–1949
Price: $750 £500

BLUE BEARD (Style two)
HN2105
Designer: L. Harradine
Height: 11in., 27.9cm.
Issued: 1953–1992
Colour variation
Price: $410 £275

BLUE BIRD HN1280
Designer: L. Harradine
Height: 4³/₄in., 12cm.
Issued: 1928–1938
Price: $410 £275

FIGURES

BOATMAN HN2417
Designer: M. Nicholl
Height: 6¹/₂in., 16.5cm.
Issued: 1971–1987
Price: $250 £165

BOBBY HN2778
Designer: William K. Harper
Height: 9in., 23cm.
Issued: 1992
Price: R.R.P.

BOLERO HN3076
Designer: A. Hughes
Height: 13¹/₂in., 34.5cm.
Issued: 1987–1989
Price: $150 £100

BON APPETIT HN2444
Designer: M. Nicholl
Height: 6in., 15.2cm.
Issued: 1972–1976
Price: $190 £125

BONJOUR HN1879
Designer: L. Harradine
Height: 6³/₄in., 17.2cm.
Issued: 1938–1949
Price: $750 £500

BONJOUR HN1888
Designer: L. Harradine
Height: 6³/₄in., 17.2cm.
Issued: 1938–1949
  Colour variation
Price: $750 £500

BONNIE LASSIE HN1626
Designer: L. Harradine
Height: 5¹/₄in., 13.3cm.
Issued: 1934–1953
Price: $440 £295

BONNIE LASSIE HN1626A
Designer: L. Harradine
Height: 5¹/₄in., 13.3cm.
Issued: Unknown
  Colour variation
Price: $440 £295

BO-PEEP (Style one) HN777
Designer: L. Harradine
Height: 6³/₄in., 17.2cm.
Issued: 1926–1938
Price: $750 £500

BO-PEEP (Style one) HN1202
Designer: L. Harradine
Height: 6³/₄in., 17.2cm.
Issued: 1926–1938
  Colour variation
Price: $750 £500

BO-PEEP (Style one) HN1327
Designer: L. Harradine
Height: 6³/₄in., 17.2cm.
Issued: 1929–1938
  Colour variation
Price: $750 £500

BO-PEEP (Style one) HN1328
Designer: L. Harradine
Height: 6³/₄in., 17.2cm.
Issued: 1929–1938
  Colour variation
Price: $750 £500

BOATMAN HN2417

BLUE BEARD (Style two)
HN2105

BLACKSMITH OF
WILLIAMSBURG HN2240

BONNIE LASSIE HN1626

BON APPETIT HN2444

BOBBY HN2778

BO-PEEP (Style two) HN1810
Designer: L. Harradine
Height: 5in., 12.7cm.
Issued: 1937–1949
Price: $340 £225

BO-PEEP (Style two) HN1811
Designer: L. Harradine
Height: 5in., 12.7cm.
Issued: 1937–
Colour variation
Price: R.R.P.

BO-PEEP M82
Designer: L. Harradine
Height: 4in., 10.1cm.
Issued: 1939–1949
Price: $340 £225

BO-PEEP M83
Designer: L. Harradine
Height: 4in., 10.1cm.
Issued: 1939–1949
Colour variation
Price: $340 £225

BOROMIR HN2918
Designer: Harry Sales
Height: 6³/₄in., 17.2cm.
Issued: 1980–1984
Price: $180 £120

BOUDOIR HN2542
Designer: E. J. Griffiths
Height: 12¹/₄in., 31.1cm.
Issued: 1974–1977
Price: $290 £195

BOUQUET HN406
Designer: G. Lambert
Height: 9in., 22.9cm.
Issued: 1920–1938
Price: $975 £650

BOUQUET HN414
Designer: G. Lambert
Height: 9in., 22.9cm.
Issued: 1920–1938
Price: $975 £650

BOUQUET HN422
Designer: G. Lambert
Height: 9in., 22.9cm.
Issued: 1920–1938
Colour variation
Price: $975 £650

BOUQUET HN428
Designer: G. Lambert
Height: 9in., 22.9cm.
Issued: 1921–1938
Colour variation
Price: $975 £650

BOUQUET HN429
Designer: G. Lambert
Height: 9in., 22.9cm.
Issued: 1921–1938
Colour variation
Price: $975 £650

BOUQUET HN567
Designer: G. Lambert
Height: 9¹/₂in., 24.1cm.
Issued: 1923–1938
Colour variation
Price: $975 £650

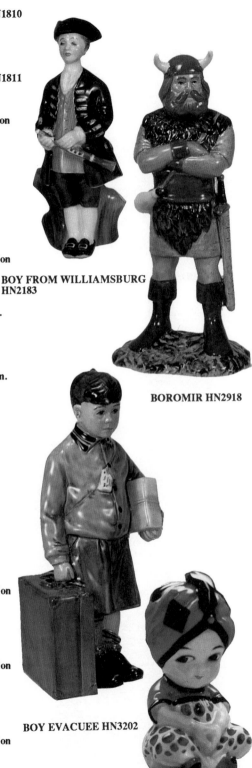

BOY FROM WILLIAMSBURG
HN2183

BOROMIR HN2918

BOY EVACUEE HN3202

BOY WITH TURBAN HN1210

BOUQUET HN794
Designer: G. Lambert
Height: 9in., 22.9cm.
Issued: 1926–1938
Colour variation
Price: $975 £650

BOY EVACUEE HN3202
Designer: A. Hughes
Height: 8¹/₂in., 21.5cm.
Issued: 1989 in a limited
edition of 9500
Price: $220 £145

**BOY FROM WILLIAMSBURG
HN2183**
Designer: P. Davies
Height: 5¹/₂in., 14cm.
Issued: 1969–1983
Price: $150 £100

BOY ON CROCODILE HN373
Designer: C. J. Noke
Height: 5in., 12.7cm.
Length: 14¹/₂in., 36.8cm.
Issued: 1920–1938
Price: $3000 £2000

BOY ON PIG HN1369
Designer: C. J. Noke
Height: 4in., 10.1cm.
Issued: 1930–1938
Price: $2250 £1500

BOY WITH TURBAN HN586
Designer: L. Harradine
Height: 3³/₄in., 9.5cm.
Issued: 1923–1938
Price: $525 £350

BOY WITH TURBAN HN587
Designer: L. Harradine
Height: 3³/₄in., 9.5cm.
Issued: 1923–1938
Price: $525 £350

BOY WITH TURBAN HN661
Designer: L. Harradine
Height: 3³/₄in., 9.5cm.
Issued: 1924–1938
Price: $525 £350

BOY WITH TURBAN HN662
Designer: L. Harradine
Height: 3³/₄in., 9.5cm.
Issued: 1924–1938
Colour variation
Price: $525 £350

BOY WITH TURBAN HN1210
Designer: L. Harradine
Height: 3³/₄in., 9.5cm.
Issued: 1926–1938
Colour variation
Price: $525 £350

BOY WITH TURBAN HN1212
Designer: L. Harradine
Height: 3³/₄in., 9.5cm.
Issued: 1926–1938
Price: $525 £350

BOY WITH TURBAN HN1213
Designer: L. Harradine
Height: 3³/₄in., 9.5cm.
Issued: 1926–1938
Colour variation
Price: $525 £350

BOY WITH TURBAN HN1214
Designer: L. Harradine
Height: 3¹/₂in., 8.9cm.
Issued: 1926–1938
Colour variation
Price: $525 £350

BOY WITH TURBAN HN1225
Designer: L. Harradine
Height: 3³/₄in., 9.5cm.
Issued: 1927–1938
Colour variation
Price: $525 £350

BREEZY DAYS HN3162
Designer: A. Hughes
Height: 8¹/₂in., 21.5cm.
Issued: 1988–1990
Price: $150 £100

BRETON DANCER HN2383
Designer: P. Davies
Height: 8¹/₂in., 21.5cm.
Issued: 1981 in a limited
edition of 750
Price: $560 £375

BRIDE (Style one) HN1588
Designer: L. Harradine
Height: 8³/₄in., 22.2cm.
Issued: 1933–1938
Price: $675 £450

BRIDE (Style one) HN1600
Designer: L. Harradine
Height: 8³/₄in., 22.2cm.
Issued: 1933–1949
Colour variation
Price: $525 £350

BRIDE (Style one) HN1762
Designer: L. Harradine
Height: 8³/₄in., 22.2cm.
Issued: 1936–1949
Colour variation
Price: $525 £350

BRIDE (Style one) HN1841
Designer: L. Harradine
Height: 9¹/₂in., 24.1cm.
Issued: 1938–1949
Colour variation
Price: $675 £450

BRIDE (Style two) HN2166
Designer: P. Davies
Height: 8in., 20.3cm.
Issued: 1956–1976
Price: $225 £150

BRIDE (Style three) HN2873
Designer: P. Davies
Height: 8in., 20.3cm.
Issued: 1980–1989
Price: $180 £120

BRIDE (White) HN3284
Designer: D. V. Tootle
Height: 8¹/₄in., 21cm.
Issued: 1990
Price: R.R.P.

BRIDE (Ivory) HN3285
Designer: D. V. Tootle
Height: 8¹/₄in., 21cm.
Issued: 1990
Price: R.R.P.

BOY WITH TURBAN HN586

BRIDE (White) HN3284

BRIDE (Style one) HN1841

BRETON DANCER HN2383

BRIDE (Style two) HN2166

FIGURES

BRIDE & GROOM HN3281
Designer: Robert Tabbenor
Height: 6¼in., 16cm.
Issued: 1991
Price: R.R.P.

BRIDESMAID (Style one)
HN1433
Designer: L. Harradine
Height: 5¼in., 13.3cm.
Issued: 1930–1951
Price: $190 £125

BRIDESMAID (Style one)
HN1434
Designer: L. Harradine
Height: 5in., 12.7cm.
Issued: 1930–1949
Colour variation
Price: $220 £145

BRIDESMAID (Style one)
HN1530
Designer: L. Harradine
Height: 5in., 12.7cm.
Issued: 1932–1938
Colour variation
Price: $290 £195

BRIDESMAID (Style two)
HN2148
Designer: P. Davies
Height: 5½in., 14cm.
Issued: 1955–1959
Price: $225 £150

BRIDESMAID (Style three)
HN2196
Designer: P. Davies
Height: 5¼in., 13.3cm.
Issued: 1960–1976
Price: $140 £95

BRIDESMAID (Style four)
HN2874
Designer: P. Davies
Height: 5¼in., 13.3cm.
Issued: 1980–1989
Price: $110 £75

BRIDESMAID M11
Designer: L. Harradine
Height: 3¾in., 9.5cm.
Issued: 1932–1938
Price: $375 £250

BRIDESMAID M12
Designer: L. Harradine
Height: 3¾in., 9.5cm.
Issued: 1932–1945
Colour variation
Price: $225 £150

BRIDESMAID M30
Designer: L. Harradine
Height: 3¾in., 9.5cm.
Issued: 1932–1945
Colour variation
Price: $225 £150

BRIDESMAID HN3280
Designer: Robert Tabbenor
Height: 8½in., 21.5cm.
Issued: 1991
Price: R.R.P.

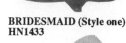

BROTHERS HN3191   BRIDESMAID (Style one)
                   HN1433

BRIDESMAID (Style three)
HN2196

BROTHER & SISTER
HN3460

BRIDE & GROOM HN3281   BRIDESMAID HN3280

BRIDGET HN2070
Designer: L. Harradine
Height: 7¾in., 19.7cm.
Issued: 1951–1973
Price: $280 £185

BRIGHT WATER HN3529
Designer: R. Jefferson
Height: 8½in., 21.5cm.
Issued: 1983–1986
Price: $48 £30

BROKEN LANCE HN2041
Designer: P. Davies
Height: 8¾in., 22.2cm.
Issued: 1949–1975
Price: $490 £325

BROTHER & SISTER HN3460
Designer: Adrian Hughes
Height: 7¾in., 19.5cm.
Issued: 1993
Price: R.R.P.

BROTHERS HN3191
Designer: Eric Griffiths
Height: 8¼in., 21cm.
Issued: 1991
Price: R.R.P.

BUDDIES HN2546
Designer: E. J. Griffiths
Height: 6in., 15.2cm.
Issued: 1973–1976
Price: $250 £165

BUDDIES HN3396
Designer: Alan Maslankowski
Height: 4¼in., 11cm.
Issued: 1992
Price: R.R.P.

BUMBLE M76
Designer: L. Harradine
Height: 4in., 10.1cm.
Issued: 1939–1982
Price: $60 £40

BUNNY HN2214
Designer: P. Davies
Height: 5in., 12.7cm.
Issued: 1960–1975
Price: $165 £110

BUNNY'S BEDTIME HN3370
Designer: N. Pedley
Height: 6in., 15.2cm.
Issued: 1991 in a limited
        edition of 9500
Price: $150 £100

BUTTERCUP HN2309
Designer: P. Davies
Height: 7in., 17.8cm.
Issued: 1964–
Price: R.R.P.

BUTTERCUP HN2399
Designer: P. Davies
Height: 7½in., 19cm.
Issued: 1983–
Price: R.R.P.

BUTTERCUP HN3268
Designer: Peggy Davies
Height: 3¾in., 9.5cm.
Issued: 1990
Price: R.R.P.

BUTTERFLY HN719
Designer: L. Harradine
Height: 6¹/₂in., 16.5cm.
Issued: 1925–1938
Price: $975 £650

BUTTERFLY HN720
Designer: L. Harradine
Height: 6¹/₂in., 16.5cm.
Issued: 1925–1938
Colour variation
Price: $975 £650

BUTTERFLY HN730
Designer: L. Harradine
Height: 6¹/₂in., 16.5cm.
Issued: 1925–1938
Colour variation
Price: $975 £650

BUTTERFLY HN1203
Designer: L. Harradine
Height: 6¹/₂in., 16.5cm.
Issued: 1926–1938
Colour variation
Price: $975 £650

BUTTERFLY HN1456
Designer: L. Harradine
Height: 6¹/₂in., 16.5cm.
Issued: 1931–1938
Price: $975 £650

BUZ FUZ HN538
Designer: L. Harradine
Height: 3³/₄in., 9.5cm.
Issued: 1922–1932
Price: $70 £45

BUZ FUZ M53
Designer: L. Harradine
Height: 4in., 10.1cm.
Issued: 1932–1983
Price: $60 £40

C

CALLED LOVE, A LITTLE BOY HN1545
Designer: Unknown
Height: 3¹/₂in., 8.9cm.
Issued: 1933–1949
Price: $260 £175

CALUMET HN1428
Designer: C. J. Noke
Height: 6in., 15.2cm.
Issued: 1930–1949
Price: $600 £400

CALUMET HN1689
Designer: C. J. Noke
Height: 6¹/₂in., 16.5cm.
Issued: 1935–1949
Colour variation
Price: $600 £400

CALUMET HN2068
Designer: C. J. Noke
Height: 6¹/₄in., 15.9cm.
Issued: 1950–1953
Colour variation
Price: $600 £400

BRIDGET HN2070   BUTTERCUP HN2309

BUDDIES HN3396

BROKEN LANCE HN2041

BUNNY'S BEDTIME HN3370

BUTTERFLY HN1456

FIGURES

CAMELLIA HN2222
Designer: P. Davies
Height: 7¾in., 19.7cm.
Issued: 1960–1971
Price: $340 £225

CAMELLIA HN1710
Designer: L. Harradine
Height: 7in., 17.8cm.
Issued: 1935–1949
Price: $675 £450

CAMELLIA HN1711
Designer: L. Harradine
Height: 7in., 17.8cm.
Issued: 1935–1949
Colour variation
Price: $675 £450

CAMILLE HN1586
Designer: L. Harradine
Height: 6½in., 16.5cm.
Issued: 1933–1949
Price: $440 £295

CAMILLE HN1648
Designer: L. Harradine
Height: 6½in., 16.5cm.
Issued: 1934–1949
Colour variation
Price: $440 £295

CAMILLE HN1736
Designer: L. Harradine
Height: 6½in., 16.5cm.
Issued: 1935–1949
Colour variation
Price: $440 £295

CAMILLE HN3171
U.S.A. edition
Price: R.R.P.

CAPTAIN (Style one) HN778
Designer: L. Harradine
Height: 7in., 17.8cm.
Issued: 1926–1938
Price: $975 £650

CAPTAIN (Style two) HN2260
Designer: M. Nicholl
Height: 9½in., 24.1cm.
Issued: 1965–1982
Price: $290 £195

CAPTAIN COOK HN2889
Designer: W. K. Harper
Height: 8in., 20.3cm.
Issued: 1980–1984
Price: $370 £245

CAPTAIN CUTTLE M77
Designer: L. Harradine
Height: 4in., 10.1cm.
Issued: 1939–1982
Price: $60 £40

CAPTAIN MacHEATH HN464
Designer: L. Harradine
Height: 7in., 17.8cm.
Issued: 1921–1949
Price: $600 £400

CAMILLE HN1586

CAMILLE HN3171

CAPTAIN MacHEATH HN590
Designer: L. Harradine
Height: 7in., 17.8cm.
Issued: 1924–1949
Price: $600 £400

CAPTAIN MacHEATH HN1256
Designer: L. Harradine
Height: 7in., 17.8cm.
Issued: 1927–1949
Price: $600 £400

CAPTAIN, 2ND NEW YORK REGIMENT 1755 HN2755
Designer: E. J. Griffiths
Height: 10in., 25.4cm.
Issued: 1976 in a limited edition of 350
Price: $825 £550

CAREFREE (Black) HN3029
Designer: R. Jefferson
Height: 12¼in., 31cm.
Issued: 1986
Price: R.R.P.

CAREFREE (White) HN3026
Designer: R. Jefferson
Height: 12¼in., 31cm.
Issued: 1986
Price: R.R.P.

CARMEN (Style one) HN1267
Designer: L. Harradine
Height: 7in., 17.8cm.
Issued: 1928–1938
Price: $640 £400

CARMEN (Style one) HN1300
Designer: L. Harradine
Height: 7in., 17.8cm.
Issued: 1928–1938
Colour variation
Price: $640 £400

CARMEN (Style two) HN2545
Designer: E. J. Griffiths
Height: 11½in., 29.2cm.
Issued: 1974–1977
Price: $340 £225

CARNIVAL HN1260
Designer: L. Harradine
Height: 8¼in., 21cm.
Issued: 1927–1938
Price: $1425 £950

CARNIVAL HN1278
Designer: L. Harradine
Height: 8½in., 21.6cm.
Issued: 1928–1938
Colour variation
Price: $1425 £950

CAROL HN2961
Designer: P. Parsons
Height: 7½in., 19cm.
Issued: 1982–
Price: R.R.P.

CAROLINE HN3170
Designer: P. Davies
Height: 7½in., 19.5cm.
Issued: 1988–1992
Price: $165 £110

CAPTAIN COOK HN2889

FIGURES

CAROLYN HN2112
Designer: L. Harradine
Height: 7in., 17.8cm.
Issued: 1953–1965
Price: $340 £225

CAROLYN HN2974
Designer: A. Hughes
Height: 5¹/₂in., 14cm.
Issued: 1983–1986
Price: $250 £165

CARPENTER HN2678
Designer: M. Nicholl
Height: 8in., 20cm.
Issued: 1986–1992
Price: $250 £165

CARPET SELLER (Style one)
HN1464
Designer: L. Harradine
Height: 9¹/₄in., 23.5cm.
Issued: 1931–?
Price: $250 £165

CARPET SELLER (Style two)
HN1464A
Designer: L. Harradine
Height: 9in., 22.9cm.
Issued: 1924–1969
Price: $250 £165

CARPET SELLER SITTING
HN3277
Designer: R. Tabbenor
Height: 7¹/₂in., 19cm.
Issued: 1990
Price: R.R.P.

CARPET SELLER STANDING
HN2776
Designer: W.K. Harper
Height: 9in., 22.9cm.
Issued: 1990
Price: R.R.P.

CARPET VENDOR (Style one)
HN38
Designer: C. J. Noke
Height: Unknown
Issued: 1914–1938
Price: $2250 £1500

CARPET VENDOR (Style one)
HN38A
Designer: C. J. Noke
Height: Unknown
Issued: 1914–1938
Price: $2250 £1500

CARPET VENDOR (Style one)
HN348
Designer: C. J. Noke
Height: Unknown
Issued: 1919–1938
Price: $2250 £1500

CARPET VENDOR (Style two)
HN76
Designer: C. J. Noke
Height: 5¹/₂in., 14cm.
Issued: 1917–1938
Price: $2250 £1500

CARPET SELLER STANDING
HN2776

CAPTAIN (Style two) HN2260

CARPENTER HN2678

CARPET SELLER SITTING
HN3277

CARPET SELLER (Style two)
HN1464A

FIGURES

CARPET VENDOR (Style two) HN350
Designer: C. J. Noke
Height: 5¹/₂in., 14cm.
Issued: 1919–1938
Price: $2250 £1500

CARRIE HN2800
Designer: P. Davies
Height: 6in., 15.2cm.
Issued: 1976–1980
Price: $250 £165

CASSIM (Style one) HN1231
Designer: L. Harradine
Height: 3in., 7.6cm.
Issued: 1927–1938
Price: $450 £300

CASSIM (Style one) HN1232
Designer: L. Harradine
Height: 3in., 7.6cm.
Issued: 1927–1938
Colour variation
Price: $450 £300

CASSIM (Style two) HN1311
Designer: L. Harradine
Height: 3³/₄in., 9.5cm.
Issued: 1929–1938
Price: $450 £300

CASSIM (Style two) HN1312
Designer: L. Harradine
Height: 3³/₄in., 9.5cm.
Issued: 1929–1938
Price: $450 £300

CATHERINE HN3044
Designer: P. Parsons
Height: 5in., 12.5cm.
Issued: 1985–
Price: R.R.P.

CATHERINE HN3451
Designer: P. Parsons
Height: 5in., 12.7cm.
Issued: 1993
Colour vairation
Price: R.R.P.

CATHERINE HOWARD HN3449
Designer: Pauline Parsons
Height: 8in., 20cm.
Issued: 1993
Price: R.R.P.

CATHERINE OF ARAGON HN3233
Designer: Pauline Parsons
Height: 6¹/₂in., 16.5cm.
Issued: 1993
Price: R.R.P.

CAVALIER (Style one) HN369
Designer: Unknown
Height: Unknown
Issued: 1920–1938
Price: $1500 £1000

CAVALIER (Style two) HN2716
Designer: E. J. Griffiths
Height: 9³/₄in., 24.7cm.
Issued: 1976–1982
Price: $280 £185

CATHERINE HN3451

CATHERINE HOWARD HN3449

CAVALIER (Style two) HN2716

CATHERINE OF ARAGON HN3233

CHARLIE CHAPLIN HN2771

CELESTE HN2237
Designer: P. Davies
Height: 6³/₄in., 17.2cm.
Issued: 1959–1971
Price: $250 £165

CELIA HN1726
Designer: L. Harradine
Height: 11¹/₂in., 29.2cm.
Issued: 1935–1949
Price: $975 £650

CELIA HN1727
Designer: L. Harradine
Height: 11¹/₂in., 29.2cm.
Issued: 1935–1949
Price: $975 £650

CELLIST HN2226
Designer: P. Davies
Height: 8in., 20.3cm.
Issued: 1960–1967
Price: $440 £295

CELLO HN2331
Designer: P. Davies
Height: 6in., 15.2cm.
Issued: 1970 in a limited edition of 750
Price: $675 £450

CENTURION HN2726
Designer: W. K. Harper
Height: 9¹/₄in., 23.5cm.
Issued: 1982–1984
Price: $260 £175

CERISE HN1607
Designer: L. Harradine
Height: 5¹/₄in., 13.3cm.
Issued: 1933–1949
Price: $300 £200

CHARISMA HN3090
Designer: P. Parsons
Height: 12¹/₂in., 31.5cm.
Issued: 1987–1990
Price: $150 £100

CHARITY HN3087
Designer: E. J. Griffiths
Height: 8¹/₂in., 21.5cm.
Issued: 1987 in a limited edition of 9500
Price: $250 £165

CHARLEY'S AUNT (Style one) HN35
Designer: A. Toft
Height: 6³/₄in., 17.2cm.
Issued: 1914–1938
Price: $450 £300

CHARLEY'S AUNT HN640
Designer: A. Toft
Height: 7in., 17.8cm.
Issued: 1924–1938
Colour variation
Price: $900 £600

CHARLEY'S AUNT (Style two) HN1411
Designer: H. Fenton
Height: 8in., 20.3cm.
Issued: 1930–1938
Price: $750 £500

FIGURES

CHARLEY'S AUNT (Style two)
HN1554
Designer: H. Fenton
Height: 8in., 20.3cm.
Issued: 1933–1938
Price: $750 £500

CHARLEY'S AUNT (Style three) **HN1703**
Designer: A. Toft
Height: 6in., 15.2cm.
Issued: 1935–1938
Price: $750 £500

CHARLIE CHAPLIN HN2771
Designer: W. K. Harper
Height: 9in., 22.4cm.
Issued: 1989 in a limited edition of 5000
Price: $225 £150

CHARLOTTE HN2421
Designer: J. Bromley
Height: 6¹/₂in., 16.5cm.
Issued: 1972–1986
Price: $250 £165

CHARLOTTE HN2423
Designer: J. Bromley
Height: 6³/₄in., 17cm.
Issued: 1986–1992
Price: $165 £110

CHARMIAN HN1568
Designer: L. Harradine
Height: 6¹/₂in., 16.5cm.
Issued: 1933–1938
Price: $525 £350

CHARMIAN HN1569
Designer: L. Harradine
Height: 6¹/₂in., 16.5cm.
Issued: 1933–1938
Colour variation
Price: $525 £350

CHARMIAN HN1651
Designer: L. Harradine
Height: 6¹/₂in., 16.5cm.
Issued: 1934–1938
Colour variation
Price: $525 £350

CHELSEA PAIR (Woman) **HN577**
Designer: L. Harradine
Height: 6in., 15.2cm.
Issued: 1923–1938
Price: $480 £300

CHELSEA PAIR (Woman) **HN578**
Designer: L. Harradine
Height: 6in., 15.2cm.
Issued: 1923–1938
Colour variation
Price: $480 £300

CHELSEA PAIR (Man) **HN579**
Designer: L. Harradine
Height: 6in., 15.2cm.
Issued: 1923–1938
Price: $480 £300

CENTURION HN2726

CHARLOTTE HN2421

CELLO HN2331

CELLIST HN2226

CHARITY HN3087

CHARMIAN HN1568

CHELSEA PAIR (Man) HN580
Designer: L. Harradine
Height: 6in., 15.2cm.
Issued: 1923–1938
        Colour variation
Price: $480 £300

CHELSEA PENSIONER HN689
Designer: L. Harradine
Height: 5³/₄in., 14.6cm.
Issued: 1924–1938
Price: $750 £500

CHERIE HN2341
Designer: P. Davies
Height: 5¹/₂in., 14cm.
Issued: 1966–1992
Price: $110 £75

CHERRY BLOSSOM HN3092
Designer: P. Parsons
Height: 12¹/₄in., 31cm.
Issued: 1987–1989
Price: $150 £100

CHERYL HN3253
Designer: D. Tootle
Height: 7¹/₂in., 19.1cm.
Issued: 1989
Price: R.R.P.

CHIC HN2997
Designer: R. Tabbenor
Height: 13in., 33cm.
Issued: 1987–1990
Price: $150 £100

CHIEF HN2892
Designer: W. K. Harper
Height: 7in., 17.8cm.
Issued: 1979–1988
Price: $250 £165

CHIEFTAIN HN2929
Designer: S. Keenan
Height: 8³/₄in., 22.2cm.
Issued: 1982 in a limited
        edition of 950
Price: $450 £300

CHILD AND CRAB HN32
Designer: C. J. Noke
Height: 5¹/₄in., 13.3cm.
Issued: 1913–1938
Price: $1875 £1250

**CHILD FROM
WILLIAMSBURG HN2154**
Designer: P. Davies
Height: 5¹/₂in., 14cm.
Issued: 1964–1984
Price: $140 £95

**CHILD STUDY (Style one)
HN603A**
Designer: L. Harradine
Height: 4³/₄in., 12cm.
Issued: 1924–1938
Price: $260 £175

**CHILD STUDY (Style one)
HN603B**
Designer: L. Harradine
Height: 4³/₄in., 12cm.
Issued: 1924–1938
        Colour variation
Price: $260 £175

CHIEF HN2892

CHINA REPAIRER HN2943

CHILD STUDY HN606A
Designer: L. Harradine
Height: 5in., 12.7cm.
Issued: 1924–1938
Price: $323 £145

CHILD STUDY HN1441
Designer: L. Harradine
Height: 5in., 12.7cm.
Issued: 1931–1938
Price: $296 £185

**CHILD STUDY (Style two)
HN604A**
Designer: L. Harradine
Height: 5¹/₂in., 14cm.
Issued: 1924–1938
Price: $272 £170

**CHILD STUDY (Style two)
HN604B**
Designer: L. Harradine
Height: 5¹/₂in., 14cm.
Issued: 1924–1938
        Colour variation
Price: $272 £170

**CHILD STUDY (Style two)
HN1442**
Designer: L. Harradine
Height: 6¹/₄in., 15.9cm.
Issued: 1931–1938
Price: $296 £185

**CHILD STUDY (Style two)
HN1443**
Designer: L. Harradine
Height: 5in., 12.7cm.
Issued: 1931–1938
Price: $272 £170

**CHILD STUDY (Style three)
HN605A**
Designer: L. Harradine
Height: 5¹/₂in., 14cm.
Issued: 1924–1938
Price: $260 £175

**CHILD STUDY (Style three)
HN605B**
Designer: L. Harradine
Height: 5¹/₂in., 14cm.
Issued: 1924–1938
Price: $260 £175

CHILD'S GRACE HN62
Designer: L. Perugini
Height: 6³/₄in., 17.2cm.
Issued: 1916–1938
Price: $1500 £1000

CHILD'S GRACE HN62A
Designer: L. Perugini
Height: 6³/₄in., 17.2cm.
Issued: 1916–1938
        Colour variation
Price: $1500 £1000

CHILD'S GRACE HN510
Designer: L. Perugini
Height: 6³/₄in., 17.1cm.
Issued: 1921–1938
Price: $1500 £1000

CHINA REPAIRER HN2943
Designer: R. Tabbenor
Height: 6³/₄in., 17cm.
Issued: 1983–1988
Price: $250 £165

CHINESE DANCER HN2840
Designer: P. Davies
Height: 9in., 22.9cm.
Issued: 1980 in a limited
edition of 750
Price: $750 £500

CHITARRONE HN2700
Designer: P. Davies
Height: 7¹/₂in., 19.1cm.
Issued: 1974 in a limited
edition of 750
Price: $675 £450

CHLOE HN1470
Designer: L. Harradine
Height: 5¹/₂in., 14cm.
Issued: 1931–1949
Price: $375 £250

CHLOE HN1476
Designer: L. Harradine
Height: 5¹/₂in., 14cm.
Issued: 1931–1938
Colour variation
Price: $375 £250

CHLOE HN1479
Designer: L. Harradine
Height: 5¹/₂in., 14cm.
Issued: 1931–1949
Colour variation
Price: $375 £250

CHLOE HN1498
Designer: L. Harradine
Height: 6in., 15.2cm.
Issued: 1932–1938
Colour variation
Price: $375 £250

CHLOE HN1765
Designer: L. Harradine
Height: 6in., 15.2cm.
Issued: 1936–1950
Colour variation
Price: $375 £250

CHLOE HN1956
Designer: L. Harradine
Height: 6in., 15.2cm.
Issued: 1940–1949
Colour variation
Price: $375 £250

CHLOE M9
Designer: L. Harradine
Height: 2³/₄in., 7cm.
Issued: 1932–1945
Price: $300 £200

CHLOE M10
Designer: L. Harradine
Height: 2³/₄in., 7cm.
Issued: 1932–1945
Colour variation
Price: $300 £200

CHILD FROM
WILLIAMSBURG HN2154

CHLOE HN1479

CHITARRONE HN2700

CHINESE DANCER HN2840

FIGURES

CHLOE M29
Designer: L. Harradine
Height: 2³/₄in., 7cm.
Issued: 1932–1945
       Colour variation
Price: $300 £200

CHOICE HN1959
Designer: L. Harradine
Height: 7¹/₄in., 18.4cm.
Issued: 1941–1949
Price: $600 £400

CHOICE HN1960
Designer: L. Harradine
Height: 7¹/₄in., 18.4cm.
Issued: 1941–1949
       Colour variation
Price: $600 £400

CHOIR BOY HN2141
Designer: P. Davies
Height: 4³/₄in., 12cm.
Issued: 1954–1975
Price: $145 £95

CHORUS GIRL HN1401
Designer: L. Harradine
Height: 8¹/₂in., 21.6cm.
Issued: 1930–1938
Price: $750 £500

CHRISTENING DAY (Pink) HN3211
Designer: P. A. Northcroft
Height: 8¹/₂in., 21.5cm.
Issued: 1988–1990
Price: $165 £110

CHRISTENING DAY (Blue) HN3210
Designer: P. A. Northcroft
Height: 8¹/₂in., 21.5cm.
Issued: 1988–1990
Price: $165 £110

CHRISTINE (Style one) HN1839
Designer: L. Harradine
Height: 7³/₄in., 19.7cm.
Issued: 1938–1949
Price: $600 £400

CHRISTINE (Style one) HN1840
Designer: L. Harradine
Height: 7³/₄in., 19.7cm.
Issued: 1938–1949
       Colour variation
Price: $600 £400

CHRISTINE (Style two) HN2792
Designer: P. Davies
Height: 7¹/₂in., 19.1cm.
Issued: 1978–
Price: R.R.P.

CHRISTINE HN3269
Designer: Peggy Davies
Height: 4in., 10cm.
Issued: 1990
Price: R.R.P.

CHRISTMAS DAY HN3488
Designer: Alan Maslankowski
Height: 6in., 15cm.
Issued: 1993
Price: R.R.P.

CHRISTINE (Style two)
HN2792

CHRISTMAS
MORN HN1992

CHRISTMAS DAY
HN3488

CHRISTMAS PARCELS HN2851

CHRISTMAS MORN HN1992
Designer: P. Davies
Height: 7in., 17.8cm.
Issued: 1947–
Price: R.R.P.

CHRISTMAS MORN HN3212
Designer: P. Davies
Height: 4in., 10cm.
Issued: 1988
Price: R.R.P.

CHRISTMAS PARCELS HN2851
Designer: W. K. Harper
Height: 8³/₄in., 22.2cm.
Issued: 1978–1982
Price: $260 £175

CHRISTMAS TIME HN2110
Designer: P. Davies
Height: 6¹/₂in., 16.5cm.
Issued: 1953–1967
Price: $365 £245

CHRISTOPHER COLUMBUS HN3392
Designer: A. Maslankowski
Height: 12in., 13.5cm.
Issued: 1992 in a limited
       edition of 1492
Price: $1125 £750

CICELY HN1516
Designer: L. Harradine
Height: 5³/₄in., 14.6cm.
Issued: 1932–1949
Price: $675 £450

CIRCE HN1249
Designer: L. Harradine
Height: 7³/₄in., 19.7cm.
Issued: 1927–1938
Price: $975 £650

CIRCE HN1250
Designer: L. Harradine
Height: 7¹/₂in., 19.1cm.
Issued: 1927–1938
Price: $975 £650

CIRCE HN1254
Designer: L. Harradine
Height: 7¹/₂in., 19.1cm.
Issued: 1927–1938
       Colour variation
Price: $975 £650

CIRCE HN1255
Designer: L. Harradine
Height: 7¹/₂in., 19.1cm.
Issued: 1927–1938
       Colour variation
Price: $975 £650

CISSIE HN1808
Designer: L. Harradine
Height: 5in., 12.7cm.
Issued: 1937–1951
Price: $225 £150

CISSIE HN1809
Designer: L. Harradine
Height: 5in., 12.7cm.
Issued: 1937–1993
       Colour variation
Price: $110 £75

CHRISTINE (Style two)
HN2792

FIGURES

CLAIRE HN3209
Designer: A. Hughes
Height: 8$\frac{1}{2}$in., 11.6cm.
Issued: 1990–1992
Price: $155 £110

CLARE HN2793
Designer: P. Davies
Height: 7$\frac{1}{2}$in., 19.1cm.
Issued: 1980–1984
Price: $250 £165

CLARIBEL HN1950
Designer: L. Harradine
Height: 4$\frac{3}{4}$in., 12cm.
Issued: 1940–1949
Price: $300 £200

CLARIBEL HN1951
Designer: L. Harradine
Height: 4$\frac{3}{4}$in., 12cm.
Issued: 1940–1949
Colour variation
Price: $300 £200

CLARINDA HN2724
Designer: W. K. Harper
Height: 8$\frac{1}{2}$in., 21.6cm.
Issued: 1975–1980
Price: $250 £165

CLARISSA (Style one) HN1525
Designer: L. Harradine
Height: 10in., 25.4cm.
Issued: 1932–1938
Price: $490 £325

CLARISSA (Style one) HN1687
Designer: L. Harradine
Height: 9$\frac{3}{4}$in., 24.8cm.
Issued: 1935–1949
Colour variation
Price: $450 £300

CLARISSA (Style two) HN2345
Designer: P. Davies
Height: 7$\frac{1}{2}$in., 19.1cm.
Issued: 1968–1982
Price: $190 £125

CLEAR WATER HN3530
Designer: R. Jefferson
Height: 8$\frac{1}{4}$in., 21cm.
Issued: 1983–1986
Price: $72 £45

CLEMENCY HN1633
Designer: L. Harradine
Height: 7in., 17.8cm.
Issued: 1934–1938
Price: $450 £300

CLEMENCY HN1634
Designer: L. Harradine
Height: 7in., 17.8cm.
Issued: 1934–1949
Colour variation
Price: $450 £300

CLEMENCY HN1643
Designer: L. Harradine
Height: 7in., 17.8cm.
Issued: 1934–1938
Colour variation
Price: $450 £300

CISSIE HN1809

CLARISSA (Style two) HN2345

CLAIRE HN3209

CHRISTINE HN3269

CLARE HN2793

CLARINDA HN2724

CHRISTOPHER COLUMBUS HN3392

FIGURES

CLEOPATRA HN2868
Designer: P. Davies
Height: 7¹/₄in., 18.4cm.
Issued: 1980 in a limited
edition of 750
Price: $1125 £750

CLOCKMAKER HN2279
Designer: M. Nicholl
Height: 7in., 17.8cm.
Issued: 1961–1975
Price: $340 £225

CLOTHILDE HN1598
Designer: L. Harradine
Height: 7¹/₄in., 18.4cm.
Issued: 1933–1949
Price: $450 £300

CLOTHILDE HN1599
Designer: L. Harradine
Height: 7¹/₄in., 18.4cm.
Issued: 1933–1949
Colour variation
Price: $450 £300

CLOUD HN1831
Designer: R. Garbe
Height: 23in., 58.4cm.
Issued: 1937–1949
Price: $2250 £1500

CLOWN HN2890
Designer: W. K. Harper
Height: 9in., 22.9cm.
Issued: 1979–1988
Price: $250 £165

COACHMAN HN2282
Designer: M. Nicholl
Height: 7¹/₄in., 18.4cm.
Issued: 1963–1971
Price: $340 £225

COBBLER (Style one) HN542
Designer: C. J. Noke
Height: 7¹/₂in., 19.1cm.
Issued: 1922–1939
Price: $525 £350

COBBLER (Style one) HN543
Designer: C. J. Noke
Height: 7¹/₂in., 19.1cm.
Issued: 1922–1938
Colour variation
Price: $675 £450

COBBLER (Style one) HN682
Designer: C. J. Noke
Height: 7¹/₂in., 19.1cm.
Issued: 1924–1938
Colour variation
Price: $600 £400

COBBLER (Style two) HN681
Designer: C. J. Noke
Height: 8¹/₂in., 21.6cm.
Issued: 1924–1938
Price: $675 £450

COBBLER (Style two) HN1251
Designer: C. J. Noke
Height: 8¹/₂in., 21.6cm.
Issued: 1927–1938
Colour variation
Price: $675 £450

CLOCKMAKER
HN2279

CLOWN HN2890

COLUMBINE HN2738

COBBLER (Style two) HN1283
Designer: C. J. Noke
Height: 8¹/₂in., 21.6cm.
Issued: 1928–1949
Colour variation
Price: $375 £250

COBBLER (Style three) HN1705
Designer: C. J. Noke
Height: 8in., 20.3cm.
Issued: 1935–1949
Price: $375 £250

COBBLER (Style three) HN1706
Designer: C. J. Noke
Height: 8¹/₂in., 21.6cm.
Issued: 1935–1969
Colour variation
Price: $260 £175

COCKTAILS HN3070
Designer: A. Hughes
Height: 10³/₄in., 27.5cm.
Issued: 1987
Price: R.R.P.

COLLINETTE HN1998
Designer: L. Harradine
Height: 7¹/₄in., 18.4cm.
Issued: 1947–1949
Price: $410 £275

COLLINETTE HN1999
Designer: L. Harradine
Height: 7¹/₄in., 18.4cm.
Issued: 1947–1949
Colour variation
Price: $410 £275

COLONEL FAIRFAX HN2903
Designer: W. K. Harper
Height: 11¹/₂in., 29cm.
Issued: 1982–1986
Price: $490 £325

**COLUMBINE (Style one)
HN1296**
Designer: L. Harradine
Height: 6in., 15.2cm.
Issued: 1928–1938
Price: $675 £450

**COLUMBINE (Style one)
HN1297**
Designer: L. Harradine
Height: 6in., 15.2cm.
Issued: 1928–1938
Colour variation
Price: $675 £450

**COLUMBINE (Style one)
HN1439**
Designer: L. Harradine
Height: 6in., 15.2cm.
Issued: 1930–1938
Colour variation
Price: $675 £450

**COLUMBINE (Style two)
HN2185**
Designer: P. Davies
Height: 7in., 17.8cm.
Issued: 1957–1969
Price: $240 £160

128

COLUMBINE HN2738
Designer: D. Tootle
Height: 12¹/₂in., 31cm.
Issued: 1982–
Price: R.R.P.

COLUMBINE HN3288
U.S.A. edition
Price: R.R.P.

COMING OF SPRING HN1722
Designer: L. Harradine
Height: 12¹/₂in., 31.7cm.
Issued: 1935–1949
Price: $1875 £1250

COMING OF SPRING HN1723
Designer: L. Harradine
Height: 12¹/₂in., 31.7cm.
Issued: 1935–1949
Colour variation
Price: $1875 £1250

CONFUCIUS HN3314
Designer: P. Gee
Height: 9in., 22.9cm.
Issued: 1990
Price: R.R.P.

CONGRATULATIONS HN3351
Designer: Peter Gee
Height: 11in., 28cm.
Issued: 1991
Price: R.R.P.

CONSTANCE HN1510
Designer: L. Harradine
Height: 6³/₄in., 17.1cm.
Issued: 1932–1938
Price: $640 £400

CONSTANCE HN1511
Designer: L. Harradine
Height: Unknown
Issued: 1932–1938
Colour variation
Price: $640 £400

CONTEMPLATION HN2213
Designer: P. Davies
Height: 12in., 30cm.
Issued: 1982–1986
Price: $150 £100

CONTEMPLATION HN2241
Designer: P. Davies
Height: 12in., 30cm.
Issued: 1982–1986
Colour variation
Price: $150 £100

CONTENTMENT HN395
Designer: L. Harradine
Height: 7¹/₄in., 18.4cm.
Issued: 1920–1938
Price: $975 £650

CONTENTMENT HN396
Designer: L. Harradine
Height: 7¹/₄in., 18.4cm.
Issued: 1920–1938
Colour variation
Price: $975 £650

CONFUCIUS HN3314

COLUMBINE HN3288

COLUMBINE (Style two)
HN2185

COLONEL FAIRFAX HN2903

CONTENTMENT HN421
Designer: L. Harradine
Height: 7¹/₄in., 18.4cm.
Issued: 1920–1938
Colour variation
Price: $975 £650

CONTENTMENT HN468
Designer: L. Harradine
Height: 7¹/₄in., 18.4cm.
Issued: 1921–1938
Colour variation
Price: $975 £650

CONTENTMENT HN572
Designer: L. Harradine
Height: 7¹/₄in., 18.4cm.
Issued: 1923–1938
Colour variation
Price: $975 £650

CONTENTMENT HN685
Designer: L. Harradine
Height: 7¹/₄in., 18.4cm.
Issued: 1923–1938
Colour variation
Price: $975 £650

CONTENTMENT HN686
Designer: L. Harradine
Height: 7¹/₄in., 18.4cm.
Issued: 1924–1938
Colour variation
Price: $975 £650

CONTENTMENT HN1323
Designer: L. Harradine
Height: 7¹/₄in., 18.4cm.
Issued: 1929–1938
Colour variation
Price: $975 £650

COOKIE HN2218
Designer: P. Davies
Height: 4³/₄in., 12cm.
Issued: 1958–1975
Price: $140 £95

COPPELIA HN2115
Designer: P. Davies
Height: 7¹/₄in., 18.4cm.
Issued: 1953–1959
Price: $590 £395

COQUETTE HN20
Designer: W. White
Height: 9¹/₄in., 23.5cm.
Issued: 1913–1938
Price: $2250 £1500

COQUETTE HN37
Designer: W. White
Height: 9¹/₄in., 23.5cm.
Issued: 1913–1938
Price: $2250 £1500

CORALIE HN2307
Designer: P. Davies
Height: 7¹/₄in., 18.4cm.
Issued: 1964–1988
Price: $200 £135

CORINTHIAN HN1973
Designer: H. Fenton
Height: 7³/₄in., 19.7cm.
Issued: 1941–1949
Price: $900 £600

COPPELIA HN2115

CORALIE HN2307

COUNTRY ROSE HN3221

CORPORAL, 1st NEW HAMPSHIRE REGIMENT 1778 HN2780
Designer: E. J. Griffiths
Height: 13in., 33cm.
Issued: 1975 in a limited edition of 350
Price: $750 £500

COUNTESS MARY HOWE HN3007
Designer: P. Gee
Height: 9¹/₄in., 23.5cm.
Issued: 1950 in a limited edition of 5000
Price: R.R.P.

COUNTESS OF HARRINGTON HN3317
Designer: Peter Gee
Height: 9¹/₂in., 24cm.
Issued: 1992 in a limited edition of 5000
Price: R.R.P.

COUNTESS SPENCER HN3320
Designer: Peter Gee
Height: 9¹/₂in., 24cm.
Issued: 1993 in a limited edition of 5000
Price: R.R.P.

COUNTRY GIRL HN3051
Designer: A. Hughes
Height: 7³/₄in., 19.5cm.
Issued: 1987–1991
Price: $100 £65

COUNTRY LASS HN1991
Designer: L. Harradine
Height: 7¹/₄in., 18.4cm.
Issued: 1975–1981
Price: $250 £165
Also called MARKET DAY HN1991

COUNTRY LOVE HN2418
Designer: J. Bromley
Height: 8in., 20.3cm.
Issued: 1990 in a limited edition of 12500
Price: R.R.P.

COUNTRY MAID HN3163
Designer: P. Hughes
Height: 8¹/₄in., 21cm.
Issued: 1988–1991
Price: $165 £110

COUNTRY ROSE HN3221
Designer: P. Davies
Height: 8¹/₂in., 21.5cm.
Issued: 1989
Price: R.R.P.

COURT SHOEMAKER HN1755
Designer: L. Harradine
Height: 6³/₄in., 17.2cm.
Issued: 1936–1949
Price: $1120 £700

COURTIER HN1338
Designer: L. Harradine
Height: 4¹/₂in., 11.4cm.
Issued: 1929–1938
Price: $1875 £1250

COURTSHIP HN3525
Designer: Russell Willis
Height: 14¹/₄in., 36cm.
Issued: 1982
Price: R.R.P.

COVENT GARDEN HN1339
Designer: L. Harradine
Height: 9in., 22.9cm.
Issued: 1929–1938
Price: $975 £650

COVENT GARDEN HN2857
Designer: W. K. Harper
Height: 10in., 25.5cm.
Issued: 1988–1990
Price: $150 £100

CRADLE SONG HN2246
Designer: P. Davies
Height: 5¹/₂in., 14cm.
Issued: 1959–1962
Price: $370 £245

CRAFTSMAN HN2284
Designer: M. Nicholl
Height: 8¹/₄in., 21cm.
Issued: 1961–1965
Price: $590 £395

CRINOLINE HN21
Designer: G. Lambert
Height: 6¹/₄in., 15.8cm.
Issued: 1913–1938
Colour variation
Price: $1125 £750

CRINOLINE HN8
Designer: G. Lambert
Height: 6¹/₄in., 15.8cm.
Issued: 1913–1938
Price: $1125 £750

CRINOLINE HN9
Designer: G. Lambert
Height: 6¹/₄in., 15.8cm.
Issued: 1913–1938
Colour variation
Price: $1125 £750

CRINOLINE HN9A
Designer: G. Lambert
Height: 6¹/₄in., 15.8cm.
Issued: 1913–1938
Colour variation
Price: $1125 £750

CRINOLINE HN21A
Designer: G. Lambert
Height: 6¹/₄in., 15.8cm.
Issued: 1913–1938
Colour variation
Price: $1125 £750

CRINOLINE HN413
Designer: G. Lambert
Height: 6¹/₄in., 15.8cm.
Issued: 1920–1938
Colour variation
Price: $1125 £750

CRINOLINE HN566
Designer: G. Lambert
Height: 6¹/₄in., 15.8cm.
Issued: 1923–1938
Colour variation
Price: $1125 £750

COUNTRY LOVE HN2418

COUNTESS SPENCER HN3320

COUNTESS OF
HARRINGTON HN3317

COVENT GARDEN HN1339

COUNTRY LASS HN1991

131

CRINOLINE HN628
Designer: G. Lambert
Height: 6¹/₄in., 15.8cm.
Issued: 1924–1938
Colour variation
Price: $1125 £750

CRINOLINE LADY HN650
Designer: Unknown
Height: 3in., 7.6cm.
Issued: 1924–1938
Price: $750 £500

CRINOLINE LADY HN651
Designer: Unknown
Height: 3in., 7.6cm.
Issued: 1924–1938
Colour variation
Price: $750 £500

CRINOLINE LADY HN652
Designer: Unknown
Height: 3in., 7.6cm.
Issued: 1924–1938
Colour variation
Price: $750 £500

CRINOLINE LADY HN653
Designer: Unknown
Height: 3in., 7.6cm.
Issued: 1924–1938
Colour variation
Price: $750 £500

CRINOLINE LADY HN654
Designer: Unknown
Height: 3in., 7.6cm.
Issued: 1924–1938
Colour variation
Price: $750 £500

CRINOLINE LADY HN655
Designer: Unknown
Height: 3in., 7.6cm.
Issued: 1924–1938
Colour variation
Price: $750 £500

CROQUET HN3470
Designer: Valerie Annand
Height: 8in., 20cm.
Issued: 1996 in a limited
edition of 5000
Price: R.R.P.

CROUCHING NUDE HN457
Designer: Unknown
Height: 5¹/₂in., 14cm.
Issued: 1921–1938
Price: $825 £550

CUP OF TEA HN2322
Designer: M. Nicholl
Height: 7in., 17.8cm.
Issued: 1964–1983
Price: $250 £165

CURLY KNOB HN1627
Designer: L. Harradine
Height: 6in., 15.2cm.
Issued: 1934–1949
Price: $440 £295

CROQUET HN3470

CUP OF TEA HN2322

CURLY LOCKS HN2049
Designer: P. Davies
Height: 4¹/₂in., 11.4cm.
Issued: 1949–1953
Price: $450 £300

CURTSEY HN57
Designer: E. W. Light
Height: 11in., 27.9cm.
Issued: 1916–1938
Price: $975 £650

CURTSEY HN57B
Designer: E. W. Light
Height: 11in., 27.9cm.
Issued: 1916–1938
Colour variation
Price: $975 £650

CURTSEY HN66A
Designer: E. W. Light
Height: 11in., 27.9cm.
Issued: 1916–1938
Colour variation
Price: $975 £650

CURTSEY HN327
Designer: E. W. Light
Height: 11in., 27.9cm.
Issued: 1918–1938
Colour variation
Price: $975 £650

CURTSEY HN334
Designer: E. W. Light
Height: 11in., 27.9cm.
Issued: 1918–1938
Colour variation
Price: $975 £650

CURTSEY HN363
Designer: E. W. Light
Height: 11in., 27.9cm.
Issued: 1919–1938
Colour variation
Price: $975 £650

CURTSEY HN371
Designer: E. W. Light
Height: 11in., 27.9cm.
Issued: 1920–1938
Colour variation
Price: $975 £650

CURTSEY HN518
Designer: E. W. Light
Height: 11in., 27.9cm.
Issued: 1921–1938
Colour variation
Price: $975 £650

CURTSEY HN547
Designer: E. W. Light
Height: 11in., 27.9cm.
Issued: 1922–1938
Colour variation
Price: $975 £650

CURTSEY HN629
Designer: E. W. Light
Height: 11in., 27.9cm.
Issued: 1924–1938
Colour variation
Price: $975 £650

CURTSEY HN670
Designer: E. W. Light
Height: 11in., 27.9cm.
Issued: 1924–1938
Colour variation
Price: $975 £650

CYMBALS HN2699
Designer: P. Davies
Height: 7½in., 19.1cm.
Issued: 1974 in a limited
edition of 750
Price: $675 £450

CYNTHIA HN1685
Designer: L. Harradine
Height: 5¾in., 14.6cm.
Issued: 1935–1949
Price: $600 £400

CYNTHIA HN1686
Designer: L. Harradine
Height: 5¾in., 14.6cm.
Issued: 1935–1949
Colour variation
Price: $600 £400

CYNTHIA HN1686A
Designer: L. Harradine
Height: 5¾in., 14.6cm.
Issued: 1935–1949
Colour variation
Price: $600 £400

CYNTHIA HN2440
Designer: P. Davies
Height: 7¼in., 18cm.
Issued: 1984–
Price: $600 £400

CYNTHIA HN2440

CYMBALS HN2699

D

DADDY'S GIRL HN3435
Designer: Alan Maslankowski
Height: 4in., 10cm.
Issued: 1993
Price: R.R.P.

**DAFFY-DOWN-DILLY
HN1712**
Designer: L. Harradine
Height: 8¼in., 20.9cm.
Issued: 1935–1975
Price: $410 £275

**DAFFY-DOWN-DILLY
HN1713**
Designer: L. Harradine
Height: 8¼in., 20.9cm.
Issued: 1935–1949
Colour variation
Price: $525 £350

DAINTY MAY HN1639
Designer: L. Harradine
Height: 6in., 15.2cm.
Issued: 1934–1949
Price: $410 £275

DADDY'S GIRL HN3435

DAFFY-DOWN-DILLY
HN1712

133

FIGURES

DAINTY MAY HN1656
Designer: L. Harradine
Height: 6in., 15.2cm.
Issued: 1934–1949
Colour variation
Price: $410 £275

DAINTY MAY M67
Designer: L. Harradine
Height: 4in., 10.1cm.
Issued: 1935–1949
Price: $375 £250

DAINTY MAY M73
Designer: L. Harradine
Height: 4in., 10.1cm.
Issued: 1936–1949
Colour variation
Price: $375 £250

DAISY HN1575
Designer: L. Harradine
Height: 3³/₄in., 9.5cm.
Issued: 1933–1949
Price: $410 £275

DAISY HN1961
Designer: L. Harradine
Height: 3¹/₂in., 8.9cm.
Issued: 1941–1949
Colour variation
Price: $410 £275

DAMARIS HN2079
Designer: P. Davies
Height: 7¹/₄in., 18.4cm.
Issued: 1951–1952
Price: $675 £450

DANCING DELIGHT HN3078
Designer: A. Hughes
Height: 12³/₄in., 32cm.
Issued: 1987–1989
Price: $150 £100

**"DANCING EYES AND
SUNNY HAIR" HN1543**
Designer: Unknown
Height: 5in., 12.7cm.
Issued: 1933–1949
Price: $375 £250

DANCING FIGURE HN311
Designer: Unknown
Height: 17³/₄in., 45cm.
Issued: 1918–1938
Price: $2250 £1500

DANCING YEARS HN2235
Designer: P. Davies
Height: 6³/₄in., 17.2cm.
Issued: 1965–1971
Price: $340 £225

DANDY HN753
Designer: L. Harradine
Height: 6³/₄in., 17.2cm.
Issued: 1925–1938
Price: $900 £600

DANIELLE HN3001
Designer: Peter Gee
Height: 7¹/₄in., 15.5cm.
Issued: 1990
Price: R.R.P.

DANCING YEARS HN2235

DANIELLE HN3001

DARBY HN1427

DAPHNE HN2268
Designer: P. Davies
Height: 8¹/₄in., 21cm.
Issued: 1963–1975
Price: $250 £165

DARBY HN1427
Designer: L. Harradine
Height: 5¹/₂in., 14cm.
Issued: 1930–1949
Price: $290 £195

DARBY HN2024
Designer: L. Harradine
Height: 5³/₄in., 14.6cm.
Issued: 1949–1959
Price: $290 £195

DARLING (Style one) HN1
Designer: C. Vyse
Height: 7³/₄in., 19.5cm.
Issued: 1913–1928
Price: $675 £450

DARLING (Style one) HN1319
Designer: C. Vyse
Height: 7¹/₂in., 19.1cm.
Issued: 1929–1959
Colour variation
Price: $210 £140

DARLING (Style one) HN1371
Designer: C. Vyse
Height: 7¹/₂in., 19.1cm.
Issued: 1930–1938
Colour variation
Price: $450 £300

DARLING (Style one) HN1372
Designer: C. Vyse
Height: 7³/₄in., 19.7cm.
Issued: 1930–1938
Colour variation
Price: $450 £300

DARLING (Style two) HN1985
Designer: C. Vyse
Height: 5¹/₄in., 13.3cm.
Issued: 1946–
Price: R.R.P.

DARLING HN3613
Designer: C. Vyse
Height: 5¹/₄in., 13.3cm.
Issued: 1993
Colour variation
Price: R.R.P.

DAVID COPPERFIELD M88
Designer: L. Harradine
Height: 4¹/₄in., 10.8cm.
Issued: 1949–1983
Price: $60 £40

DAWN HN1858
Designer: L. Harradine
Height: 10in., 25.4cm.
Issued: 1938–?
Price: $1125 £750

DAWN HN1858A
Designer: L. Harradine
Height: 9³/₄in., 24.7cm.
Issued: ?–1949
Colour variation
Price: $1125 £750

FIGURES

DAWN HN3600
Designer: Nada Pedley
Height: 7½in., 19cm.
Issued: 1993
Price: R.R.P.

DAYBREAK HN3107
Designer: R. Jefferson
Height: 11¾in., 30cm.
Issued: 1987–1989
Price: $150 £100

DAYDREAMS HN1731
Designer: L. Harradine
Height: 5¾in., 14.6cm.
Issued: 1935–
Price: R.R.P.

DAYDREAMS HN1732
Designer: L. Harradine
Height: 5½in., 14cm.
Issued: 1935–1949
Colour variation
Price: $375 £250

DAYDREAMS HN1944
Designer: L. Harradine
Height: 5½in., 14cm.
Issued: 1940–1949
Colour variation
Price: $375 £250

DEAUVILLE HN2344
Designer: P. Davies
Height: 8¼in., 20.9cm.
Issued: 1982 in a limited
edition of 1500
Price: $225 £150

DEBBIE HN2385
Designer: P. Davies
Height: 5½in., 14cm.
Issued: 1969–1982
Price: $140 £95

DEBBIE HN2400
Designer: P. Davies
Height: 6in., 15cm.
Issued: 1983–
Price: R.R.P.

DEBUT HN3046
Designer: P. Parsons
Height: 12¼in., 31cm.
Issued: 1987–1989
Price: $150 £100

DEBUTANTE HN2210
Designer: P. Davies
Height: 5in., 12.7cm.
Issued: 1963–1967
Price: $290 £195

DECEMBER HN2696
Designer: P. Davies
Height: 7¾in., 19.7cm.
Issued: 1987
Price: $165 £110

DARLING HN3613

DAYDREAMS HN1731

DAWN HN3600

DAWN HN1858

DEAUVILLE HN2344

135

FIGURES

DECEMBER HN3329
Designer: P. Davies
Height: 7½in., 19cm.
Issued: 1991
Price: $165 £110

DEIRDRE HN2020
Designer: L. Harradine
Height: 7in., 17.8cm.
Issued: 1949–1955
Price: $300 £200

DELICIA HN1662
Designer: L. Harradine
Height: 5¾in., 14.6cm.
Issued: 1934–1938
Price: $600 £400

DELICIA HN1663
Designer: L. Harradine
Height: 5¾in., 14.6cm.
Issued: 1934–1938
 Colour variation
Price: $600 £400

DELICIA HN1681
Designer: L. Harradine
Height: 5¾in., 14.6cm.
Issued: 1935–1938
 Colour variation
Price: $600 £400

DELIGHT HN1772
Designer: L. Harradine
Height: 7in., 17.8cm.
Issued: 1936–1967
Price: $290 £195

DELIGHT HN1773
Designer: L. Harradine
Height: 6¾in., 17.2cm.
Issued: 1936–1949
 Colour variation
Price: $375 £250

DELPHINE HN2136
Designer: P. Davies
Height: 7¾in., 18.4cm.
Issued: 1954–1967
Price: $290 £195

DEMURE HN3045
Designer: P. Parsons
Height: 12½in., 31.5cm.
Issued: 1987–1989
Price: $135 £90

DENISE HN2273
Designer: P. Davies
Height: 7in., 17.8cm.
Issued: 1964–1971
Price: $290 £195

DENISE M34
Designer: Unknown
Height: 4½in., 11.4cm.
Issued: 1933–1945
Price: $340 £225

DENISE M35
Designer: Unknown
Height: 4½in., 11.4cm.
Issued: 1933–1945
 Colour variation
Price: $340 £225

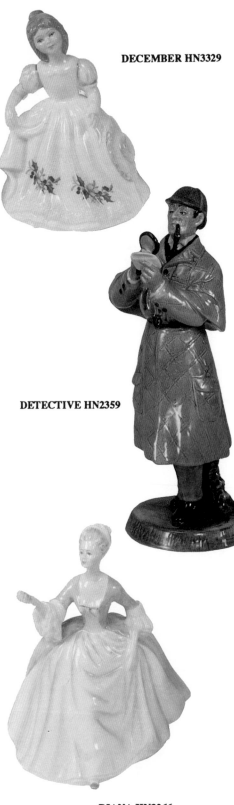

DECEMBER HN3329

DETECTIVE HN2359

DIANA HN3266

DENISE HN2477
Designer: P. Davies
Height: 7¾in., 19.5cm.
Issued: 1987
Price: R.R.P.

DERRICK HN1398
Designer: L. Harradine
Height: 8in., 20.3cm.
Issued: 1930–1938
Price: $525 £350

DESPAIR HN596
Designer: Unknown
Height: 4½in., 11.4cm.
Issued: 1924–1938
Price: $900 £600

DETECTIVE HN2359
Designer: E. J. Griffiths
Height: 9¼in., 23.5cm.
Issued: 1977–1983
Price: $280 £185

DEVOTION HN3228
Designer: P. Parsons
Height: 9½in., 24cm.
Issued: 1989
Price: R.R.P.

DIANA HN1716
Designer: L. Harradine
Height: 5¾in., 14.6cm.
Issued: 1935–1949
Price: $225 £150

DIANA HN1717
Designer: L. Harradine
Height: 5¾in., 14.6cm.
Issued: 1935–1949
 Colour variation
Price: $300 £200

DIANA HN1986
Designer: L. Harradine
Height: 5¾in., 14.6cm.
Issued: 1946–1975
 Colour variation
Price: $190 £125

DIANA HN2468
Designer: P. Davies
Height: 8in., 20cm.
Issued: 1987
Price: R.R.P.

DIANA HN3266
Designer: P. Davies
Height: 8in., 10.3cm.
Issued: 1990
Price: $218 £145

DIANA HN3310
Designer: Peggy Davies
Height: 4½in., 11.5cm.
Issued: 1991
Price: R.R.P.

DIANA THE HUNTRESS HN2829
Designer: R. Jefferson
Height: 11¼in., 28.5cm.
Issued: 1986 in a limited
 edition of 300
Price: $1520 £950

DIANE HN3604
Designer: Nada Pedley
Height: 8³/₄in., 22cm.
Issued: 1994
Price: R.R.P.

DICK SWIVELLER M90
Designer: L. Harradine
Height: 4¹/₄in., 10.8cm.
Issued: 1949–1982
Price: $60 £40

DICK TURPIN HN3272
Designer: G. Tounge
Height: 12in., 30.5cm.
Issued: 1989 in a limited
edition of 5000
Price: $675 £450

DIGGER (Australian) HN322
Designer: E. W. Light
Height: 11¹/₄in., 28.5cm.
Issued: 1918–1938
Price: $975 £650

DIGGER (Australian) HN353
Designer: E. W. Light
Height: 11¹/₄in., 28.5cm.
Issued: 1919–1938
Price: $975 £650

DIGGER (New Zealand) HN321
Designer: E. W. Light
Height: 11¹/₄in., 28.5cm.
Issued: 1918–1938
Price: $975 £650

DILIGENT SCHOLAR HN26
Designer: W. White
Height: 7in., 17.8cm.
Issued: 1913–1938
Price: $1875 £1250

DIMITY HN2169
Designer: L. Harradine
Height: 5³/₄in., 14.6cm.
Issued: 1956–1959
Price: $340 £225

DINKY DO HN1678
Designer: L. Harradine
Height: 4³/₄in., 12cm.
Issued: 1934–
Colour variation
Price: R.R.P.

DINKY DO HN2120
Designer: L. Harradine
Height: 4³/₄in., 12cm.
Issued: 1983
Price: R.R.P.

DINKY DO HN3618
Designer: L. Harradine
Height: 4³/₄in., 12cm.
Issued: 1994
Colour variation
Price: R.R.P.

DISCOVERY HN3428
Designer: A. Munslow
Height: 12in., 30.5cm.
Issued: 1992 in a special
edition for Expo 92
Price: $165 £110

DICK TURPIN HN3272

DINKY DO HN1678

DINKY DO HN3618

DISCOVERY HN3428

137

"DO YOU WONDER..."
HN1544
Designer: Unknown
Height: 5in., 12.7cm.
Issued: 1933–1949
Price: $290 £195

DOCTOR HN2858
Designer: W. K. Harper
Height: 7½in., 19.1cm.
Issued: 1979–1992
Price: $260 £175

DOLLY HN355
Designer: C. J. Noke
Height: 7¼in., 18.4cm.
Issued: 1919–1938
Price: $1875 £1250

DOLLY VARDON HN1514
Designer: L. Harradine
Height: 8½in., 21.6cm.
Issued: 1932–1938
Price: $675 £450

DOLLY VARDON HN1515
Designer: L. Harradine
Height: 8½in., 21.6cm.
Issued: 1932–1949
Price: $490 £325

DONNA HN2939
Designer: P. Gee
Height: 7¾in., 19.5cm.
Issued: 1986
Price: R.R.P.

DORCAS HN1490
Designer: L. Harradine
Height: 7in., 17.8cm.
Issued: 1932–1938
Price: $340 £225

DORCAS HN1491
Designer: L. Harradine
Height: 6¾in., 17.2cm.
Issued: 1932–1938
Price: $340 £225

DORCAS HN1558
Designer: L. Harradine
Height: 6¾in., 17.2cm.
Issued: 1932–1952
        Colour variation
Price: $260 £175

DOREEN HN1363
Designer: L. Harradine
Height: 5¼in., 13.3cm.
Issued: 1929–1938
Price: $600 £375

DOREEN HN1389
Designer: L. Harradine
Height: 5¼in., 13.3cm.
Issued: 1930–1938
        Colour variation
Price: $600 £375

DOREEN HN1390
Designer: L. Harradine
Height: 5¾in., 14.6cm.
Issued: 1929–1938
        Colour variation
Price: $600 £375

DOCTOR HN2858

DREAM WEAVER HN2283

DORIS KEENE as CAVALLINI
(Style one) HN90
Designer: C. J. Noke
Height: 11in., 27.9cm.
Issued: 1918–1936
Price: $1350 £900

DORIS KEENE as CAVALLINI
(Style one) HN467
Designer: C. J. Noke
Height: 11in., 27.9cm.
Issued: 1921–1936
        Colour variation
Price: $1350 £900

DORIS KEENE as CAVALLINI
(Style two) HN96
Designer: C. J. Noke
Height: 10¾in., 27.8cm.
Issued: 1918–1938
Price: $1350 £900

DORIS KEENE as CAVALLINI
(Style two) HN345
Designer: C. J. Noke
Height: 10½in., 26.6cm.
Issued: 1919–1949
        Colour variation
Price: $1350 £900

DOROTHY HN3098
Designer: P. Parsons
Height: 7in., 18cm.
Issued: 1987–1990
Price: $250 £165

DOUBLE JESTER HN365
Designer: C. J. Noke
Height: Unknown
Issued: 1920–1938
Price: $3000 £2000

DREAM WEAVER HN2283
Designer: M. Nicholl
Height: 8¼in., 21cm.
Issued: 1972–1976
Price: $210 £145

DREAMING HN3133
Designer: P. Parsons
Height: 9in., 22.5cm.
Issued: 1987
Price: R.R.P.

DREAMLAND HN1473
Designer: L. Harradine
Height: 4¾in., 12cm.
Issued: 1931–1938
Price: $1600 £1000

DREAMLAND HN1481
Designer: L. Harradine
Height: 4¾in., 12cm.
Issued: 1931–1938
        Colour variation
Price: $1500 £1000

DRESSING UP HN2964
Designer: P. Parsons
Height: 7½in., 19cm.
Issued: 1982–1986
Price: $210 £145

FIGURES

DRESSING UP HN3300
Designer: N. Pedley
Height: 6³/₄in., 17.1cm.
Issued: 1991 in a limited
edition of 9500
Price: $150 £100

DRUMMER BOY HN2679
Designer: M. Nicholl
Height: 8¹/₂in., 21.6cm.
Issued: 1976–1982
Price: $440 £295

**DRYAD OF THE PINES
HN1869**
Designer: R. Garbe
Height: 23in., 58.4cm.
Issued: 1938–1949
Price: $2250 £1500

DUCHESS OF YORK HN3086
Designer: E. J. Griffiths
Height: 8¹/₂in., 21.5cm.
Issued: 1986 in a limited
edition of 1500
Price: $490 £325

**DUKE OF WELLINGTON
HN3432**
Designer: Alan Maslankowski
Height: 12in., 30.5cm.
Issued: 1992 in a limited
edition of 1500
Price: R.R.P.

DULCIE HN2305
Designer: P. Davies
Height: 7¹/₄in., 18.4cm.
Issued: 1981–1984
Price: $190 £125

DULCIMER HN2798
Designer: P. Davies
Height: 6¹/₂in., 16.5cm.
Issued: 1975 in a limited
edition of 750
Price: $675 £450

DULCINEA HN1343
Designer: L. Harradine
Height: 5¹/₂in., 14cm.
Issued: 1929–1938
Price: $1120 £700

DULCINEA HN1419
Designer: L. Harradine
Height: 5¹/₂in., 14cm.
Issued: 1930–1938
Colour variation
Price: $1120 £700

DUNCE HN6
Designer: C. J. Noke
Height: 10¹/₂in., 26.7cm.
Issued: 1913–1938
Price: $1575 £1250

DUNCE HN310
Designer: C. J. Noke
Height: 10¹/₂in., 26.7cm.
Issued: 1918–1938
Colour variation
Price: $1575 £1250

DRESSING UP HN3300

DULCIMER HN2798

DRUMMER BOY HN2679

DULCINEA HN1419

DUKE OF WELLINGTON
HN3432

DUNCE HN357
Designer: C. J. Noke
Height: 10½in., 26.7cm.
Issued: 1919–1938
Colour variation
Price: $1575 £1250

E

EASTER DAY HN1976
Designer: P. Davies
Height: 7¼in., 18.4cm.
Issued: 1945–1951
Price: $440 £295

EASTER DAY HN2039
Designer: P. Davies
Height: 7¼in., 18.4cm.
Issued: 1949–1969
Colour variation
Price: $365 £245

EASTERN GRACE HN3138
Designer: P. Parsons
Height: 12in., 30.5cm.
Issued: 1988–1989
Price: $150 £100

EDITH HN2957
Designer: P. Parsons
Height: 5¾in., 14.5cm.
Issued: 1982–1985
Price: $246 £165

ELAINE HN2791
Designer: P. Davies
Height: 7½in., 19.1cm.
Issued: 1980
Price: R.R.P.

ELAINE HN3214
Designer: P. Davies
Height: 3¾in., 9.5cm.
Issued: 1988
Price: R.R.P.

ELAINE (Pink) HN3307
Designer: Peggy Davies
Height: 7¼in., 18cm.
Issued: 1990
Price: R.R.P.

ELEANOR OF PROVENCE HN2009
Designer: P. Davies
Height: 9½in., 24.1cm.
Issued: 1948–1953
Price: $520 £325

ELEANORE HN1753
Designer: L. Harradine
Height: 7in., 17.8cm.
Issued: 1936–1949
Price: $675 £450

ELEANORE HN1754
Designer: L. Harradine
Height: 7in., 17.8cm.
Issued: 1936–1949
Colour variation
Price: $675 £450

ELAINE (Pink) HN3307

ELAINE HN3214

ELAINE HN2791

ELEGANCE HN2264
Designer: P. Davies
Height: 7¼in., 18.4cm.
Issued: 1961–1985
Price: $210 £145

ELFREDA HN2078
Designer: L. Harradine
Height: 7¼in., 18.4cm.
Issued: 1951–1955
Price: $450 £300

ELIZA HN2543
Designer: E. J. Griffiths
Height: 11¼in., 28.6cm.
Issued: 1974–1975
Price: $340 £225

ELIZA HN2543A
Designer: E. J. Griffiths
Height: 11¾in., 29.8cm.
Issued: 1975–1977
Colour variation
Price: $340 £225

ELIZA HN3179
Designer: D. Tootle
Height: 7½in., 19cm.
Issued: 1988
Price: $165 £110

ELIZA FARRELL, COUNTESS OF DERBY HN3442
Designer: Peter Gee
Height: 7½in., 19cm.
Issued: 1992
Price: R.R.P.

ELIZABETH HN2946
Designer: B. Franks
Height: 8in., 20cm.
Issued: 1982–1986
Price: $250 £165

ELIZABETH HN2465
Designer: John Bromley
Height: 8½in., 21.5cm.
Issued: 1990
Price: R.R.P.

ELIZABETH FRY HN2
Designer: C. Vyse
Height: 17in., 43.2cm.
Issued: 1913–1938
Price: $2400 £1500

ELIZABETH FRY HN2A
Designer: C. Vyse
Height: 17in., 43.2cm.
Issued: 1913–1938
Price: $2400 £1500

ELLEN HN3020
Designer: P. Parsons
Height: 3½in., 9cm.
Issued: 1984–1987
Price: $220 £145

ELLEN TERRY as QUEEN CATHERINE HN379
Designer: C. J. Noke
Height: 12½in., 31.7cm.
Issued: 1920–1949
Price: $1425 £950

ELSIE MAYNARD HN639
Designer: C. J. Noke
Height: 7in., 17.8cm.
Issued: 1924–1949
Price: $525 £350

ELSIE MAYNARD HN2902
Designer: W. K. Harper
Height: 11¼in., 28.5cm.
Issued: 1982–1986
Price: $440 £295

ELYSE HN2429
Designer: P. Davies
Height: 5¾in., 14.6cm.
Issued: 1972–
Price: R.R.P.

ELYSE (Green) HN2474
Designer: P. Davies
Height: 6¾in., 17cm.
Issued: 1987
Price: R.R.P.

EMBROIDERING HN2855
Designer: W. K. Harper
Height: 7¼in., 18.4cm.
Issued: 1980–1990
Price: $220 £145

EMIR HN1604
Designer: C. J. Noke
Height: 7½in., 19.1cm.
Issued: 1933–1949
Price: $525 £350

EMIR HN1605
Designer: C. J. Noke
Height: 7¼in., 18.4cm.
Issued: 1933–1949
Price: $525 £350
(Also called Ibrahim HN2095)

EMMA HN2834
Designer: P. Davies
Height: 5¾in., 14.6cm.
Issued: 1977–1982
Price: $260 £175

EMMA HN3208
Designer: Adrian Hughes
Height: 4½in., 11.5cm.
Issued: 1990
Price: R.R.P.

ENCHANTING EVENING HN3108
Designer: R. Jefferson
Height: 11¾in., 30cm.
Issued: 1987–1991
Price: $150 £100

ENCHANTMENT HN2178
Designer: P. Davies
Height: 7½in., 19.1cm.
Issued: 1957–1982
Price: $200 £135

ENCORE HN2751
Designer: D. Tootle
Height: 10in., 25.5cm.
Issued: 1988–1989
Price: $150 £100

ELIZA FARRELL, COUNTESS OF DERBY HN3442

EMBROIDERING HN2855

EMMA HN3208

ENCHANTMENT HN2178

ELIZABETH HN2946

141

FIGURES

ENIGMA HN3110
Designer: R. Jefferson
Height: 12³/₄in., 32cm.
Issued: 1987
Price: R.R.P.

ENTRANCED HN3186
Designer: E. J. Griffiths
Height: 7¹/₄in., 18.5cm.
Issued: 1988–1989
Price: $135 £90

ERMINE COAT HN1981
Designer: L. Harradine
Height: 6³/₄in., 17.2cm.
Issued: 1945–1967
Price: $340 £225

ERMINE MUFF HN54
Designer: C. J. Noke
Height: 8¹/₂in., 21.6cm.
Issued: 1916–1938
Price: $900 £600

ERMINE MUFF HN332
Designer: C. J. Noke
Height: 8¹/₂in., 21.6cm.
Issued: 1918–1938
        Colour variation
Price: $900 £600

ERMINE MUFF HN671
Designer: C. J. Noke
Height: 8¹/₂in., 21.6cm.
Issued: 1924–1938
        Colour variation
Price: $900 £600

ERMINIE M40
Designer: Unknown
Height: 4in., 10.1cm.
Issued: 1933–1945
Price: $450 £300

ESMERALDA HN2168
Designer: P. Davies
Height: 5¹/₂in., 14cm.
Issued: 1956–1959
Price: $290 £195

ESTELLE HN1566
Designer: L. Harradine
Height: 8in., 20.3cm.
Issued: 1933–1938
Price: $600 £375

ESTELLE HN1802
Designer: L. Harradine
Height: 8in., 20.3cm.
Issued: 1937–1949
        Colour variation
Price: $480 £300

ETE HN3067
Designer: R. Jefferson
Height: 11¹/₂in., 29cm.
Issued: 1989 in a limited
        edition of 300
Price: $975 £650

EUGENE HN1520
Designer: L. Harradine
Height: 5³/₄in., 14.6cm.
Issued: 1932–1938
Price: $675 £450

ERMINE COAT HN1981

ESTELLE HN1802

ESMERALDA HN2168

ERMINE MUFF HN54

EUGENE HN1520

EUGENE HN1521
Designer: L. Harradine
Height: 5in., 12.7cm.
Issued: 1932–1938
Colour variation
Price: $675 £450

EUROPA AND THE BULL HN95
Designer: H. Tittensor
Height: 9³/₄in., 24.7cm.
Issued: 1918–1938
Price: $3000 £2000

EUROPA AND THE BULL HN2828
Designer: R. Jefferson
Height: 10¹/₂in., 26.5cm.
Issued: 1985 in a limited edition of 300
Price: $1520 £950

EVE HN2466
Designer: P. Davies
Height: 9¹/₄in., 23.5cm.
Issued: 1984 in a limited edition of 750
Price: $720 £450

EVELYN HN1622
Designer: L. Harradine
Height: 6¹/₄in., 15.9cm.
Issued: 1934–1949
Price: $595 £395

EVELYN HN1637
Designer: L. Harradine
Height: 6in., 15.2cm.
Issued: 1934–1938
Colour variation
Price: $595 £395

EVENTIDE HN2814
Designer: W. K. Harper
Height: 7³/₄in., 19.7cm.
Issued: 1977–
Price: $245 £165

F

FAGIN HN534
Designer: L. Harradine
Height: 4in., 10.1cm.
Issued: 1922–1932
Price: $45 £30

FAGIN M49
Designer: L. Harradine
Height: 4in., 10.1cm.
Issued: 1932–1983
Price: $48 £30

FAIR LADY HN2835
Designer: P. Davies
Height: 7¹/₄in., 18.4cm.
Issued: 1977–
Colour variation
Price: R.R.P.

FAIR LADY HN2832
Designer: P. Davies
Height: 7¹/₄in., 18.4cm.
Issued: 1977–
Colour variation
Price: R.R.P.

EUROPA AND THE BULL
HN2828

EVENTIDE HN2814

EVE HN2466

FAIR LADY HN2193
Designer: P. Davies
Height: 7¼in., 18.4cm.
Issued: 1963–
Price: R.R.P.

FAIR LADY HN3216
Designer: P. Davies
Height: 3¾in., 9.5cm.
Issued: 1988
Price: R.R.P.

FAIR MAIDEN HN2211
Designer: P. Davies
Height: 5¼in., 13.3cm.
Issued: 1967
Price: R.R.P.

FAIR MAIDEN HN2434
Designer: P. Davies
Height: 5¼in., 13.3cm.
Issued: 1983–
        Colour variation
Price: R.R.P.

FAIRY (Style one) HN1324
Designer: L. Harradine
Height: 6½in., 16.5cm.
Issued: 1929–1938
Price: $525 £350

FAIRY (Style two) HN1374
Designer: L. Harradine
Height: 4in., 10.1cm.
Issued: 1930–1938
Price: $525 £350

FAIRY (Style two) HN1380
Designer: L. Harradine
Height: 4in., 10.1cm.
Issued: 1930–1938
        Colour variation
Price: $525 £350

FAIRY (Style two) HN1532
Designer: L. Harradine
Height: 4in., 10.1cm.
Issued: 1932–1938
Price: $525 £350

FAIRY (Style three) HN1375
Designer: L. Harradine
Height: 3in., 7.6cm.
Issued: 1930–1938
Price: $525 £350

FAIRY (Style three) HN1395
Designer: L. Harradine
Height: 3in., 7.6cm.
Issued: 1930–1938
        Colour variation
Price: $525 £350

FAIRY (Style three) HN1533
Designer: L. Harradine
Height: 3in., 7.6cm.
Issued: 1932–1938
Price: $525 £350

FAIRY (Style four) HN1376
Designer: L. Harradine
Height: 2½in., 6.3cm.
Issued: 1930–1938
Price: $525 £350

FAIRY (Style one) HN1324

FAIR LADY HN2193

FAIRY SPELL HN2979

FAIRY (Style four) HN1536
Designer: L. Harradine
Height: 2½in., 6.3cm.
Issued: 1932–1938
Price: $525 £350

FAIRY (Style five) HN1378
Designer: L. Harradine
Height: 2½in., 6.3cm.
Issued: 1930–1938
Price: $525 £350

FAIRY (Style five) HN1396
Designer: L. Harradine
Height: 2½in., 6.3cm.
Issued: 1930–1938
        Colour variation
Price: $525 £350

FAIRY (Style five) HN1535
Designer: L. Harradine
Height: 2½in., 6.3cm.
Issued: 1932–1938
        Colour variation
Price: $525 £350

FAIRY (Style six) HN1379
Designer: L. Harradine
Height: 2½in., 6.3cm.
Issued: 1930–1938
Price: $525 £350

FAIRY (Style six) HN1394
Designer: L. Harradine
Height: 2½in., 6.3cm.
Issued: 1930–1938
        Colour variation
Price: $525 £350

FAIRY (Style six) HN1534
Designer: L. Harradine
Height: 2½in., 6.3cm.
Issued: 1932–1938
Price: $525 £350

FAIRY (Style seven) HN1393
Designer: L. Harradine
Height: 2½in., 6.3cm.
Issued: 1930–1938
Price: $525 £350

FAIRY SPELL HN2979
Designer: A. Hughes
Height: 5¼in., 13cm.
Issued: 1983–1986
Price: $150 £100

FAITH HN3082
Designer: E. J. Griffiths
Height: 8½in., 21.5cm.
Issued: 1986 in a limited
        edition of 9500
Price: $220 £145

FALSTAFF (Style one) HN571
Designer: C. J. Noke
Height: 7in., 17.8cm.
Issued: 1923–1938
Price: $600 £400

FALSTAFF (Style one) HN575
Designer: C. J. Noke
Height: 7in., 17.8cm.
Issued: 1923–1938
Price: $600 £400

FIGURES

FALSTAFF (Style one) HN608
Designer: C. J. Noke
Height: 7in., 17.8cm.
Issued: 1924–1938
          Colour variation
Price: $660 £400

FALSTAFF (Style one) HN609
Designer: C. J. Noke
Height: 7in., 17.8cm.
Issued: 1924–1938
          Colour variation
Price: $660 £400

FALSTAFF (Style one) HN619
Designer: C. J. Noke
Height: 7in., 17.8cm.
Issued: 1924–1938
          Colour variation
Price: $660 £400

FALSTAFF (Style one) HN638
Designer: C. J. Noke
Height: 7in., 17.8cm.
Issued: 1924–1938
          Colour variation
Price: $660 £400

FALSTAFF (Style one) HN1216
Designer: C. J. Noke
Height: 7in., 17.8cm.
Issued: 1926–1949
          Colour variation
Price: $450 £300

FALSTAFF (Style one) HN1606
Designer: C. J. Noke
Height: 7in., 17.8cm.
Issued: 1933–1949
          Colour variation
Price: $450 £300

FALSTAFF (Style two) HN618
Designer: C. J. Noke
Height: 7in., 17.8cm.
Issued: 1924–1938
Price: $660 £400

FALSTAFF (Style two) HN2054
Designer: C. J. Noke
Height: 7in., 17.8cm.
Issued: 1950–1992
          Colour variation
Price: $190 £125

FALSTAFF HN3236
Designer: C. J. Noke
Height: 4in., 10cm.
Issued: 1989–1992
Price: $100 £65

FAMILY HN2720 (White)
Designer: E. Griffiths
Height: 12in., 30.5cm.
Issued: 1981
Price: R.R.P.

FAMILY HN2721 (Black)
Designer: E. Griffiths
Height: 12in., 30.5cm.
Issued: 1981–1992
Price: $150 £100

FAIRY (Style two) HN1380

FAIRY (Style three) HN1395

FAITH HN3082

FALSTAFF (Style two) HN2054

FALSTAFF (Style one) HN1606

FAMILY HN2721 (Black)

FAMILY ALBUM HN2321
Designer: M. Nicholl
Height: 6¹/₄in., 15.9cm.
Issued: 1966–1973
Price: $368 £245

FANTASY HN3296
Designer: A. Hughes
Height: 12¹/₂in., 31.7cm.
Issued: 1990–1992
Price: $188 £125

FARAWAY HN2133
Designer: P. Davies
Height: 2¹/₂in., 6.3cm.
Issued: 1958–1962
Price: $340 £225

FARMER HN3195
Designer: A. Hughes
Height: 9in., 23cm.
Issued: 1988–1991
Price: $190 £125

FARMER'S BOY HN2520
Designer: W. M. Chance
Height: 8¹/₂in., 21.6cm.
Issued: 1938–1960
Price: $975 £650

FARMER'S WIFE HN2069
Designer: L. Harradine
Height: 9in., 22.9cm.
Issued: 1951–1955
Price: $410 £275

FARMER'S WIFE HN3164
Designer: A. Hughes
Height: 8³/₄in., 22cm.
Issued: 1988–1991
Price: $190 £125

FAT BOY (Style one) HN530
Designer: L. Harradine
Height: 3¹/₂in., 8.9cm.
Issued: 1922–1932
Price: $70 £45

FAT BOY (Style two) HN555
Designer: L. Harradine
Height: 7in., 17.8cm.
Issued: 1923–1939
Price: $340 £225

FAT BOY (Style two) HN1893
Designer: L. Harradine
Height: 7in., 17.8cm.
Issued: 1938–1952
Colour variation
Price: $340 £225

FAT BOY (Style three) HN2096
Designer: L. Harradine
Height: 7¹/₄in., 18.4cm.
Issued: 1952–1967
Price: $340 £225

FAT BOY M44
Designer: L. Harradine
Height: 4¹/₄in., 10.8cm.
Issued: 1932–1982
Price: $60 £40

FAMILY ALBUM HN2321

FATHER CHRISTMAS
HN3399

FANTASY HN3296

FIDDLER HN2171

FATHER CHRISTMAS
HN3399
Designer: Robert Tabbenor
Height: 9in., 23cm.
Issued: 1992
Price: R.R.P.

FAVOURITE HN2249
Designer: M. Nicholl
Height: 7³/₄in., 19.7cm.
Issued: 1960–1990
Price: $180 £120

FEBRUARY HN2703
Designer: P. Davies
Height: 7³/₄in., 19.7cm.
Issued: 1987
Price: $165 £110

FEEDING TIME HN3373
Designer: Nada Pedley
Height: 7¹/₄in., 18.5cm.
Issued: 1991 in a limited
            edition of 9500
Price: R.R.P.

FIDDLER HN2171
Designer: M. Nicholl
Height: 8³/₄in., 22.2cm.
Issued: 1956–1962
Price: $750 £500

FIELD MARSHAL
MONTGOMERY HN3405
Designer: Robert Tabbenor
Height: 11³/₄in., 30cm.
Issued: 1994 in a limited
            edition of 1944
Price: R.R.P.

FIONA (Style one) HN1924
Designer: L. Harradine
Height: 5³/₄in., 14.6cm.
Issued: 1940–1949
Price: $675 £450

FIONA (Style one) HN1925
Designer: L. Harradine
Height: 5³/₄in., 14.6cm.
Issued: 1940–1949
            Colour variation
Price: $675 £450

FIONA (Style one) HN1933
Designer: L. Harradine
Height: 5³/₄in., 14.6cm.
Issued: 1940–1949
            Colour variation
Price: $675 £450

FIONA (Style two) HN2694
Designer: P. Davies
Height: 7¹/₂in., 19.1cm.
Issued: 1974–1980
Price: $250 £165

FIONA HN3252
Designer: D. Tootle
Height: 7in., 17.8cm.
Issued: 1989–1992
Price: $200 £135

FAVOURITE HN2249   FEBRUARY HN2703

FIONA (Style one) HN1924   FIONA HN3252

FIGURES

FIRST DANCE HN2803
Designer: P. Davies
Height: 7¼in., 18.4cm.
Issued: 1977–1992
Price: $190 £125

FIRST LOVE (White) HN2747
Designer: D. Tootle
Height: 13in., 33cm.
Issued: 1987
Price: R.R.P.

FIRST OUTING HN3377
Designer: Nada Pedley
Height: 7½in., 19.5cm.
Issued: 1991 in a limited
edition of 9500
Price: R.R.P.

FIRST STEPS HN2242
Designer: P. Davies
Height: 6½in., 16.5cm.
Issued: 1959–1965
Price: $340 £225

FIRST STEPS HN3282
Designer: Robert Tabbenor
Height: 10in., 25.5cm.
Issued: 1991
Price: R.R.P.

FIRST STEPS HN3361
U.S.A. edition
Price: R.R.P.

FIRST WALTZ HN2862
Designer: P. Davies
Height: 7¼in., 18.4cm.
Issued: 1979–1983
Price: $250 £165

FISHERWOMEN HN80
Designer: Unknown
Height: Unknown
Issued: 1917–1938
Price: $2250 £1500

FISHERWOMEN HN349
Designer: Unknown
Height: Unknown
Issued: 1919–1938
Colour variation
Price: $2250 £1500

FISHERWOMEN HN359
Designer: Unknown
Height: Unknown
Issued: 1919–1938
Colour variation
Price: $2250 £1500

FISHERWOMEN HN631
Designer: Unknown
Height: Unknown
Issued: 1924–1938
Colour variation
Price: $2250 £1500

FITZHERBERT, MRS HN2007
Designer: P. Davies
Height: 9¼in., 23.5cm.
Issued: 1948–1953
Price: $560 £350

FIRST OUTING
HN3377

FIRST STEPS
HN3361

FIRST DANCE
HN2803

FLEURETTE HN1587

FLOWER OF LOVE
HN2460

FLEUR HN2368
Designer: J. Bromley
Height: 7¼in., 18.4cm.
Issued: 1968–
Price: R.R.P.

FLEUR (Red) HN2369
Designer: J. Bromley
Height: 7¾in., 19.5cm.
Issued: 1983–1986
Colour variation
Price: $165 £110

FLEURETTE HN1587
Designer: L. Harradine
Height: 6½in., 16.5cm.
Issued: 1933–1949
Price: $410 £275

FLIRTATION HN3071
Designer: A. Hughes
Height: 10in., 25.5cm.
Issued: 1987
Price: R.R.P.

FLORA HN2349
Designer: M. Nicholl
Height: 7¾in., 19.7cm.
Issued: 1966–1973
Price: $260 £175

FLORENCE HN2745
Designer: D. Tootle
Height: 8in., 20cm.
Issued: 1988
Price: $180 £120

FLORENCE NIGHTINGALE
HN3144
Designer: P. Parsons
Height: 8¼in., 21cm.
Issued: 1988 in a limited
edition of 500
Price: $825 £550

FLOUNCED SKIRT HN57A
Designer: E. W. Light
Height: 9¾in., 24.7cm.
Issued: 1916–1938
Price: $1125 £750

FLOUNCED SKIRT HN66
Designer: E. W. Light
Height: 9¾in., 24.7cm.
Issued: 1916–1938
Colour variation
Price: $1125 £750

FLOUNCED SKIRT HN77
Designer: E. W. Light
Height: 9¾in., 24.7cm.
Issued: 1917–1938
Colour variation
Price: $1125 £750

FLOUNCED SKIRT HN78
Designer: E. W. Light
Height: 9¾in., 24.7cm.
Issued: 1917–1938
Colour variation
Price: $1125 £750

FLOUNCED SKIRT HN333
Designer: E. W. Light
Height: 9³/₄in., 24.7cm.
Issued: 1918–1938
Colour variation
Price: $1125 £750

FLOWER ARRANGING HN3040
Designer: P. Parsons
Height: 8³/₄in., 22cm.
Issued: 1988 in a limited edition of 750
Price: $825 £550

FLOWER OF LOVE HN2460
Designer: John Bromley
Height: 7¹/₂in., 19cm.
Issued: 1991
Price: R.R.P.

FLOWER SELLER HN789
Designer: L. Harradine
Height: 8³/₄in., 22.2cm.
Issued: 1926–1938
Price: $720 £450

FLOWER SELLER'S CHILDREN HN525
Designer: L. Harradine
Height: 8¹/₄in., 21cm.
Issued: 1921–1949
Price: $675 £450

FLOWER SELLER'S CHILDREN HN551
Designer: L. Harradine
Height: 8¹/₄in., 21cm.
Issued: 1922–1949
Colour variation
Price: $675 £450

FLOWER SELLER'S CHILDREN HN1206
Designer: L. Harradine
Height: 8¹/₄in., 21cm.
Issued: 1926–1949
Colour variation
Price: $525 £350

FLOWER SELLER'S CHILDREN HN1342
Designer: L. Harradine
Height: 8in., 20.3cm.
Issued: 1929–
Colour variation
Price: $450 £300

FLOWER SELLER'S CHILDREN HN1406
Designer: L. Harradine
Height: 8¹/₄in., 21cm.
Issued: 1930–1938
Colour variation
Price: $675 £450

FLOWERS FOR MOTHER HN3454
Designer: Pauline Parsons
Height: 5³/₄in., 14.5cm.
Issued: 1994
Price: R.R.P.

FLOWER SELLER'S CHILDREN HN1342

FLOWER ARRANGING HN3040

FLUTE HN2483
Designer: P. Davies
Height: 6in., 15.2cm.
Issued: 1973 in a limited
edition of 750
Price: $675 £450

FOAMING QUART HN2162
Designer: P. Davies
Height: 6in., 15.2cm.
Issued: 1955–
Price: $190 £125

FOLLY HN1335
Designer: L. Harradine
Height: 9in., 22.9cm.
Issued: 1929–1938
Price: $1125 £750

FOLLY HN1750
Designer: L. Harradine
Height: 9½in., 24.1cm.
Issued: 1936–1949
Colour variation
Price: $1125 £750

FORGET-ME-NOT HN1812
Designer: L. Harradine
Height: 6in., 15.2cm.
Issued: 1937–1949
Price: $450 £300

FORGET-ME-NOT HN1813
Designer: L. Harradine
Height: 6in., 15.2cm.
Issued: 1937–1949
Colour variation
Price: $450 £300

FORGET-ME-NOT HN3388
Designer: A. Maslankowski
Height: 6in., 15cm.
Issued: 1991
Price: R.R.P.

FORTUNE TELLER HN2159
Designer: L. Harradine
Height: 6½in., 16.5cm.
Issued: 1955–1967
Price: $370 £245

FORTY WINKS HN1974
Designer: H. Fenton
Height: 6¾in., 17cm.
Issued: 1945–1973
Price: $260 £175

FOUR O'CLOCK HN1760
Designer: L. Harradine
Height: 6in., 15.2cm.
Issued: 1936–1949
Price: $450 £300

FRAGRANCE HN2334
Designer: P. Davies
Height: 7¼in., 18.4cm.
Issued: 1966–
Price: R.R.P.

FRAGRANCE HN3220
Designer: P. Davies
Height: 3½in., 9cm.
Issued: 1988
Price: $100 £65

FLUTE HN2483

FOLLY HN1335

FORTY WINKS HN1974

FOAMING QUART HN2162

FIGURES

FRANCES DUNCOMBE
HN3009
Designer: Peter Gee
Height: 9³/₄in., 24.7cm.
Issued: 1991 in a limited
edition of 5000
Price: R.R.P.

FRANCINE HN2422
Designer: J. Bromley
Height: 5in., 12.7cm.
Issued: 1972–1980
Price: $165 £110

FRANÇON HN1720
Designer: L. Harradine
Height: 7¹/₂in., 19.1cm.
Issued: 1935–1949
Price: $600 £400

FRANÇON HN1721
Designer: L. Harradine
Height: 7¹/₄in., 18.4cm.
Issued: 1935–1949
Colour variation
Price: $600 £400

FREE SPIRIT (White) HN3157
Designer: A. Hughes
Height: 10¹/₂in., 26.5cm.
Issued: 1987
Price: $150 £100

FREE SPIRIT (Black) HN3159
Designer: A. Hughes
Height: 10¹/₂in., 26.5cm.
Issued: 1987
Price: $150 £100

FREE AS THE WIND HN3139
Designer: P. Parsons
Height: 9¹/₂in., 24cm.
Issued: 1989
Price: R.R.P.

FREEDOM HN3528
Designer: R. Jefferson
Height: 8¹/₂in., 22cm.
Issued: 1983–1986
Price: $72 £45

FRENCH HORN HN2795
Designer: P. Davies
Height: 6in., 15.2cm.
Issued: 1976 in a limited
edition of 750
Price: $675 £450

FRENCH PEASANT HN2075
Designer: L. Harradine
Height: 9¹/₄in., 23.5cm.
Issued: 1951–1955
Price: $450 £300

FRIAR TUCK HN2143
Designer: P. Davies
Height: 7¹/₂in., 19.1cm.
Issued: 1954–1965
Price: $375 £250

FRIENDSHIP HN3491
Designer: Alan Maslankowski
Height: 6in., 15cm.
Issued: 1994
Price: R.R.P.

FORGET-ME-NOT HN3388

FORTUNE TELLER HN2159

FRAGRANCE HN2334

FRANCES DUNCOMBE
HN3009

FRENCH HORN HN2795

151

FRODO HN2912
Designer: H. Sales
Height: 4¹/₂in., 11.4cm.
Issued: 1979–1984
Price: $110 £75

FRUIT GATHERING HN449
Designer: L. Harradine
Height: 7³/₄in., 19.7cm.
Issued: 1921–1938
Price: $1500 £1000

FRUIT GATHERING HN476
Designer: L. Harradine
Height: 7³/₄in., 19.7cm.
Issued: 1921–1938
Colour variation
Price: $1500 £1000

FRUIT GATHERING HN503
Designer: L. Harradine
Height: 7³/₄in., 19.7cm.
Issued: 1921–1938
Colour variation
Price: $1500 £1000

FRUIT GATHERING HN561
Designer: L. Harradine
Height: 7³/₄in., 19.7cm.
Issued: 1923–1938
Colour variation
Price: $1500 £1000

FRUIT GATHERING HN562
Designer: L. Harradine
Height: 7³/₄in., 19.7cm.
Issued: 1923–1938
Colour variation
Price: $1500 £1000

FRUIT GATHERING HN707
Designer: L. Harradine
Height: 7¹/₄in., 18.4cm.
Issued: 1925–1938
Colour variation
Price: $1500 £1000

FRUIT GATHERING HN706
Designer: L. Harradine
Height: 7¹/₄in., 18.4cm.
Issued: 1925–1938
Colour variation
Price: $1500 £1000

G

GAFFER HN2053
Designer: L. Harradine
Height: 7³/₄in., 19.7cm.
Issued: 1950–1959
Price: $300 £200

GAIETY HN3140
Designer: P. Parsons
Height: 10¹/₄in., 26cm.
Issued: 1988
Price: $190 £125

GAIL HN2937
Designer: P. Gee
Height: 7¹/₂in., 19cm.
Issued: 1986
Price: R.R.P.

FRODO HN2912

GAIL HN3321

FRUIT GATHERING HN707

GALADRIEL HN2915

GAIL HN3321
Designer: Peter Gee
Height: 3³/₄in., 9.5cm.
Issued: 1992
Price: R.R.P.

GAINSBOROUGH HAT HN46
Designer: H. Tittensor
Height: 8³/₄in., 22.2cm.
Issued: 1915–1938
Price: $1275 £850

GAINSBOROUGH HAT HN46A
Designer: H. Tittensor
Height: 8³/₄in., 22.2cm.
Issued: 1915–1938
Colour variation
Price: $1275 £850

GAINSBOROUGH HAT HN47
Designer: H. Tittensor
Height: 8³/₄in., 22.2cm.
Issued: 1915–1938
Colour variation
Price: $1275 £850

GAINSBOROUGH HAT HN329
Designer: H. Tittensor
Height: 8³/₄in., 22.2cm.
Issued: 1918–1938
Colour variation
Price: $1275 £850

GAINSBOROUGH HAT HN352
Designer: H. Tittensor
Height: 8³/₄in., 22.2cm.
Issued: 1919–1938
Colour variation
Price: $1275 £850

GAINSBOROUGH HAT HN383
Designer: H. Tittensor
Height: 8³/₄in., 22.2cm.
Issued: 1920–1938
Colour variation
Price: $1275 £850

GAINSBOROUGH HAT HN453
Designer: H. Tittensor
Height: 8³/₄in., 22.2cm.
Issued: 1921–1938
Colour variation
Price: $1275 £850

GAINSBOROUGH HAT HN675
Designer: H. Tittensor
Height: 8³/₄in., 22.2cm.
Issued: 1924–1938
Colour variation
Price: $1275 £850

GAINSBOROUGH HAT HN705
Designer: H. Tittensor
Height: 9in., 22.9cm.
Issued: 1925–1938
Colour variation
Price: $1275 £850

GALADRIEL HN2915
Designer: H. Sales
Height: 5¹/₂in., 14cm.
Issued: 1979–1984
Price: $130 £85

GAMEKEEPER HN2879
Designer: E. Griffiths
Height: 7in., 17.8cm.
Issued: 1984–
Price: $190 £125

GANDALF HN2911
Designer: H. Sales
Height: 7in., 17.8cm.
Issued: 1979–1984
Price: $130 £85

GARDENER HN3161
Designer: A. Hughes
Height: 8¼in., 21cm.
Issued: 1989
Price: $190 £125

GARDENING TIME HN3401
Designer: Robert Tabbenor
Height: 5in., 12.5cm.
Issued: 1992
Price: R.R.P.

GAY MORNING HN2135
Designer: P. Davies
Height: 7in., 17.8cm.
Issued: 1954–1967
Price: $290 £195

GEISHA (Style one) HN354
Designer: H. Tittensor
Height: 10¾in., 27.3cm.
Issued: 1919–1938
Price: $2250 £1500

GEISHA (Style one) HN376
Designer: H. Tittensor
Height: 10¾in., 27.3cm.
Issued: 1920–1938
        Colour variation
Price: $2250 £1500

GEISHA (Style one) HN387
Designer: H. Tittensor
Height: 10¾in., 27.3cm.
Issued: 1920–1938
        Colour variation
Price: $2250 £1500

GEISHA (Style one) HN634
Designer: H. Tittensor
Height: 10¾in., 27.3cm.
Issued: 1924–1938
        Colour variation
Price: $2250 £1500

GEISHA (Style one) HN741
Designer: H. Tittensor
Height: 10¾in., 27.3cm.
Issued: 1925–1938
        Colour variation
Price: $2250 £1500

GEISHA (Style one) HN779
Designer: H. Tittensor
Height: 10¾in., 27.3cm.
Issued: 1926–1938
        Colour variation
Price: $2250 £1500

GEISHA (Style one) HN1321
Designer: H. Tittensor
Height: 10¾in., 27.3cm.
Issued: 1929–1938
        Colour variation
Price: $2250 £1500

GAINSBOROUGH HAT HN705

GARDENING TIME HN3401

GANDALF HN2911

GAMEKEEPER HN2879

GAFFER HN2053

153

GEISHA (Style one) HN1322
Designer: H. Tittensor
Height: 10³/₄in., 27.3cm.
Issued: 1929–1938
Colour variation
Price: $2250 £1500

GEISHA (Style two) HN1223
Designer: C. J. Noke
Height: 6³/₄in., 17.2cm.
Issued: 1927–1938
Price: $640 £400

GEISHA (Style two) HN1234
Designer: C. J. Noke
Height: 6³/₄in., 17.2cm.
Issued: 1927–1938
Colour variation
Price: $640 £400

GEISHA (Style two) HN1292
Designer: C. J. Noke
Height: 6³/₄in., 17.2cm.
Issued: 1928–1938
Colour variation
Price: $640 £400

GEISHA (Style two) HN1310
Designer: C. J. Noke
Height: 6³/₄in., 17.2cm.
Issued: 1929–1938
Colour variation
Price: $640 £400

GEISHA (Flambe) HN3229
Designer: P. Parsons
Height: 9¹/₂in., 24cm.
Issued: 1989
Price: $190 £125

GENEVIEVE HN1962
Designer: L. Harradine
Height: 7in., 17.8cm.
Issued: 1941–1975
Price: $290 £195

GENIE HN2989
Designer: R. Tabbenor
Height: 9³/₄in., 24.5cm.
Issued: 1983–
Price: $165 £110

GENIE (Flambe) HN2999
Designer: R. Tabbenor
Height: 9³/₄in., 24.5cm.
Issued: 1989
Price: R.R.P.

GENTLEMAN FROM
WILLIAMSBURG HN2227
Designer: P. Davies
Height: 6¹/₄in., 15.9cm.
Issued: 1960–1983
Price: $220 £145

GENTLEWOMAN HN1632
Designer: L. Harradine
Height: 7¹/₂in., 19.1cm.
Issued: 1934–1949
Price: $525 £350

GEISHA (Flambe) HN3229

GEISHA (Style two) HN1234

GENEVIEVE HN1962

GENIE HN2989

FIGURES

GEORGE WASHINGTON AT PRAYER HN2861
Designer: L. Ispanky
Height: 12¹/₂in., 31.7cm.
Issued: 1977 in a limited edition of 750
Price: $1500 £1000

GEORGIANA HN2093
Designer: P. Davies
Height: 8¹/₄in., 21cm.
Issued: 1952–1955
Price: $750 £500

GEORGINA HN2377
Designer: P. Davies
Height: 5³/₄in., 14.6cm.
Issued: 1981–1986
Price: $165 £110

GERALDINE HN2348
Designer: P. Davies
Height: 7¹/₄in., 18.4cm.
Issued: 1972–1976
Price: $165 £110

GIFT OF FREEDOM HN3443
Designer: Peter Gee
Height: 9³/₄in., 25cm.
Issued: 1993
Price: R.R.P.

GIFT OF LIFE HN3524
Designer: Russell Willis
Height: 8¹/₄in., 21cm.
Issued: 1982
Price: R.R.P.

GIFT OF LOVE HN3427
Designer: Nada Pedley
Height: 7¹/₂in., 19cm.
Issued: 1993
Price: R.R.P.

GILLIAN HN1670
Designer: L. Harradine
Height: 7³/₄in., 19.7cm.
Issued: 1934–1949
Price: $450 £300

GILLIAN HN1670A
Designer: L. Harradine
Height: 7³/₄in., 19.7cm.
Issued: Unknown Colour variation
Price: $450 £300

GILLIAN HN3042
Designer: P. Parsons
Height: 8¹/₄in., 21cm.
Issued: 1985–
Price: $180 £120

GIMLI HN2922
Designer: H. Sales
Height: 5¹/₂in., 14cm.
Issued: 1980–1984
Price: $110 £75

GENTLEMAN FROM WILLIAMSBURG HN2227

GIFT OF FREEDOM HN3443

GIFT OF LOVE HN3427

GIMLI HN2922

GERALDINE HN2348

155

GIRL EVACUEE HN3023
Designer: A. Hughes
Height: 8in., 20.3cm.
Issued: 1989 in a limited
edition of 9500
Price: $300 £200

GIRL WITH YELLOW FROCK HN588
Designer: Unknown
Height: 6¼in., 15.9cm.
Issued: 1923–1938
Price: $1500 £1000

GISELLE HN2139
Designer: P. Davies
Height: 6in., 15.2cm.
Issued: 1954–1969
Price: $490 £325

GISELLE, THE FOREST GLADE HN2140
Designer: P. Davies
Height: 7in., 17.8cm.
Issued: 1954–1965
Price: $410 £275

GLADYS HN1740
Designer: L. Harradine
Height: 5¼in., 13.3cm.
Issued: 1935–1949
Price: $480 £300

GLADYS HN1741
Designer: L. Harradine
Height: 5in., 12.7cm.
Issued: 1935–1938
Colour variation
Price: $480 £300

GLEANER HN1302
Designer: Unknown
Height: 14½in., 36.8cm.
Issued: 1928–1938
Price: $2400 £1500

GLORIA HN1488
Designer: L. Harradine
Height: 7¼in., 18.4cm.
Issued: 1932–1938
Price: $900 £600

GLORIA HN1700
Designer: L. Harradine
Height: 7in., 17.8cm.
Issued: 1935–1938
Colour variation
Price: $900 £600

GLORIA HN3200
Designer: A. Hughes
Height: 9in., 23cm.
Issued: 1989
Price: $165 £110

GNOME HN319
Designer: H. Tittensor
Height: 6¼in., 15.9cm.
Issued: 1918–1938
Price: $1125 £750

GNOME HN380
Designer: H. Tittensor
Height: 6¼in., 15.9cm.
Issued: 1920–1938
Colour variation
Price: $1125 £750

GIRL EVACUEE HN3023

GOOD CATCH HN2258

GNOME HN381
Designer: H. Tittensor
Height: 6¼in., 15.9cm.
Issued: 1920–1938
Colour variation
Price: $1125 £750

GOD BLESS YOU HN3400
Designer: Robert Tabbenor
Height: 8in., 20cm.
Issued: 1992
Price: R.R.P.

GOING HOME HN3527
Designer: Adrian Hughes
Height: 6¼in., 16cm.
Issued: 1982
Price: R.R.P.

GOLDEN DAYS HN2274
Designer: P. Davies
Height: 3¾in., 9.5cm.
Issued: 1964–1973
Price: $165 £110

GOLFER HN2992
Designer: R. Tabbenor
Height: 9½in., 24cm.
Issued: 1988
Price: $180 £120

GOLLUM HN2913
Designer: H. Sales
Height: 3¼in., 8.3cm.
Issued: 1979–1984
Price: $130 £85

GOLLYWOG HN1979
Designer: L. Harradine
Height: 5¼in., 13.3cm.
Issued: 1945–1959
Price: $290 £195

GOLLYWOG HN2040
Designer: L. Harradine
Height: 5¼in., 13.3cm.
Issued: 1949–1959
Colour variation
Price: $340 £225

GOOD CATCH HN2258
Designer: M. Nicholl
Height: 7¼in., 18.4cm.
Issued: 1966–1986
Price: $225 £150

GOOD COMPANION HN3608
Designer: Nada Pedley
Height: 8¼in., 21cm.
Issued: 1994
Price: R.R.P.

GOOD DAY SIR HN2896
Designer: W. K. Harper
Height: 8½in., 21.5cm.
Issued: 1986–1989
Price: $180 £120

GOOD FRIENDS HN2783
Designer: W. K. Harper
Height: 9in., 23cm.
Issued: 1985–
Price: $165 £110

FIGURES

GOOD KING WENCESLAS
HN2118
Designer: P. Davies
Height: 8¹⁄₂in., 21.6cm.
Issued: 1953–1976
Price: $370 £245

GOOD KING WENCESLAS
HN3262
Designer: P. Davies
Height: 4¹⁄₄in., 11cm.
Issued: 1989
Price: $100 £65

GOOD MORNING HN2671
Designer: M. Nicholl
Height: 8in., 20.3cm.
Issued: 1974–1976
Price: $225 £150

GOOD PALS HN3132
Designer: P. Parsons
Height: 6¹⁄₄in., 15.5cm.
Issued: 1987
Price: $110 £75

GOODY TWO SHOES HN1889
Designer: L. Harradine
Height: 4³⁄₄in., 12cm.
Issued: 1938–1949
Price: $200 £135

GOODY TWO SHOES HN1905
Designer: L. Harradine
Height: 4³⁄₄in., 12cm.
Issued: 1939–1949
        Colour variation
Price: $195 £130

GOODY TWO SHOES HN2037
Designer: L. Harradine
Height: 5in., 12.7cm.
Issued: 1949–1989
        Colour variation
Price: $135 £90

GOODY TWO SHOES M80
Designer: L. Harradine
Height: 4in., 10.1cm.
Issued: 1939–1949
Price: $345 £230

GOODY TWO SHOES M81
Designer: L. Harradine
Height: 4in., 10.1cm.
Issued: 1939–1949
        Colour variation
Price: $345 £230

GOOSEGIRL HN425
Designer: L. Harradine
Height: 8in., 20.3cm.
Issued: 1921–1938
Price: $1875 £1250

GOOSEGIRL HN436
Designer: L. Harradine
Height: 8in., 20.3cm.
Issued: 1921–1938
        Colour variation
Price: $1875 £1250

GOODY TWO SHOES HN2037

GISELLE HN2139

GOD BLESS YOU HN3400

GOOD MORNING HN2671

GOOD DAY SIR HN2896

GOLLUM HN2913

GOOSEGIRL HN437
Designer: L. Harradine
Height: 8in., 20.3cm.
Issued: 1921–1938
Colour variation
Price: $1875 £1250

GOOSEGIRL HN448
Designer: L. Harradine
Height: 8in., 20.3cm.
Issued: 1921–1938
Colour variation
Price: $1875 £1250

GOOSEGIRL HN559
Designer: L. Harradine
Height: 8in., 20.3cm.
Issued: 1923–1938
Colour variation
Price: $1875 £1250

GOOSEGIRL HN560
Designer: L. Harradine
Height: 8in., 20.3cm.
Issued: 1923–1938
Colour variation
Price: $1875 £1250

GOOSEGIRL HN2419
Designer: J. Bromley
Height: 8in., 20.3cm.
Issued: 1990 in a limited
edition of 12500
Price: R.R.P.

GOSSIPS HN1426
Designer: L. Harradine
Height: 5³/₄in., 14.6cm.
Issued: 1930–1949
Price: $450 £300

GOSSIPS HN1429
Designer: L. Harradine
Height: 5³/₄in., 14.6cm.
Issued: 1930–1949
Colour variation
Price: $450 £300

GOSSIPS HN2025
Designer: L. Harradine
Height: 5¹/₂in., 14cm.
Issued: 1949–1967
Colour variation
Price: $410 £275

GRACE HN2318
Designer: M. Nicholl
Height: 7³/₄in., 19.7cm.
Issued: 1966–1980
Price: $220 £145

GRACE DARLING HN3089
Designer: E. J. Griffiths
Height: 9in., 22.5cm.
Issued: 1987 in a limited
edition of 9500
Price: $200 £125

GRADUATE (The Female)
HN3016
Designer: P. Parsons
Height: 8³/₄in., 22cm.
Issued: 1984
Price: $225 £150

GOOSEGIRL HN2419

GRACE DARLING HN3089

GRAND MANNER HN2723

GRADUATE
(The Female) HN3016

GRADUATE (The Male)
HN3017
Designer: P. Parsons
Height: 9¹/₄in., 23.5cm.
Issued: 1984–
Price: $225 £150

GRAND MANNER HN2723
Designer: W. K. Harper
Height: 7³/₄in., 19.7cm.
Issued: 1975–1982
Price: $220 £145

GRANDMA HN2052
Designer: L. Harradine
Height: 6³/₄in., 17.2cm.
Issued: 1950–1959
Price: $260 £175

GRANDMA HN2052A
Designer: L. Harradine
Height: 6³/₄in., 17.2cm.
Issued: 1950–1959
Colour variation
Price: $260 £175

GRANNY HN1804
Designer: L. Harradine
Height: 7in., 17.8cm.
Issued: 1937–1949
Price: $900 £600

GRANNY HN1832
Designer: L. Harradine
Height: 6³/₄in., 17.1cm.
Issued: 1937–1949
Colour variation
Price: $900 £600

GRANNY'S HERITAGE
HN1873
Designer: L. Harradine
Height: 6³/₄in., 17.1cm.
Issued: 1938–1949
Price: $560 £375

GRANNY'S HERITAGE
HN1874
Designer: L. Harradine
Height: 6¹/₄in., 15.9cm.
Issued: 1938–1949
Colour variation
Price: $560 £375

GRANNY'S HERITAGE
HN2031
Designer: L. Harradine
Height: 6³/₄in., 17.1cm.
Issued: 1949–1969
Colour variation
Price: $375 £250

GRANNY'S SHAWL HN1642
Designer: L. Harradine
Height: 5³/₄in., 14.6cm.
Issued: 1934–1949
Price: $300 £200

GRANNY'S SHAWL HN1647
Designer: L. Harradine
Height: 5³/₄in., 14.6cm.
Issued: 1934–1949
Colour variation
Price: $300 £200

GRETA HN1485
Designer: L. Harradine
Height: 5¹/₂in., 14cm.
Issued: 1931–1953
Price: $300 £200

GRETCHEN HN1397
Designer: L. Harradine
Height: 7³/₄in., 19.7cm.
Issued: 1930–1938
Price: $525 £350

GRETCHEN HN1562
Designer: L. Harradine
Height: 7³/₄in., 19.7cm.
Issued: 1933–1938
         Colour variation
Price: $525 £350

GRIEF HN595
Designer: Unknown
Height: 2in., 5.1cm.
Issued: 1924–1938
Price: $900 £600

GRISELDA HN1993
Designer: L. Harradine
Height: 5³/₄in., 14.6cm.
Issued: 1947–1953
Price: $560 £375

GRIZEL HN1629
Designer: L. Harradine
Height: 6³/₄in., 17.2cm.
Issued: 1934–1938
Price: $525 £350

GROSSMITH'S TSANG IHANG HN582
Designer: Unknown
Height: 11¹/₂in., 29.2cm.
Issued: 1923–?
Price: $720 £450

GROUCHO MARX HN2777
Designer: W.K. Harper
Height: 9¹/₂in., 24.1cm.
Issued: 1991 in a limited edition of 9500
Price: R.R.P.

GUARDSMAN HN2784
Designer: William K. Harper
Height: 9³/₄in., 24.5cm.
Issued: 1992
Price: R.R.P.

GUY FAWKES HN98
Designer: C. J. Noke
Height: 10¹/₂in., 26.7cm.
Issued: 1918–1949
Price: $1125 £750

GUY FAWKES HN347
Designer: C. J. Noke
Height: 10¹/₂in., 26.7cm.
Issued: 1919–1938
         Colour variation
Price: $1125 £750

GUY FAWKES HN445
Designer: C. J. Noke
Height: 10¹/₂in., 26.7cm.
Issued: 1921–1938
         Colour variation
Price: $1125 £750

GROUCHO MARX HN2777

GRADUATE (The Male) HN3017

GRANDMA HN2052

GRACE HN2318

GUARDSMAN HN2784

GUY FAWKES HN3271
Designer: C. J. Noke
Height: 4¼in., 11cm.
Issued: 1989
Price: $100 £65

GWENDOLEN HN1494
Designer: L. Harradine
Height: 6in., 15.2cm.
Issued: 1932–1938
Price: $600 £400

GWENDOLEN HN1503
Designer: L. Harradine
Height: 6in., 15.2cm.
Issued: 1932–1949
Colour variation
Price: $410 £275

GWENDOLEN HN1570
Designer: L. Harradine
Height: 6in., 15.2cm.
Issued: 1933–1949
Colour variation
Price: $410 £275

GWYNNETH HN1980
Designer: L. Harradine
Height: 7in., 17.8cm.
Issued: 1934–1952
Price: $300 £200

GYPSY DANCE (Style one)
HN2157
Designer: P. Davies
Height: 7in., 17.8cm.
Issued: 1955–1957
Price: $300 £200

GYPSY DANCE (Style two)
HN2230
Designer: P. Davies
Height: 7in., 17.8cm.
Issued: 1959–1971
Price: $290 £195

GYPSY WOMAN WITH
CHILD HN1301
Designer: Unknown
Height: 14¼in., 36.2cm.
Issued: 1928–1938
Price: $2250 £1500

H

HANNAH HN3369
Designer: Nada Pedley
Height: 8¼in., 21cm.
Issued: 1991
Price: R.R.P.

HAPPY ANNIVERSARY
HN3097
Designer: P. Parsons
Height: 6½in., 16.5cm.
Issued: 1987
Price: $220 £145

HAPPY ANNIVERSARY
HN3254
Designer: D. Tootle
Height: 12in., 30.5cm.
Issued: 1989
Price: R.R.P.

GYPSY DANCE (Style two)
HN2230

GWENDOLEN HN1494

HANNAH HN3369

GYPSY DANCE (Style one)
HN2157

HAPPY BIRTHDAY HN3095
Designer: P. Parsons
Height: 7¹/₂in., 19.5cm.
Issued: 1987
Price: R.R.P.

"HAPPY JOY BABY BOY..."
HN1541
Designer: Unknown
Height: 6¹/₄in., 15.9cm.
Issued: 1933–1949
Price: $300 £200

HARLEQUIN HN2186
Designer: P. Davies
Height: 7¹/₄in., 18.4cm.
Issued: 1957–1969
Price: $240 £160

HARLEQUIN HN2737
Designer: D. Tootle
Height: 12¹/₂in., 31cm.
Issued: 1982–
Price: R.R.P.

HARLEQUIN HN3287
U.S.A. edition
Price: R.R.P.

HARLEQUINADE HN585
Designer: L. Harradine
Height: 6¹/₂in., 16.5cm.
Issued: 1923–1938
Price: $720 £450

HARLEQUINADE HN635
Designer: L. Harradine
Height: 6¹/₂in., 16.5cm.
Issued: 1924–1938
        Colour variation
Price: $675 £450

HARLEQUINADE HN711
Designer: L. Harradine
Height: 6¹/₂in., 16.5cm.
Issued: 1925–1938
        Colour variation
Price: $720 £450

HARLEQUINADE HN780
Designer: L. Harradine
Height: 6¹/₂in., 16.5cm.
Issued: 1926–1939
        Colour variation
Price: $720 £450

HARLEQUINADE MASKED
HN768
Designer: L. Harradine
Height: 6¹/₂in., 16.5cm.
Issued: 1925–1938
Price: $1125 £750

HARLEQUINADE MASKED
HN1304
Designer: L. Harradine
Height: 6¹/₂in., 16.5cm.
Issued: 1928–1938
        Colour variation
Price: $1125 £750

HAPPY ANNIVERSARY
HN3254

HARLEQUIN HN3287   HARLEQUIN HN2186

HARLEQUINADE HN585   HARLEQUIN HN2737   HARLEQUINADE MASKED
                                        HN1304

FIGURES

HARLEQUINADE MASKED HN769
Designer: L. Harradine
Height: 6¹/₂in., 16.5cm.
Issued: 1925–1938
Colour variation
Price: $1125 £750

HARLEQUINADE MASKED HN1274
Designer: L. Harradine
Height: 6¹/₂in., 16.5cm.
Issued: 1928–1938
Colour variation
Price: $1125 £750

HARMONY HN2824
Designer: R. Jefferson
Height: 8in., 20.3cm.
Issued: 1978–1984
Price: $220 £145

HARP HN2482
Designer: P. Davies
Height: 8³/₄in., 22.2cm.
Issued: 1973 in a limited edition of 750
Price: $975 £650

HARRIET HN3177
Designer: D. Tootle
Height: 7¹/₄in., 18.5cm.
Issued: 1988
Price: $190 £125

HARVESTIME HN3084
Designer: E. J. Griffiths
Height: 8in., 20cm.
Issued: 1988
Price: $150 £100

HAZEL HN1797
Designer: L. Harradine
Height: 5¹/₄in., 13.3cm.
Issued: 1936–1949
Colour variation
Price: $375 £250

HAZEL HN3167
Designer: P. Davies
Height: 8in., 20cm.
Issued: 1988
Price: $150 £100

HE LOVES ME HN2046
Designer: L. Harradine
Height: 5¹/₂in., 14cm.
Issued: 1949–1962
Price: $220 £145

HEART TO HEART HN2276
Designer: P. Davies
Height: 5¹/₂in., 14cm.
Issued: 1961–1971
Price: $450 £300

HEATHER HN2956
Designer: P. Parsons
Height: 6in., 15cm.
Issued: 1982–
Price: R.R.P.

HEIDI HN2975
Designer: A. Hughes
Height: 4¹/₂in., 11.5cm.
Issued: 1983–1986
Price: $180 £120

HELEN HN1509

HENLEY HN3367

HARP HN2482

HARMONY HN2824

FIGURES

HELEN HN1508
Designer: L. Harradine
Height: 8in., 20.3cm.
Issued: 1932–1938
Price: $600 £400

HELEN HN1509
Designer: L. Harradine
Height: 8in., 20.3cm.
Issued: 1932–1938
Colour variation
Price: $600 £400

HELEN HN1572
Designer: L. Harradine
Height: 8in., 20.3cm.
Issued: 1933–1938
Colour variation
Price: $600 £400

HELEN HN2294
Designer: R. Tabbenor
Height: 5in., 12.5cm.
Issued: 1985–1987
Price: $135 £90

HELEN HN3601
Designer: Nada Pedley
Height: 8in., 20cm.
Issued: 1993
Price: R.R.P.

HELEN OF TROY HN2387
Designer: P. Davies
Height: 9¼in., 23.4cm.
Issued: 1981 as a limited
edition of 750
Price: $1125 £750

HELMSMAN HN2499
Designer: M. Nicoll
Height: 9in., 22.9cm.
Issued: 1974–1986
Price: $260 £175

HENLEY HN3367
Designer: Valerie Annand
Height: 8in., 20cm.
Issued: 1993 in a limited
edition of 5000
Price: R.R.P.

HENRIETTA MARIA HN2005
Designer: P. Davies
Height: 9½in., 24.1cm.
Issued: 1948–1953
Price: $600 £375

HENRY VIII (Style one) HN370
Designer: C. J. Noke
Height: Unknown
Issued: 1920–1938
Price: $1600 £1000

HENRY VIII (Style one) HN673
Designer: C. J. Noke
Height: Unknown
Issued: 1924–1938
Colour variation
Price: $1600 £1000

**HENRY VIII (Style two)
HN1792**
Designer: C. J. Noke
Height: 11½in., 29.2cm.
Issued: 1933 in a limited
edition of 200
Price: $1500 £1000

HELEN HN3601

HENRIETTA MARIA HN2005

HELMSMAN HN2499

HELEN OF TROY HN2387

HENRY VIII HN3350
Designer: Pauline Parsons
Height: Unknown
Issued: 1991 in a limited
edition of 1991
Price: R.R.P.

**HENRY IRVING AS
CARDINAL WOLSEY HN344**
Designer: C. J. Noke
Height: 13¼in., 33.7cm.
Issued: 1919–1949
Price: $1425 £950

**HENRY LYTTON AS JACK
POINT HN610**
Designer: C. J. Noke
Height: 6½in., 16.5cm.
Issued: 1924–1949
Price: $525 £350

HER LADYSHIP HN1977
Designer: L. Harradine
Height: 7¼in., 18.4cm.
Issued: 1945–1959
Price: $330 £220

**HER MAJESTY QUEEN
ELIZABETH II HN2878**
Designer: E. J. Griffiths
Height: 10½in., 27cm.
Issued: 1983 in a limited
edition of 2500
Price: $410 £275

**HER MAJESTY QUEEN
ELIZABETH, THE QUEEN
MOTHER HN2882**
Designer: E. J. Griffiths
Height: 11¾in., 29.8cm.
Issued: 1980 in a limited
edition of 1500
Price: $750 £500

**"HERE A LITTLE CHILD I
STAND" HN1546**
Designer: Unknown
Height: 6¼in., 15.9cm.
Issued: 1933–1949
Price: $300 £200

HERMINIA HN1644
Designer: L. Harradine
Height: 6½in., 16.5cm.
Issued: 1934–1938
Price: $560 £350

HERMINIA HN1646
Designer: L. Harradine
Height: 6½in., 16.5cm.
Issued: 1934–1938
Colour variation
Price: $608 £380

HERMINIA HN1704
Designer: L. Harradine
Height: 6¾in., 17.2cm.
Issued: 1935–1938
Colour variation
Price: $560 £350

HERMIONE HN2058
Designer: P. Davies
Height: ¾in., 19.7cm.
Issued: 1950–1952
Price: $675 £450

HENRY VIII HN3350

HER MAJESTY QUEEN
ELIZABETH II HN2878

HER LADYSHIP HN1977

HINGED PARASOL HN1578

FIGURES

HIBERNIA HN2932
Designer: S. Keenan
Height: 9in., 23cm.
Issued: 1983 in a limited
edition of 950
Price: $525 £350

HIGHWAYMAN HN527
Designer: L. Harradine
Height: 6¹/₂in., 16.5cm.
Issued: 1921–1949
Price: $480 £300

HIGHWAYMAN HN592
Designer: L. Harradine
Height: 6¹/₂in., 16.5cm.
Issued: 1924–1949
Price: $480 £300

HIGHWAYMAN HN1257
Designer: L. Harradine
Height: 6¹/₂in., 16.5cm.
Issued: 1927–1949
Price: $480 £300

HILARY HN2335
Designer: P. Davies
Height: 7¹/₄in., 18.4cm.
Issued: 1967–1980
Price: $190 £125

HINGED PARASOL HN1578
Designer: L. Harradine
Height: 6¹/₂in., 16.5cm.
Issued: 1933–1949
Price: $450 £300

HINGED PARASOL HN1579
Designer: L. Harradine
Height: 6¹/₂in., 16.5cm.
Issued: 1933–1949
Colour variation
Price: $450 £300

**HIS ROYAL HIGHNESS
PRINCE PHILIP DUKE OF
EDINBURGH HN2386**
Designer: P. Davies
Height: 8¹/₄in., 21cm.
Issued: 1981 in a limited
edition of 1500
Price: $410 £275

HIVER HN3069
Designer: R. Jefferson
Height: 11¹/₂in., 29cm.
Issued: 1988 in a limited
edition of 300
Price: $975 £650

HOLD TIGHT HN3298
Designer: Adrian Hughes
Height: 8¹/₂in., 21.5cm.
Issued: 1990
Price: R.R.P.

HOME AGAIN HN2167
Designer: P. Davies
Height: 3¹/₄in., 8.3cm.
Issued: 1956–
Price: R.R.P.

HOMECOMING HN3295
Designer: A. Hughes
Height: 7in., 17.8cm.
Issued: 1990 in a limited
edition of 9500
Price: R.R.P.

HILARY HN2335

**HIS ROYAL HIGHNESS
PRINCE PHILIP DUKE OF
EDINBURGH HN2386**

HOLD TIGHT HN3298

HOMECOMING HN3295

FIGURES

HOMECOMING HN3532
Designer: R. Willis
Height: 14³/₄in., 37.5cm.
Issued: 1987
Price: R.R.P.

HONEY HN1909
Designer: L. Harradine
Height: 7in., 17.8cm.
Issued: 1939–1949
Price: $375 £250

HONEY HN1910
Designer: L. Harradine
Height: 6³/₄in., 17.2cm.
Issued: 1939–1949
        Colour variation
Price: $375 £250

HONEY HN1963
Designer: L. Harradine
Height: 6³/₄in., 17.2cm.
Issued: 1941–1949
        Colour variation
Price: $375 £250

HOPE HN3061
Designer: E. J. Griffiths
Height: 8¹/₂in., 21.5cm.
Issued: 1984 in a limited
        edition of 9500
Price: $330 £220

HORNPIPE HN2161
Designer: M. Nicoll
Height: 9¹/₄in., 23.5cm.
Issued: 1955–1962
Price: $600 £400

HOSTESS OF
WILLIAMSBURG HN2209
Designer: P. Davies
Height: 7¹/₄in., 18.4cm.
Issued: 1960–1983
Price: $220 £145

HUCKLEBERRY FINN
HN2927
Designer: D. Lyttleton
Height: 7in., 17.5cm.
Issued: 1982–1985
Price: $150 £100

HUNTING SQUIRE HN1409
Designer: Unknown
Height: 9³/₄in., 24.7cm.
Issued: 1930–1938
Price: $1600 £1000

HUNTS LADY HN1201
Designer: L. Harradine
Height: 8¹/₄in., 21cm.
Issued: 1926–1938
Price: $1440 £900

HUNTSMAN (Style one)
HN1226
Designer: L. Harradine
Height: 8³/₄in., 22.2cm.
Issued: 1927–1938
Price: $975 £650

HOPE HN3061

HOSTESS OF
WILLIAMSBURG HN2209

HUNTSMAN (Style three)
HN2492

HUNTSMAN (Style two)
HN1815
Designer: Unknown
Height: 9¹/₂in., 24.1cm.
Issued: 1937–1949
Price: $1125 £750
Also called John Peel

HUNTSMAN (Style three)
HN2492
Designer: M. Nicoll
Height: 7¹/₂in., 19.1cm.
Issued: 1974–1978
Price: $250 £165

HURDY GURDY HN2796
Designer: P. Davies
Height: 6in., 15.2cm.
Issued: 1975 in a limited
        edition of 750
Price: $675 £450

I

IBRAHIM HN2095
Designer: C. J. Noke
Height: 7³/₄in., 19.7cm.
Issued: 1952–1955
Price: $375 £250
Also called Emir

IDLE HOURS HN3115
Designer: A. Maslankowski
Height: 12¹/₄in., 31cm.
Issued: 1987–1989
Price: $150 £100

I'M NEARLY READY HN2976
Designer: A. Hughes
Height: 7¹/₂in., 19cm.
Issued: 1984–1986
Price: $190 £125

IN GRANDMA'S DAYS HN339
Designer: C. J. Noke
Height: 8³/₄in., 22.2cm.
Issued: 1919–1938
Price: $900 £600

IN GRANDMA'S DAYS HN340
Designer: C. J. Noke
Height: 8³/₄in., 22.2cm.
Issued: 1919–1938
        Colour variation
Price: $900 £600

IN GRANDMA'S DAYS HN388
Designer: C. J. Noke
Height: 8³/₄in., 22.2cm.
Issued: 1920–1938
        Colour variation
Price: $900 £600

IN GRANDMA'S DAYS HN442
Designer: C. J. Noke
Height: 8³/₄in., 22.2cm.
Issued: 1921–1938
        Colour variation
Price: $900 £600
Also called Lilac Shawl and Poke
Bonnet

IN THE STOCKS (Style one)
HN1474
Designer: L. Harradine
Height: 5in., 12.7cm.
Issued: 1931–1938
Price: $1280 £800

IN THE STOCKS (Style one)
HN1475
Designer: L. Harradine
Height: 5¼in., 13.3cm.
Issued: 1931–1938
          Colour variation
Price: $1280 £800

IN THE STOCKS (Style two)
HN2163
Designer: M. Nicoll
Height: 5¾in., 14.6cm.
Issued: 1955–1959
Price: $600 £400

INDIAN BRAVE HN2376
Designer: P. Davies
Height: 16in., 40.6cm.
Issued: 1967 in a limited
          edition of 500
Price: $3200 £2000

INDIAN MAIDEN HN3117
Designer: A. Maslankowski
Height: 12in., 30.5cm.
Issued: 1988
Price: $150 £100

INDIAN TEMPLE DANCER
HN2830
Designer: P. Davies
Height: 9¼in., 23.5cm.
Issued: 1977 in a limited
          edition of 750
Price: $520 £325

INNOCENCE HN2842
Designer: E. J. Griffiths
Height: 7½in., 19.1cm.
Issued: 1979–1983
Price: $210 £140

INNOCENCE HN3226
Designer: P. Parsons
Height: 7¾in., 19.7cm.
Issued: 1988 in a limited
          edition of 9500
Price: R.R.P.

INVITATION HN2170
Designer: P. Davies
Height: 5½in., 14cm.
Issued: 1956–1975
Price: $190 £125

IONA HN1346
Designer: L. Harradine
Height: 7½in., 19.1cm.
Issued: 1929–1938
Price: $1600 £1000

IRENE HN1621
Designer: L. Harradine
Height: 6½in., 16.5cm.
Issued: 1934–1951
Price: $375 £250

INDIAN BRAVE HN2376

INDIAN TEMPLE DANCER
HN2830

IONA HN1346

FIGURES

IRENE HN1697
Designer: L. Harradine
Height: 7in., 17.8cm.
Issued: 1935–1949
Colour variation
Price: $375 £250

IRENE HN1952
Designer: L. Harradine
Height: 6³/₄in., 17.2cm.
Issued: 1940–1950
Colour variation
Price: $375 £250

IRISH COLLEEN HN766
Designer: L. Harradine
Height: 6¹/₂in., 16.5cm.
Issued: 1925–1938
Price: $1200 £800

IRISH COLLEEN HN767
Designer: L. Harradine
Height: 6¹/₂in., 16.5cm.
Issued: 1925–1938
Price: $1200 £800

IRISHMAN HN1307
Designer: H. Fenton
Height: 6³/₄in., 17.2cm.
Issued: 1928–1938
Price: $1275 £850

ISABELLA, COUNTESS OF SEFTON HN3010
Designer: P. Gee
Height: 9³/₄in., 24.7cm.
Issued: 1991 in a limited
edition of 5000
Price: R.R.P.

ISADORA HN2938
Designer: P. Gee
Height: 8in., 20cm.
Issued: 1986
Price: $250 £165

IT WON'T HURT HN2963
Designer: P. Parsons
Height: 7¹/₂in., 19cm.
Issued: 1982–1986
Price: $110 £75

IVY HN1768
Designer: L. Harradine
Height: 4³/₄in., 12cm.
Issued: 1936–1979
Price: $165 £110

IVY HN1769
Designer: L. Harradine
Height: 4³/₄in., 12cm.
Issued: 1936–1979
Colour variation
Price: $165 £110

J

JACK HN2060
Designer: L. Harradine
Height: 5¹/₂in., 14cm.
Issued: 1950–1971
Price: $190 £125

IRISH COLLEEN HN766

ISABELLA, COUNTESS OF SEFTON HN3010

ISADORA HN2938

IT WON'T HURT HN2963

JACK POINT HN85
Designer: C. J. Noke
Height: 16¼in., 41.2cm.
Issued: 1918–1938
Price: $2250 £1500

JACK POINT HN91
Designer: C. J. Noke
Height: 16¼in., 41.2cm.
Issued: 1918–1938
          Colour variation
Price: $2250 £1500

JACK POINT HN99
Designer: C. J. Noke
Height: 16¼in., 41.2cm.
Issued: 1918–1938
          Colour variation
Price: $1500 £1000

JACK POINT HN2080
Designer: C. J. Noke
Height: 16in., 40.6cm.
Issued: 1952–
          Colour variation
Price: R.R.P.

JACQUELINE HN2000
Designer: L. Harradine
Height: 7¼in., 18.4cm.
Issued: 1947–1951
Price: $375 £250

JACQUELINE HN2333
Designer: P. Davies
Height: 7½in., 19cm.
Issued: 1983–
Price: $220 £145

JACQUELINE HN2001
Designer: L. Harradine
Height: 7¼in., 18.4cm.
Issued: 1947–1951
          Colour variation
Price: $375 £250

JAMES HN3013
Designer: P. Parsons
Height: 6in., 15cm.
Issued: 1983–1987
Price: $375 £250

JANE HN2014
Designer: L. Harradine
Height: 6¼in., 15.9cm.
Issued: 1948–1951
Price: $525 £350

JANE HN2806
Designer: P. Davies
Height: 8in., 20cm.
Issued: 1983–1986
Price: $250 £165

JANE HN3260
Designer: D. V. Tootle
Height: 7¾in., 19.5cm.
Issued: 1990
Price: R.R.P.

JANE SEYMOUR HN3349
Designer: P. Parsons
Height: 9in., 22.9cm.
Issued: 1991 in a limited
          edition of 9500
Price: R.R.P.

JANE HN2806

JACQUELINE HN2333

JACQUELINE HN2000

JANE HN3260

JANE SEYMOUR HN3349

JANET (Style one) HN1537
Designer: L. Harradine
Height: 6¼in., 15.9cm.
Issued: 1932–
Price: R.R.P.

JANET (Style one) HN1538
Designer: L. Harradine
Height: 6¼in., 15.9cm.
Issued: 1932–1949
Colour variation
Price: $375 £250

JANET (Style one) HN1652
Designer: L. Harradine
Height: 6½in., 16.5cm.
Issued: 1934–1949
Colour variation
Price: $375 £250

JANET (Style one) HN1737
Designer: L. Harradine
Height: 6¼in., 15.9cm.
Issued: 1935–1949
Colour variation
Price: $375 £250

JANET (Style two) HN1916
Designer: L. Harradine
Height: 5¼in., 13.3cm.
Issued: 1939–1949
Price: $225 £150

JANET (Style two) HN1964
Designer: L. Harradine
Height: 5in., 12.7cm.
Issued: 1941–1949
Colour variation
Price: $300 £200

JANET M69
Designer: L. Harradine
Height: 4in., 10.1cm.
Issued: 1936–1949
Price: $300 £200

JANET M75
Designer: L. Harradine
Height: 4in., 10.1cm.
Issued: 1936–1949
Colour variation
Price: $300 £200

JANICE HN2022
Designer: P. Davies
Height: 7¼in., 18.4cm.
Issued: 1949–1955
Price: $450 £300

JANICE HN2165
Designer: P. Davies
Height: 7¼in., 18.4cm.
Issued: 1955–1965
Colour variation
Price: $450 £300

JANICE HN 3624
Designer: Valerie Annand
Height: Unknown
Issued: 1994 special
commission
Price: R.R.P.

JANET (Style one) HN1537

JANINE HN2461

JANINE HN2461
Designer: J. Bromley
Height: 7½in., 19.1cm.
Issued: 1971–
Price: R.R.P.

JANUARY HN2697
Designer: P. Davies
Height: 7¾in., 19.7cm.
Issued: 1987
Price: $165 £110

JANUARY HN3330
Designer: P. Davies
Height: 7½in., 19cm.
Issued: 1991
U.S.A. only
Price: $165 £110

JANUARY HN3341
Designer: P. Davies
Height: 7½in., 19cm.
Issued: 1991
Canada only
Price: $165 £110

JAPANESE FAN HN399
Designer: H. Tittensor
Height: 4¾in., 12.1cm.
Issued: 1920–1938
Price: $1250 £850

JAPANESE FAN HN405
Designer: H. Tittensor
Height: 4¾in., 12.1cm.
Issued: 1920–1938
Colour variation
Price: $1250 £850

JAPANESE FAN HN439
Designer: H. Tittensor
Height: 4½in., 12.1cm.
Issued: 1921–1938
Colour variation
Price: $1250 £850

JAPANESE FAN HN440
Designer: H. Tittensor
Height: 4¾in., 12.1cm.
Issued: 1921–1938
Colour variation
Price: $1250 £850

JASMINE HN1862
Designer: L. Harradine
Height: 7¼in., 18.4cm.
Issued: 1938–1949
Price: $450 £300

JASMINE HN1863
Designer: L. Harradine
Height: 7½in., 19.1cm.
Issued: 1938–1949
Colour variation
Price: $525 £350

JASMINE HN1876
Designer: L. Harradine
Height: 7½in., 19.1cm.
Issued: 1938–1949
Colour variation
Price: $560 £375

FIGURES

JEAN HN1877
Designer: L. Harradine
Height: 7^1/₂in., 19.1cm.
Issued: 1938–1949
Price: $216 £135

JEAN HN1878
Designer: L. Harradine
Height: 7^1/₂in., 19.1cm.
Issued: 1938–1949
Colour variation
Price: $490 £325

JEAN HN2032
Designer: L. Harradine
Height: 7^1/₂in., 19.1cm.
Issued: 1949–1959
Colour variation
Price: $450 £300

JEAN HN2710
Designer: P. Davies
Height: 5^3/₄in., 14.5cm.
Issued: 1983–1986
Price: $220 £145

JEMMA HN3168
Designer: P. Davies
Height: 8^1/₂in., 21cm.
Issued: 1988
Price: $220 £145

JENNIFER HN1484
Designer: L. Harradine
Height: 6^1/₂in., 16.5cm.
Issued: 1931–1949
Price: $375 £250

JENNIFER HN2392
Designer: P. Davies
Height: 7in., 17.5cm.
Issued: 1982–
Price: $220 £145

JENNIFER HN3447
Designer: Peter Gee
Height: 7^3/₄in., 19.5cm.
Issued: 1994
Price: R.R.P.

JERSEY MILKMAID HN2057
Designer: L. Harradine
Height: 6^1/₂in., 16.5cm.
Issued: 1950–1959
Price: $290 £195
Also called The Milkmaid

JESSICA HN3169
Designer: P. Davies
Height: 7in., 18cm.
Issued: 1988
Price: R.R.P.

JESSICA HN3497
Designer: P. Davies
Height: 7in., 17.8cm.
Issued: 1993
Colour variation
U.S.A. only
Price: R.R.P.

JESTER (Style one) HN45
Designer: C. J. Noke
Height: 9^1/₂in., 24.1cm.
Issued: 1915–1938
Price: $900 £600

JANUARY HN3330

JANUARY HN3341

JASMINE HN1862

JEAN HN2032

JESSICA HN3169

JESSICA HN3497

171

JESTER (Style one) HN71
Designer: C. J. Noke
Height: 9¹/₂in., 24.1cm.
Issued: 1917–1938
Colour variation
Price: $800 £500

JESTER (Style one) HN71A
Designer: C. J. Noke
Height: 9¹/₂in., 24.1cm.
Issued: 1917–1938
Colour variation
Price: $900 £600

JESTER (Style one) HN320
Designer: C. J. Noke
Height: 10in., 25.4cm.
Issued: 1918–1938
Colour variation
Price: $1125 £750

JESTER (Style one) HN367
Designer: C. J. Noke
Height: 10in., 25.4cm.
Issued: 1920–1938
Colour variation
Price: $800 £500

JESTER (Style one) HN412
Designer: C. J. Noke
Height: 10in., 25.4cm.
Issued: 1920–1938
Colour variation
Price: $1050 £700

JESTER (Style one) HN426
Designer: C. J. Noke
Height: 10in., 25.4cm.
Issued: 1921–1938
Colour variation
Price: $975 £650

JESTER (Style one) HN446
Designer: C. J. Noke
Height: 10in., 25.4cm.
Issued: 1921–1938
Colour variation
Price: $1050 £700

JESTER (Style one) HN552
Designer: C. J. Noke
Height: 10in., 25.4cm.
Issued: 1922–1938
Colour variation
Price: $1200 £800

JESTER (Style one) HN616
Designer: C. J. Noke
Height: 10in., 25.4cm.
Issued: 1924–1938
Colour variation
Price: $975 £650

JESTER (Style one) HN627
Designer: C. J. Noke
Height: 10in., 25.4cm.
Issued: 1924–1938
Colour variation
Price: $1200 £800

JESTER (Style one) HN1295
Designer: C. J. Noke
Height: 10in., 25.4cm.
Issued: 1928–1949
Colour variation
Price: $450 £300

JESTER (Style two)
HN45A

JESTER (Style one)
HN2016

JESTER (Style one) HN71

JESTER (Style one) HN1702
Designer: C. J. Noke
Height: 10in., 25.4cm.
Issued: 1935–1949
Colour variation
Price: $450 £300

JESTER (Style one) HN2016
Designer: C. J. Noke
Height: 10in., 25.4cm.
Issued: 1949–
Colour variation
Price: R.R.P.

JESTER (Style two) HN45A
Designer: C. J. Noke
Height: 10¹/₄in., 26cm.
Issued: 1915–1938
Price: $1200 £800

JESTER (Style two) HN45B
Designer: C. J. Noke
Height: 10¹/₄in., 26cm.
Issued: 1915–1938
Colour variation
Price: $1500 £1000

JESTER (Style two) HN55
Designer: C. J. Noke
Height: 10¹/₄in., 26cm.
Issued: 1916–1938
Colour variation
Price: $900 £600

JESTER (Style two) HN308
Designer: C. J. Noke
Height: 10¹/₄in., 26cm.
Issued: 1918–1938
Colour variation
Price: $1500 £1000

JESTER (Style two) HN630
Designer: C. J. Noke
Height: 10¹/₄in., 26cm.
Issued: 1924–1938
Colour variation
Price: $1125 £750

JESTER (Style two) HN1333
Designer: C. J. Noke
Height: 10¹/₄in., 26cm.
Issued: 1929–1949
Colour variation
Price: $900 £600

JESUS HN3487
Designer: Alan Maslankowski
Height: 2¹/₂in., 6.5cm.
Issued: 1993
Decorated
U.S.A. only
Price: R.R.P.

JESUS HN 3484
Designer: Alan Maslankowski
Height: 2¹/₂in., 6.5cm.
Issued: 1993
White – U.S.A. only
Price: R.R.P.

JILL HN2061
Designer: L. Harradine
Height: 5¹/₂in., 14cm.
Issued: 1950–1971
Price: $190 £125

FIGURES

JOAN HN1422
Designer: L. Harradine
Height: 5¹/₂in., 14cm.
Issued: 1930–1949
Price: $290 £195

JOAN HN2023
Designer: L. Harradine
Height: 5³/₄in., 14.6cm.
Issued: 1949–1959
Colour variation
Price: $290 £195

JOAN HN3217
Designer: P. Davies
Height: 7¹/₂in., 19cm.
Issued: 1988 in a limited
edition of 2000
Price: $250 £165

JOANNE HN2373
Designer: J. Bromley
Height: 5¹/₄in., 13cm.
Issued: 1982–1988
Price: $250 £165

JOANNE HN3422
Designer: Nada Pedley
Height: 7¹/₂in., 19cm.
Issued: 1993
Price: R.R.P.

JOHN PEEL HN1408
Designer: Unknown
Height: 8³/₄in., 22.2cm.
Issued: 1930–1937
Price: $1600 £1000
Also called Huntsman

JOKER HN3196
Designer: A. Hughes
Height: 9³/₄in., 23.5cm.
Issued: 1988
Price: $165 £110

JOKER HN2252
Designer: M. Nicoll
Height: 8¹/₂in., 21.6cm.
Issued: 1990–1992
Price: $165 £110

JOLLY SAILOR HN2172
Designer: M. Nicoll
Height: 6¹/₂in., 16.5cm.
Issued: 1956–1965
Price: $600 £400

JOSEPH HN3486
Designer: Alan Maslankowski
Height: 5³/₄in., 14.6cm.
Issued: 1993
U.S.A. only
Price: R.R.P.

JOSEPH (White) HN3438
Designer: Alan Maslankowski
Height: 5³/₄in., 14.6cm.
Issued: 1993
U.S.A. only
Price: R.R.P.

JOVIAL MONK HN2144
Designer: P. Davies
Height: 7³/₄in., 19.7cm.
Issued: 1954–1976
Price: $290 £195

JOKER HN2252

JOANNE HN3422

JESUS HN3487

JOAN HN2023

JOSEPH HN3486

JOVIAL MONK HN2144

173

JOY HN3184
Designer: D. Tootle
Height: 6¾in., 17cm.
Issued: 1988
Price: $135 £90

JUDGE HN2443
Designer: M. Nicoll
Height: 6½in., 16.5cm.
Issued: 1972–1976
Matte
Price: $250 £165

JUDGE HN2443A
Designer: M. Nicoll
Height: 6½in., 16.5cm.
Issued: 1976
Gloss
Price: $220 £145

JUDGE AND JURY HN1264
Designer: J. G. Hughes
Height: 6in., 15.2cm.
Issued: 1927–1938
Price: $2250 £1500

JUDITH HN2089
Designer: L. Harradine
Height: 7in., 17.8cm.
Issued: 1952–1959
Price: $260 £175

JUDITH HN2278
Designer: M. Nicoll
Height: 6¾in., 17cm.
Issued: 1987–1989
Price: $190 £125

JULIA HN2705
Designer: P. Davies
Height: 7½in., 19.1cm.
Issued: 1975–
Price: $165 £110

JULIA HN2706
Designer: P. Davies
Height: 7½in., 19.1cm.
Issued: 1985–
Colour variation
Price: $165 £110

JULIE HN2995
Designer: R. Tabbenor
Height: 5in., 12.5cm.
Issued: 1985–
Price: R.R.P.

JULIE HN3407
Designer: R. Tabbenor
Height: 5in., 12.7cm.
Issued: 1993
Colour variation
U.S.A. only
Price: R.R.P.

JULY HN2794
Designer: P. Davies
Height: 7¾in., 19.7cm.
Issued: 1987
Price: $165 £110

JULY HN3324
Designer: P. Davies
Height: 7½in., 19.1cm.
Issued: U.S.A. only
Price: $165 £110

JULY HN3324

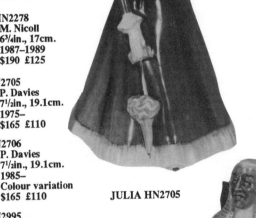

JULIA HN2705

JUDGE HN2443

JULY HN3347
Designer: P. Davies
Height: 7½in., 19.1cm.
Issued: Canada only
Price: $165 £110

JUNE HN1690
Designer: L. Harradine
Height: 7¼in., 18.4cm.
Issued: 1935–1949
Price: $375 £250

JUNE HN1691
Designer: L. Harradine
Height: 7¼in., 18.4cm.
Issued: 1935–1949
Colour variation
Price: $375 £250

JUNE HN1947
Designer: L. Harradine
Height: 7¼in., 18.4cm.
Issued: 1940–1949
Colour variation
Price: $375 £250

JUNE HN2027
Designer: L. Harradine
Height: 7¼in., 18.4cm.
Issued: 1949–1952
Colour variation
Price: $375 £250

JUNE M65
Designer: L. Harradine
Height: 4¼in., 10.8cm.
Issued: 1935–1949
Price: $375 £250

JUNE M71
Designer: L. Harradine
Height: 4¼in., 10.8cm.
Issued: 1936–1949
Colour variation
Price: $375 £250

JUNE HN2790
Designer: P. Davies
Height: 7¾in., 19.7cm.
Issued: 1987
Price: $165 £110

JUNE HN2991
Designer: R. Tabbenor
Height: 9in., 22.5cm.
Issued: 1988
Price: R.R.P.

JUNE HN3323
Designer: P. Davies
Height: 7½in., 19.1cm.
Issued: 1991 U.S.A. only
Price: $165 £110

JUNE HN3346
Designer: P. Davies
Height: 7½in., 19.1cm.
Issued: 1991 Canada only
Price: $165 £110

**JUNO AND THE PEACOCK
HN 2827**
Designer: R. Jefferson
Height: 11in., 27.9cm.
Issued: 1984 in a limited
edition of 300
Price: $1520 £950

JUST FOR YOU HN3355
Designer: Pauline Parsons
Height: 8¼in., 21cm.
Issued: 1992
Price: R.R.P.

JUST ONE MORE HN2980
Designer: A. Hughes
Height: 7in., 17.5cm.
Issued: 1984–1986
Price: $130 £85

K

KAREN HN1994
Designer: L. Harradine
Height: 8in., 20.3cm.
Issued: 1947–1955
Price: $410 £275

KAREN HN2388
Designer: P. Davies
Height: 8in., 20cm.
Issued: 1982–
Price: R.R.P.

KAREN HN3270
Designer: Peggy Davies
Height: 3¾in., 9.5cm.
Issued: 1990
Price: R.R.P.

KATE HN2789
Designer: P. Davies
Height: 7½in., 19.1cm.
Issued: 1978–1987
Price: $220 £145

KATE HANNIGAN HN3088
Designer: E. J. Griffiths
Height: 9in., 27.5cm.
Issued: 1987
Price: $220 £145

KATE HARDCASTLE HN1919
Designer: L. Harradine
Height: 8¼in., 21cm.
Issued: 1939–1949
        Colour variation
Price: $450 £300

KATE HARDCASTLE HN2028
Designer: L. Harradine
Height: 7¾in., 19.7cm.
Issued: 1949–1952
        Colour variation
Price: $450 £300

KATE HARDCASTLE HN1734
Designer: L. Harradine
Height: 8¼in., 21cm.
Issued: 1935–1949
        Colour variation
Price: $600 £400

KATE HARDCASTLE HN1861
Designer: L. Harradine
Height: 8in., 20.3cm.
Issued: 1938–1949
        Colour variation
Price: $600 £400

JUNE HN3323

JUNE HN3346

JUNO AND THE PEACOCK
HN 2827

JUST FOR YOU HN3355

KAREN HN2388

FIGURES

KATE HARDCASTLE HN1718
Designer: L. Harradine
Height: 8in., 20.3cm.
Issued: 1935–1949
Price: $450 £300

KATE HARDCASTLE HN1719
Designer: L. Harradine
Height: 8in., 20.3cm.
Issued: 1935–1949
Colour variation
Price: $490 £325

KATHARINE HN61
Designer: C. J. Noke
Height: 5³/₄in., 14.6cm.
Issued: 1916–1938
Price: $975 £650

KATHARINE HN74
Designer: C. J. Noke
Height: 5³/₄in., 14.6cm.
Issued: 1917–1938
Colour variation
Price: $975 £650

KATHARINE HN341
Designer: C. J. Noke
Height: 5³/₄in., 14.6cm.
Issued: 1919–1938
Colour variation
Price: $1125 £750

KATHARINE HN471
Designer: C. J. Noke
Height: 5³/₄in., 14.6cm.
Issued: 1921–1938
Colour variation
Price: $900 £600

KATHARINE HN615
Designer: C. J. Noke
Height: 5³/₄in., 14.6cm.
Issued: 1924–1938
Colour variation
Price: $900 £600

KATHARINE HN793
Designer: C. J. Noke
Height: 5³/₄in., 14.6cm.
Issued: 1926–1938
Colour variation
Price: $975 £650

KATHLEEN HN1252
Designer: L. Harradine
Height: 7³/₄in., 19.7cm.
Issued: 1927–1938
Colour variation
Price: $525 £350

KATHLEEN HN1253
Designer: L. Harradine
Height: 7¹/₂in., 19.1cm.
Issued: 1927–1938
Colour variation
Price: $525 £350

KATHLEEN HN1275
Designer: L. Harradine
Height: 7¹/₂in., 19.1cm.
Issued: 1928–1938
Colour variation
Price: $525 £350

KATHLEEN HN3100

KATE HARDCASTLE
HN1719

KATHRYN HN3413

KATHLEEN HN1279
Designer: L. Harradine
Height: 7³/₄in., 19.7cm.
Issued: 1928–1938
Colour variation
Price: $525 £350

KATHLEEN HN1291
Designer: L. Harradine
Height: 7¹/₂in., 19.1cm.
Issued: 1928–1938
Colour variation
Price: $525 £350

KATHLEEN HN1357
Designer: L. Harradine
Height: 7¹/₂in., 19.1cm.
Issued: 1929–1938
Colour variation
Price: $525 £350

KATHLEEN HN1512
Designer: L. Harradine
Height: 7¹/₂in., 19.1cm.
Issued: 1932–1938
Colour variation
Price: $525 £350

KATHLEEN HN2933
Designer: S. Keenan
Height: 6¹/₂in., 16.5cm.
Issued: 1984–1987
Price: $250 £165

KATHLEEN HN3100
Designer: S. Keenan
Height: 6¹/₂in., 16.5cm.
Issued: 1986
Price: $290 £195

KATHLEEN HN3609
Designer: Nada Pedley
Height: 8¹/₄in., 21cm.
Issued: 1994
Price: R.R.P.

KATHRYN HN3413
Designer: P. Davies
Height: 7¹/₂in., 19.1cm.
Issued: 1991
Price: $190 £125

KATHY HN2346
Designer: P. Davies
Height: 4³/₄in., 12cm.
Issued: 1981–1987
Price: $180 £120

KATHY HN3305
Designer: Peggy Davies
Height: 7in., 17.5cm.
Issued: 1990
Price: R.R.P.

KATIE HN3366
Designer: Valerie Annand
Height: 8¹/₄in., 21cm.
Issued: 1992
Price: R.R.P.

KATRINA HN2327
Designer: P. Davies
Height: 7¹/₂in., 19.1cm.
Issued: 1965–1969
Price: $290 £195

FIGURES

KAY HN3340
U.S.A. edition
Price: R.R.P.

KELLY HN2478
Designer: P. Davies
Height: 7¹/₂in., 19cm.
Issued: 1985–
Price: $140 £95

KERRY HN3036
Designer: A. Hughes
Height: 5¹/₄in., 13.5cm.
Issued: 1986
Price: $80 £55

KERRY HN3461
Designer: A. Hughes
Height: 5¹/₄in., 13.3cm.
Issued: 1993
           Colour variation
           U.S.A. only
Price: R.R.P.

KIMBERLEY HN3379
Designer: Tim Potts
Height: 8¹/₂in., 21.5cm.
Issued: 1992
Price: R.R.P.

KIMBERLEY HN3382
Designer: T. Potts
Height: 8¹/₂in., 21.6cm.
Issued: 1993
           Colour variation
           U.S.A. only
Price: R.R.P.

KING CHARLES HN404
Designer: C. J. Noke and
          H. Tittensor
Height: 16³/₄in., 42.5cm.
Issued: 1920–1951
Price: $1600 £1000

KING CHARLES HN2084
Designer: C. J. Noke
Height: 16in., 40.6cm.
Issued: 1952–
Price: $1275 £850

KING CHARLES I HN3459
Designer: C. J. Noke and
          H. Tittensor
Height: 16³/₄in., 42.5cm.
Issued: 1992 in a limited
          edition of 350
Price: R.R.P.

KIRSTY HN2381
Designer: P. Davies
Height: 7¹/₂in., 19.1cm.
Issued: 1971–
Price: R.R.P.

KIRSTY HN3213
Designer: P. Davies
Height: 3³/₄in., 9.5cm.
Issued: 1989
Price: R.R.P.

KIRSTY HN3480
U.S.A. edition
Price: R.R.P.

KATHY HN3305

KATIE HN3366

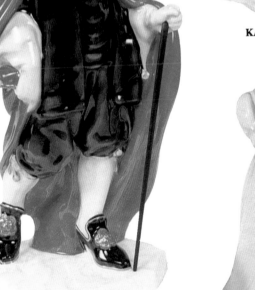

KING CHARLES I HN3459

KAY HN3340

KIMBERLEY HN3382

177

KITTY HN1367
Designer: Unknown
Height: 4in., 10.1cm.
Issued: 1930–1938
Price: $975 £650

KO-KO (Style one) HN1266
Designer: L. Harradine
Height: 5in., 12.7cm.
Issued: 1928–1949
Price: $450 £300

KO-KO (Style one) HN1286
Designer: L. Harradine
Height: 5in., 12.7cm.
Issued: 1938–1949
        Colour variation
Price: $450 £300

KO-KO (Style two) HN2898
Designer: W. K. Harper
Height: 11¹/₄in., 29.2cm.
Issued: 1980–1986
Price: $450 £300

KURDISH DANCER HN2867
Designer: P. Davies
Height: 8¹/₄in., 21cm.
Issued: 1979 in a limited
        edition of 750
Price: $525 £350

L

L'AMBITIEUSE HN3359
Designer: V. Annand
Height: 8¹/₄in., 20.9cm.
Issued: 1991 in a limited
        edition of 5000
Price: $300 £200

LA LOGE HN3472
Designer: V. Annand
Height: 8¹/₂in., 21.5cm.
Issued: 1993 in a limited
        edition of 7500
Price: R.R.P.

LA SYLPHIDE HN2138
Designer: P. Davies
Height: 7in., 17.8cm.
Issued: 1956–1965
Price: $440 £295

LADY AND BLACKAMOOR
(Style one) HN374
Designer: H. Tittensor
Height: Unknown
Issued: 1920–1938
Price: $3000 £2000

LADY AND BLACKAMOOR
(Style two) HN375
Designer: H. Tittensor
Height: Unknown
Issued: 1920–1938
Price: $3000 £2000

LADY AND BLACKAMOOR
(Style two) HN377
Designer: H. Tittensor
Height: Unknown
Issued: 1920–1938
        Colour variation
Price: $3000 £2000

KO-KO (Style two) HN2898   KURDISH DANCER HN2867

L'AMBITIEUSE HN3359   LA LOGE HN3472

FIGURES

LADY AND BLACKAMOOR
(Style two) HN470
Designer: H. Tittensor
Height: Unknown
Issued: 1921–1938
        Colour variation
Price: $3000 £2000

LADY AND THE UNICORN
HN2825
Designer: R. Jefferson
Height: 8³/₄in., 22.2cm.
Issued: 1982 in a limited
        edition of 300
Price: $1520 £950

LADY ANNE HN83
Designer: E. W. Light
Height: Unknown
Issued: 1918–1938
Price: $2250 £1500

LADY ANNE HN87
Designer: E. W. Light
Height: Unknown
Issued: 1918–1938
        Colour variation
Price: $2250 £1500

LADY ANNE HN93
Designer: E. W. Light
Height: Unknown
Issued: 1918–1938
        Colour variation
Price: $2250 £1500

LADY ANNE NEVILL HN2006
Designer: P. Davies
Height: 9³/₄in., 24.7cm.
Issued: 1948–1953
Price: $640 £400

LADY APRIL HN1958
Designer: L. Harradine
Height: 7in., 17.8cm.
Issued: 1940–1959
Price: $340 £225

LADY APRIL HN1965
Designer: L. Harradine
Height: 7in., 17.8cm.
Issued: 1941–1949
        Colour variation
Price: $525 £350

LADY BETTY HN1967
Designer: L. Harradine
Height: 6¹/₂in., 16.5cm.
Issued: 1941–1951
Price: $375 £250

LADY CHARMIAN HN1948
Designer: L. Harradine
Height: 8in., 20.3cm.
Issued: 1940–1973
Price: $300 £200

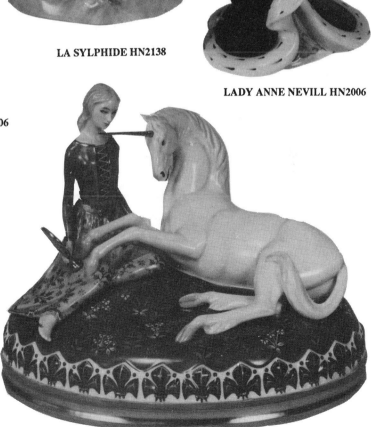

LA SYLPHIDE HN2138

LADY ANNE NEVILL HN2006

LADY AND THE UNICORN
HN2825

179

LADY CHARMIAN HN1949
Designer: L. Harradine
Height: 8in., 20.3cm.
Issued: 1940–1975
Colour variation
Price: $300 £200

LADY CLARE HN1465
Designer: L. Harradine
Height: 7³/₄in., 19.7cm.
Issued: 1931–1938
Price: $525 £350

LADY CLOWN HN717
Designer: L. Harradine
Height: 7¹/₂in., 19.1cm.
Issued: 1925–1938
Price: $1500 £1000

LADY CLOWN HN718
Designer: L. Harradine
Height: 7¹/₂in., 19.1cm.
Issued: 1925–1938
Colour variation
Price: $1500 £1000

LADY CLOWN HN738
Designer: L. Harradine
Height: 7¹/₂in., 19.1cm.
Issued: 1925–1938
Colour variation
Price: $1500 £1000

LADY CLOWN HN770
Designer: L. Harradine
Height: 7¹/₂in., 19.1cm.
Issued: 1925–1938
Colour variation
Price: $1500 £1000

LADY CLOWN HN1263
Designer: L. Harradine
Height: 7¹/₄in., 18.4cm.
Issued: 1927–1938
Colour variation
Price: $1500 £1000
Also called CLOWNETTE

LADY DIANA SPENCER HN2885
Designer: E. Griffiths
Height: 7³/₄in., 19.6cm.
Issued: 1982 as a limited edition of 1500
Price: $340 £225

LADY EATON HN3623
Designer: Valerie Annand
Height: Unknown
Issued: In a limited edition of 2500 Canada only
Price: R.R.P.

LADY FAYRE HN1265
Designer: L. Harradine
Height: 5¹/₄in., 13.3cm.
Issued: 1928–1938
Price: $450 £300

LADY FAYRE HN1557
Designer: L. Harradine
Height: 5³/₄in., 14.6cm.
Issued: 1933–1938
Colour variation
Price: $450 £300

LADY CHARMIAN HN1949

LADY FROM WILLIAMSBURG HN2228

LADY FROM WILLIAMSBURG HN2228
Designer: P. Davies
Height: 6in., 15.2cm.
Issued: 1960–1983
Price: $250 £165

LADY JESTER (Style one) HN1221
Designer: L. Harradine
Height: 7in., 17.8cm.
Issued: 1927–1938
Price: $1200 £750

LADY JESTER (Style one) HN1222
Designer: L. Harradine
Height: 7in., 17.8cm.
Issued: 1927–1938
Colour variation
Price: $1200 £750

LADY JESTER (Style one) HN1332
Designer: L. Harradine
Height: 7in., 17.8cm.
Issued: 1929–1938
Colour variation
Price: $1200 £750

LADY JESTER (Style two) HN1284
Designer: L. Harradine
Height: 4¹/₄in., 10.8cm.
Issued: 1928–1938
Price: $1200 £750

LADY JESTER (Style two) HN1285
Designer: L. Harradine
Height: 4¹/₄in., 10.8cm.
Issued: 1928–1938
Colour variation
Price: $1200 £750

LADY OF THE ELIZABETHAN PERIOD (Style one) HN40
Designer: E. W. Light
Height: 9¹/₂in., 24.1cm.
Issued: 1914–1938
Price: $1500 £1000

LADY OF THE ELIZABETHAN PERIOD (Style one) HN40A
Designer: E. W. Light
Height: 9¹/₂in., 24.1cm.
Issued: 1914–1938
Price: $1500 £1000

LADY OF THE ELIZABETHAN PERIOD (Style one) HN73
Designer: E. W. Light
Height: 9¹/₂in., 24.1cm.
Issued: 1917–1938
Colour variation
Price: $1500 £1000

LADY OF THE ELIZABETHAN PERIOD (Style one) HN411
Designer: E. W. Light
Height: 9³/₄in., 24.7cm.
Issued: 1920–1938
Colour variation
Price: $1500 £1000

**LADY OF THE
ELIZABETHAN PERIOD**
(Style two) HN309
Designer: E. W. Light
Height: 9¹/₂in., 24.1cm.
Issued: 1918–1938
Price: $1500 £1000

LADY OF THE FAN HN48
Designer: E. W. Light
Height: 9¹/₂in., 24.1cm.
Issued: 1916–1938
Price: $1500 £1000

LADY OF THE FAN HN52
Designer: E. W. Light
Height: 9¹/₂in., 24.1cm.
Issued: 1916–1938
        Colour variation
Price: $1500 £1000

LADY OF THE FAN HN335
Designer: E. W. Light
Height: 9¹/₂in., 24.1cm.
Issued: 1919–1938
        Colour variation
Price: $1500 £1000

LADY OF THE FAN HN509
Designer: E. W. Light
Height: 9¹/₂in., 24.1cm.
Issued: 1921–1938
        Colour variation
Price: $1500 £1000

LADY OF THE FAN HN53A
Designer: E. W. Light
Height: 9in., 22.9cm.
Issued: 1916–1938
        Colour variation
Price: $1500 £1000

LADY OF THE FAN HN53
Designer: E. W. Light
Height: 9¹/₂in., 24.1cm.
Issued: 1916–1938
        Colour variation
Price: $1500 £1000

**LADY OF THE GEORGIAN
PERIOD HN41**
Designer: E. W. Light
Height: 10¹/₄in., 26cm.
Issued: 1914–1938
Price: $1500 £1000

**LADY OF THE GEORGIAN
PERIOD HN331**
Designer: E. W. Light
Height: 10¹/₄in., 26cm.
Issued: 1918–1938
        Colour variation
Price: $1500 £1000

**LADY OF THE GEORGIAN
PERIOD HN444**
Designer: E. W. Light
Height: 10¹/₄in., 26cm.
Issued: 1921–1938
        Colour variation
Price: $1500 £1000

**LADY JESTER (Style two)
HN1285**

**LADY DIANA SPENCER
HN2885**

**LADY JESTER (Style one)
HN1221**

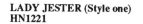

LADY OF THE FAN HN335

181

LADY OF THE GEORGIAN PERIOD HN690
Designer: E. W. Light
Height: 10¹/₄in., 26cm.
Issued: 1925–1938
Price: $1500 £1000

LADY OF THE GEORGIAN PERIOD HN702
Designer: E. W. Light
Height: 10¹/₄in., 26cm.
Issued: 1925–1938
Colour variation
Price: $1500 £1000

LADY OF THE SNOWS HN1780
Designer: R. Garbe
Height: Unknown
Issued: 1933–?
Price: $3000 £2000

LADY OF THE SNOWS HN1830
Designer: R. Garbe
Height: Unknown
Issued: 1937–1949
Price: $3000 £2000

LADY OF THE TIME OF HENRY VI HN43
Designer: E. W. Light
Height: 9¹/₄in., 23.5cm.
Issued: 1914–1938
Price: $1600 £1000

LADY PAMELA HN2718
Designer: D. V. Tootle
Height: 8in., 20.3cm.
Issued: 1974–1980
Price: $210 £140

LADY WITH ERMINE MUFF HN82
Designer: E. W. Light
Height: 6³/₄in., 17.2cm.
Issued: 1918–1938
Price: $1500 £1000
Also known as 'The Afternoon Call'

LADY WITH ROSE HN48A
Designer: E. W. Light
Height: 9¹/₂in., 24.1cm.
Issued: 1916–1938
Price: $1280 £800

LADY WITH ROSE HN52A
Designer: E. W. Light
Height: 9¹/₂in., 24.1cm.
Issued: 1916–1938
Colour variation
Price: $1280 £800

LADY WITH ROSE HN68
Designer: E. W. Light
Height: 9¹/₂in., 24.1cm.
Issued: 1916–1938
Colour variation
Price: $1280 £800

LADY WITH ROSE HN304
Designer: E. W. Light
Height: 9¹/₂in., 24.1cm.
Issued: 1918–1938
Colour variation
Price: $1280 £800

LADY PAMELA HN2718

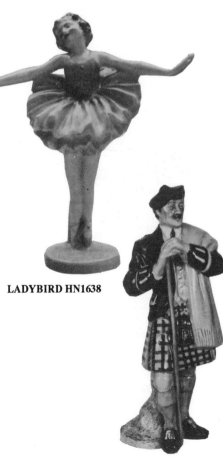

LADYBIRD HN1638

LAIRD HN2361

LADY WITH ROSE HN336
Designer: E. W. Light
Height: 9¹/₂in., 24.1cm.
Issued: 1919–1938
Colour variation
Price: $1280 £800

LADY WITH ROSE HN515
Designer: E. W. Light
Height: 9¹/₂in., 24.1cm.
Issued: 1921–1938
Colour variation
Price: $1360 £850

LADY WITH ROSE HN517
Designer: E. W. Light
Height: 9¹/₂in., 24.1cm.
Issued: 1921–1938
Colour variation
Price: $1360 £850

LADY WITH ROSE HN584
Designer: E. W. Light
Height: 9¹/₂in., 24.1cm.
Issued: 1923–1938
Colour variation
Price: $1360 £850

LADY WITH ROSE HN624
Designer: E. W. Light
Height: 9¹/₂in., 24.1cm.
Issued: 1924–1938
Colour variation
Price: $1360 £850

LADY WITH SHAWL HN447
Designer: L. Harradine
Height: 13¹/₄in., 33.7cm.
Issued: 1921–1938
Price: $1875 £1250

LADY WITH SHAWL HN458
Designer: L. Harradine
Height: 13¹/₄in., 33.7cm.
Issued: 1921–1938
Colour variation
Price: $1920 £1200

LADY WITH SHAWL HN626
Designer: L. Harradine
Height: 13¹/₄in., 33.7cm.
Issued: 1924–1938
Colour variation
Price: $1875 £1250

LADY WITH SHAWL HN678
Designer: L. Harradine
Height: 13¹/₄in., 33.7cm.
Issued: 1924–1938
Colour variation
Price: $1875 £1250

LADY WITH SHAWL HN679
Designer: L. Harradine
Height: 13¹/₄in., 33.7cm.
Issued: 1924–1938
Colour variation
Price: $1875 £1250

LADY WITHOUT BOUQUET HN393
Designer: G. Lambert
Height: 9in., 22.9cm.
Issued: 1920–1938
Price: $3000 £2000

LADY WITHOUT BOUQUET HN394
Designer: G. Lambert
Height: 9in., 22.9cm.
Issued: 1920–1938
Colour variation
Price: $3000 £2000

LADY WORSLEY HN3318
Designer: Peter Gee
Height: 9¹/₂in., 24cm.
Issued: 1991 in a limited edition of 5000
Price: R.R.P.

LADYBIRD HN1638
Designer: L. Harradine
Height: 7³/₄in., 19.7cm.
Issued: 1934–1949
Price: $1125 £750

LADYBIRD HN1640
Designer: L. Harradine
Height: 7³/₄in., 19.7cm.
Issued: 1934–1938
Colour variation
Price: $1125 £750

LAIRD HN2361
Designer: M. Nicoll
Height: 8in., 20.3cm.
Issued: 1969–
Price: R.R.P.

LALLA ROOKH HN2910
Designer: S. Keenan
Height: 9in., 22.8cm.
Issued: 1981 in a limited edition of 950
Price: $1190 £795

LAMBETH WALK HN1880
Designer: L. Harradine
Height: 10in., 25.4cm.
Issued: 1938–1949
Price: $1275 £850

LAMBETH WALK HN1881
Designer: L. Harradine
Height: 10in., 25.4cm.
Issued: 1938–1949
Colour variation
Price: $1275 £850

LAMBING TIME HN1890
Designer: L. Harradine
Height: 9¹/₄in., 23.5cm.
Issued: 1938–1980
Price: $250 £165

LAMP SELLER HN3278
Designer: R. Tabbenor
Height: 9in., 22.9cm.
Issued: 1990
Price: R.R.P.

LANCELOT & GUINEVERE HN3112
Designer: Robert Jefferson
Height: 12in., 30.5cm.
Issued: 1996 in a limited edition of 150
Price: R.R.P.

LAMP SELLER HN3278

LAST WALTZ HN2315

LAURIANNE HN2719

LAND OF NOD HN56
Designer: H. Tittensor
Height: 9¹/₂in., 24.1cm.
Issued: 1916–1938
Price: $1875 £1250

LAND OF NOD HN56A
Designer: H. Tittensor
Height: 9¹/₂in., 24.1cm.
Issued: 1916–1938
Price: $1875 £1250

LAND OF NOD HN56B
Designer: H. Tittensor
Height: 9¹/₂in., 24.1cm.
Issued: 1916–1938
Colour variation
Price: $1875 £1250

LAST WALTZ HN2315
Designer: P. Davies
Height: 7³/₄in., 19.7cm.
Issued: 1967–
Price: $190 £125

LAURA HN2960
Designer: P. Parsons
Height: 7¹/₄in., 18cm.
Issued: 1983–
Price: R.R.P.

LAURA HN3136
Designer: P. Parsons
Height: 7¹/₄in., 18.4cm.
Issued: 1988–1989
Price: $220 £145

LAURIANNE HN2719
Designer: D. V. Tootle
Height: 6¹/₄in., 15.9cm.
Issued: 1974–1978
Price: $240 £160

LAVENDER WOMAN HN22
Designer: P. Stabler
Height: 8¹/₄in., 21cm.
Issued: 1913–1938
Price: $1500 £1000

LAVENDER WOMAN HN23
Designer: P. Stabler
Height: 8¹/₄in., 21cm.
Issued: 1913–1938
Colour variation
Price: $1500 £1000

LAVENDER WOMAN HN23A
Designer: P. Stabler
Height: 8¹/₄in., 21cm.
Issued: 1913–1938
Colour variation
Price: $1500 £1000

LAVENDER WOMAN HN342
Designer: P. Stabler
Height: 8¹/₄in., 21cm.
Issued: 1919–1938
Colour variation
Price: $1500 £1000

LAVENDER WOMAN HN569
Designer: P. Stabler
Height: 8¹/₄in., 21cm.
Issued: 1924–1938
Colour variation
Price: $1500 £1000

LAVENDER WOMAN HN744
Designer: P. Stabler
Height: 8¼in., 21cm.
Issued: 1925–1938
Colour variation
Price: $1500 £1000

LAVINIA HN1955
Designer: L. Harradine
Height: 5in., 12.7cm.
Issued: 1940–1978
Price: $180 £120

LAWYER HN3041
Designer: P. Parsons
Height: 9in., 23cm.
Issued: 1985–
Price: R.R.P.

LEADING LADY HN2269
Designer: P. Davies
Height: 7¾in., 19.7cm.
Issued: 1965–1976
Price: $220 £145

THE LEAP HN3522
Designer: Adrian Hughes
Height: 8¾in., 22cm.
Issued: 1982
Price: R.R.P.

LEDA AND THE SWAN HN2826
Designer: R. Jefferson
Height: 9¾in., 25cm.
Issued: 1983 in a limited edition of 300
Price: $1520 £950

LEGOLAS HN2917
Designer: H. Sales
Height: 6¼in., 15.9cm.
Issued: 1980–1984
Price: $110 £75

LEISURE HOUR HN2055
Designer: P. Davies
Height: 7in., 17.8cm.
Issued: 1950–1965
Price: $440 £295

LESLEY HN2410
Designer: M. Nicoll
Height: 8in., 20cm.
Issued: 1986
Price: $190 £125

LET'S PLAY HN3397
Designer: Alan Maslankowski
Height: 4in., 10cm.
Issued: 1992
Price: R.R.P.

LIBERTY HN3201
Designer: A. Hughes
Height: 9½in., 23.5cm.
Issued: 1989
Price: $165 £110

LIDO LADY HN1220
Designer: L. Harradine
Height: 6¾in., 17.2cm.
Issued: 1927–1938
Price: $750 £500

LEGOLAS HN2917

LET'S PLAY HN3397

LIDO LADY HN1229

LIFEGUARD HN2781

LIDO LADY HN1229
Designer: L. Harradine
Height: 6¾in., 17.2cm.
Issued: 1927–1938
Colour variation
Price: $750 £500

LIFEBOAT MAN HN2764
Designer: W. K. Harper
Height: 9½in., 24cm.
Issued: 1987
Price: $220 £145

LIFEGUARD HN2781
Designer: William K. Harper
Height: 9½in., 24cm.
Issued: 1992
Price: R.R.P.

LIGHTS OUT HN2262
Designer: P. Davies
Height: 5in., 12.7cm.
Issued: 1965–1969
Price: $250 £165

LILAC SHAWL HN44
Designer: C. J. Noke
Height: 8¾in., 22.2cm.
Issued: 1915–1938
Price: $825 £550

LILAC SHAWL HN44A
Designer: C. J. Noke
Height: 8¾in., 22.2cm.
Issued: 1915–1938
Colour variation
Price: $825 £550
Also called In Grandma's Days and Poke Bonnet

LILAC TIME HN2137
Designer: P. Davies
Height: 7¼in., 18.4cm.
Issued: 1954–1969
Price: $290 £195

LILY HN1798
Designer: L. Harradine
Height: 5in., 12.7cm.
Issued: 1936–1949
Price: $190 £125

LILY HN1799
Designer: L. Harradine
Height: 5in., 12.7cm.
Issued: 1936–1949
Colour variation
Price: $190 £125

LINDA HN2106
Designer: L. Harradine
Height: 4¾in., 12cm.
Issued: 1953–1976
Price: $180 £120

LINDA HN2758
Designer: E. Griffiths
Height: 7¾in., 19.5cm.
Issued: 1984–1988
Price: $190 £125

LINDA HN3374
Designer: Nada Pedley
Height: 8¼in., 21cm.
Issued: 1991
Price: R.R.P.

FIGURES

LISA HN2310
Designer: P. Davies
Height: 7¼in., 18.4cm.
Issued: 1969–1982
Price: $190 £125

LISA HN2394
Designer: P. Davies
Height: 7¾in., 19.7cm.
Issued: 1983–
Price: $190 £125

LISA HN3265
Designer: P. Davies
Height: 7¾in., 19.7cm.
Issued: 1989
Price: R.R.P.

LISETTE HN1523
Designer: L. Harradine
Height: 5¼in., 13.3cm.
Issued: 1932–1938
Price: $675 £450

LISETTE HN1524
Designer: L. Harradine
Height: 5¼in., 13.3cm.
Issued: 1932–1938
Colour variation
Price: $675 £450

LISETTE HN1684
Designer: L. Harradine
Height: 6½in., 16.5cm.
Issued: 1935–1938
Colour variation
Price: $675 £450

LITTLE BALLERINA HN3395
Designer: Alan Maslankowski
Height: 6in., 15cm.
Issued: 1992
Price: R.R.P.

LITTLE BALLERINA HN3431
Designer: A. Maslankowski
Height: 6in., 15cm.
Issued: 1993 in a limited
edition of 2000
Colour variation
U.S.A. only
Price: R.R.P.

LITTLE BO-PEEP HN3030
Designer: A. Hughes
Height: 8in., 20cm.
Issued: 1984–1987
Price: $130 £85

LITTLE BOY BLUE HN2062
Designer: L. Harradine
Height: 5½in., 14cm.
Issued: 1950–1973
Price: $190 £125

LITTLE BOY BLUE HN3035
Designer: A. Hughes
Height: 7¾in., 19.7cm.
Issued: 1984–1987
Price: $130 £85

LITTLE BOY BLUE HN2062
Designer: L. Harradine
Height: 5½in., 14cm.
Issued: 1950–1973
Colour variation
Price: $128 £80

LINDA HN3374

LISETTE HN1523

LILAC TIME HN2137

LITTLE
BALLERINA
HN3395

LITTLE BOY BLUE HN2062

LISA HN2310

185

"LITTLE CHILD SO RARE AND SWEET" (Style one)
HN1540
Designer: Unknown
Height: 5in., 12.7cm.
Issued: 1933–1949
Price: $345 £230

"LITTLE CHILD SO RARE AND SWEET" (Style two)
HN1542
Designer: Unknown
Height: 5in., 12.7cm.
Issued: 1933–1949
Price: $345 £230

LITTLE JACK HORNER
HN2063
Designer: L. Harradine
Height: 4¹/₂in., 11.4cm.
Issued: 1950–1953
Price: $290 £195

LITTLE JACK HORNER
HN3034
Designer: A. Hughes
Height: 7in., 17.5cm.
Issued: 1984–1987
Price: $110 £75

LITTLE LADY MAKE BELIEVE HN1870
Designer: L. Harradine
Height: 6¹/₄in., 15.9cm.
Issued: 1938–1949
Price: $450 £300

LITTLE LAND HN63
Designer: H. Tittensor
Height: 7¹/₂in., 19.1cm.
Issued: 1916–1938
Price: $1875 £1250

LITTLE LAND HN67
Designer: H. Tittensor
Height: 7¹/₂in., 19.1cm.
Issued: 1916–1938
Price: $1875 £1250

LITTLE LORD FAUNTLEROY
HN2972
Designer: A. Hughes
Height: 6¹/₄in., 16cm.
Issued: 1982–1986
Price: $165 £110

LITTLE MISS MUFFET
HN2727
Designer: W. K. Harper
Height: 6¹/₄in., 16cm.
Issued: 1984–1987
Price: $130 £85

LITTLE MISTRESS HN1449
Designer: L. Harradine
Height: 5³/₄in., 14.6cm.
Issued: 1931–1949
Price: $300 £200

LITTLE MOTHER (Style one)
HN389
Designer: H. Tittensor
Height: Unknown
Issued: 1920–1938
Price: $2250 £1500

LITTLE LORD FAUNTLEROY HN2972

LOBSTER MAN HN2317

LITTLE MOTHER (Style one)
HN390
Designer: H. Tittensor
Height: Unknown
Issued: 1920–1938
Colour variation
Price: $2250 £1500

LITTLE MOTHER (Style one)
HN469
Designer: H. Tittensor
Height: Unknown
Issued: 1921–1938
Colour variation
Price: $2250 £1500

LITTLE MOTHER (Style two)
HN1418
Designer: L. Harradine
Height: 8in., 20.3cm.
Issued: 1930–1938
Price: $1500 £1000

LITTLE MOTHER (Style two)
HN1641
Designer: L. Harradine
Height: 8in., 20.3cm.
Issued: 1934–1949
Price: $1500 £1000
Also called Young Widow

LITTLE NELL HN540
Designer: L. Harradine
Height: 4in., 10.1cm.
Issued: 1922–1932
Price: $70 £45

LITTLE NELL M51
Designer: L. Harradine
Height: 4¹/₄in., 10.8cm.
Issued: 1932–1982
Price: $60 £40

LIZANA HN1756
Designer: L. Harradine
Height: 8¹/₂in., 21.6cm.
Issued: 1936–1949
Price: $600 £400

LIZANA HN1761
Designer: L. Harradine
Height: 8¹/₂in., 21.6cm.
Issued: 1936–1938
Price: $600 £400

LIZZIE HN2749
Designer: D. Tootle
Height: 8¹/₂in., 22cm.
Issued: 1988–1991
Price: $190 £125

LOBSTER MAN HN2317
Designer: M. Nicoll
Height: 7¹/₄in., 18.4cm.
Issued: 1964–
Price: R.R.P.

LOBSTER MAN HN2327
Designer: M. Nicoll
Height: 7¹/₂in., 19cm.
Issued: 1987
Price: R.R.P.

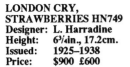

**LONDON CRY,
STRAWBERRIES HN749**
Designer: L. Harradine
Height: 6³/₄in., 17.2cm.
Issued: 1925–1938
Price: $900 £600

**LONDON CRY,
STRAWBERRIES HN772**
Designer: L. Harradine
Height: 6³/₄in., 17.2cm.
Issued: 1925–1938
 Colour variation
Price: $900 £600

**LONDON CRY, TURNIPS AND
CARROTS HN752**
Designer: L. Harradine
Height: 6³/₄in., 17.2cm.
Issued: 1925–1938
Price: $900 £600

**LONDON CRY, TURNIPS AND
CARROTS HN771**
Designer: L. Harradine
Height: 6³/₄in., 17.2cm.
Issued: 1925–1938
Price: $900 £600

LONG JOHN SILVER HN2204
Designer: M. Nicoll
Height: 9in., 22.9cm.
Issued: 1957–1965
Price: $375 £250

**LORD NELSON, VICE
ADMIRAL HN3489**
Designer: Alan Maslankowski
Height: 12¹/₂in., 32cm.
Issued: 1993 in a limited
 edition of 950
Price: R.R.P

**LORD OLIVIER AS RICHARD
III HN2881**
Designer: E. Griffiths
Height: 11¹/₄in., 28.5cm.
Issued: 1985 in a limited
 edition of 750
Price: $675 £450

LORETTA HN2337
Designer: P. Davies
Height: 7³/₄in., 19.7cm.
Issued: 1966–1980
Price: $165 £110

LORI HN2801
Designer: P. Davies
Height: 5³/₄in., 14.6cm.
Issued: 1976–1987
Price: $165 £110

LORNA HN2311
Designer: P. Davies
Height: 8¹/₄in., 21cm.
Issued: 1965–1985
Price: $190 £125

LORRAINE HN3118
Designer: A. Maslankowski
Height: 8in., 20cm.
Issued: 1988
Price: R.R.P.

LONG JOHN SILVER HN2204

LORETTA HN2337

LORD NELSON, VICE
ADMIRAL HN3489

LORNA HN2311

FIGURES

LOUISE HN2869
Designer: P. Davies
Height: 6in., 15.2cm.
Issued: 1980–1986
Price: $200 £135

LOUISE HN3207
Designer: Adrian Hughes
Height: 7½in., 19cm.
Issued: 1990
Price: R.R.P.

LOVE LETTER HN2149
Designer: P. Davies
Height: 5½in., 14cm.
Issued: 1958–1976
Price: $410 £275

LOVE LETTER, THE HN3105
Designer: R. Jefferson
Height: 12in., 30.5cm.
Issued: 1986–1988
Price: $135 £90

LOVERS HN2762 (White)
Designer: D. Tootle
Height: 12in., 30.5cm.
Issued: 1981
Price: R.R.P.

LOVERS HN2763 (Black)
Designer: D. Tootle
Height: 12in., 30.5cm.
Issued: 1981–1992
Price: $150 £100

LOVING YOU HN3389
Designer: Alan Maslankowski
Height: 6¼in., 16cm.
Issued: 1991
Price: R.R.P.

LOYAL FRIEND HN3358
Designer: Valerie Annand
Height: 8¼in., 21cm.
Issued: 1991
Price: R.R.P.

LUCREZIA BORGIA HN2342
Designer: P. Davies
Height: 8in., 20cm.
Issued: 1985 in a limited
edition of 750
Price: $975 £650

LUCY HN2863
Designer: P. Davies
Height: 6in., 15.2cm.
Issued: 1980–1984
Price: $200 £135

LUCY HN 3653
Designer: P. Davies
Height: Unknown
Issued: 1994 only
Price: R.R.P.

LUCY ANN HN1502
Designer: L. Harradine
Height: 5¼in., 13.3cm.
Issued: 1932–1951
Price: $300 £200

LUTE HN2431

LUNCHTIME HN2485

LUCREZIA BORGIA HN2342

FIGURES

LUCY ANN HN1565
Designer: L. Harradine
Height: 5¼in., 13.3cm.
Issued: 1933–1938
Colour variation
Price: $300 £200

LUCY LOCKETT (Style one)
HN485
Designer: L. Harradine
Height: 6in., 15.2cm.
Issued: 1921–1949
Price: $600 £400

LUCY LOCKETT (Style one)
HN524
Designer: L. Harradine
Height: 6in., 15.2cm.
Issued: 1921–1949
Colour variation
Price: $600 £400

LUCY LOCKETT (Style two)
HN695
Designer: L. Harradine
Height: 6in., 15.2cm.
Issued: 1925–1949
Price: $600 £400

LUCY LOCKETT (Style two)
HN696
Designer: L. Harradine
Height: 6in., 15.2cm.
Issued: 1925–1949
Colour variation
Price: $600 £400

LUNCHTIME HN2485
Designer: M. Nicoll
Height: 8in., 20.3cm.
Issued: 1973–1980
Price: $260 £175

LUTE HN2431
Designer: P. Davies
Height: 6¼in., 15.9cm.
Issued: 1972 in a limited
edition of 750
Price: $675 £450

LYDIA HN1906
Designer: L. Harradine
Height: 4¼in., 10.8cm.
Issued: 1939–1949
Price: $300 £200

LYDIA HN1907
Designer: L. Harradine
Height: 4¾in., 12cm.
Issued: 1939–1949
Colour variation
Price: $300 £200

LYDIA HN1908
Designer: L. Harradine
Height: 4¾in., 12cm.
Issued: 1939–
Colour variation
Price: R.R.P.

LYDIA HN1908

LOVING YOU HN3389

LOVE LETTER HN2149

LOYAL FRIEND HN3358   LUCY ANN HN1502   LOUISE HN3207

189

FIGURES

LYNNE HN2329
Designer: P. Davies
Height: 7in., 17.8cm.
Issued: 1971–
Price: R.R.P.

LYNSEY HN3043
Designer: P. Parsons
Height: 4³/₄in., 12cm.
Issued: 1985–
Price: R.R.P.

LYRIC HN2757
Designer: E. Griffiths
Height: 6¹/₄in., 16cm.
Issued: 1983–1986
Price: $150 £100

M

**MADONNA OF THE SQUARE
HN10**
Designer: P. Stabler
Height: 7in., 17.8cm.
Issued: 1913–1938
Price: $880 £550

**MADONNA OF THE SQUARE
HN10A**
Designer: P. Stabler
Height: 7in., 17.8cm.
Issued: 1913–1938
Colour variation
Price: $1275 £850

**MADONNA OF THE SQUARE
HN11**
Designer: P. Stabler
Height: 7in., 17.8cm.
Issued: 1913–1938
Colour variation
Price: $1275 £850

**MADONNA OF THE SQUARE
HN14**
Designer: P. Stabler
Height: 7in., 17.8cm.
Issued: 1913–1938
Colour variation
Price: $880 £550

**MADONNA OF THE SQUARE
HN27**
Designer: P. Stabler
Height: 7in., 17.8cm.
Issued: 1913–1938
Colour variation
Price: $1275 £850

**MADONNA OF THE SQUARE
HN326**
Designer: P. Stabler
Height: 7in., 17.8cm.
Issued: 1918–1938
Colour variation
Price: $975 £650

**MADONNA OF THE SQUARE
HN573**
Designer: P. Stabler
Height: 7in., 17.8cm.
Issued: 1913–1938
Colour variation
Price: $975 £650

LYNNE HN2329

LYRIC HN2757

MADONNA OF THE SQUARE
HN2034

**MADONNA OF THE SQUARE
HN576**
Designer: P. Stabler
Height: 7in., 17.8cm.
Issued: 1923–1938
Colour variation
Price: $900 £600

**MADONNA OF THE SQUARE
HN594**
Designer: P. Stabler
Height: 7in., 17.8cm.
Issued: 1924–1938
Colour variation
Price: $975 £650

**MADONNA OF THE SQUARE
HN613**
Designer: P. Stabler
Height: 7in., 17.8cm.
Issued: 1924–1938
Colour variation
Price: $880 £550

**MADONNA OF THE SQUARE
HN764**
Designer: P. Stabler
Height: 7in., 17.8cm.
Issued: 1925–1938
Colour variation
Price: $975 £650

**MADONNA OF THE SQUARE
HN1968**
Designer: P. Stabler
Height: 7in., 17.8cm.
Issued: 1941–1949
Colour variation
Price: $800 £500

**MADONNA OF THE SQUARE
HN1969**
Designer: P. Stabler
Height: 7in., 17.8cm.
Issued: 1941–1949
Colour variation
Price: $800 £500

**MADONNA OF THE SQUARE
HN2034**
Designer: P. Stabler
Height: 7in., 17.8cm.
Issued: 1949–1951
Colour variation
Price: $525 £350

MAGIC DRAGON HN2977
Designer: A. Hughes
Height: 4³/₄in., 12cm.
Issued: 1983–1986
Price: $225 £150

MAGPIE RING HN2978
Designer: A. Hughes
Height: 8in., 20cm.
Issued: 1983–1986
Price: $225 £150

MAISIE HN1618
Designer: L. Harradine
Height: 6¹/₄in., 15.9cm.
Issued: 1934–1949
Price: $410 £275

FIGURES

MAISIE HN1619
Designer: L. Harradine
Height: 6¼in., 15.9cm.
Issued: 1934–1949
Colour variation
Price: $410 £275

MAJOR, 3rd NEW JERSEY REGIMENT 1776 HN2752
Designer: E. J. Griffiths
Height: 10in., 25.4cm.
Issued: 1975 in a limited edition of 350
Price: $825 £550

MAKE BELIEVE HN2225
Designer: M. Nicoll
Height: 5¾in., 14.6cm.
Issued: 1962–1988
Price: $130 £85

MAKE BELIEVE (White) HN2224
Designer: M. Nicoll
Height: 5¾in., 14.6cm.
Issued: 1984–1988
Colour variation
Price: $130 £85

MAKING FRIENDS HN3372
Designer: Nada Pedley
Height: 5½in., 14cm.
Issued: 1991 in a limited edition of 9500
Price: R.R.P.

MAM'SELLE HN658
Designer: L. Harradine
Height: 7in., 17.8cm.
Issued: 1924–1938
Price: $900 £600

MAM'SELLE HN659
Designer: L. Harradine
Height: 7in., 17.8cm.
Issued: 1924–1938
Colour variation
Price: $900 £600

MAM'SELLE HN724
Designer: L. Harradine
Height: 7in., 17.8cm.
Issued: 1925–1938
Colour variation
Price: $900 £600

MAM'SELLE HN786
Designer: L. Harradine
Height: 7in., 17.8cm.
Issued: 1926–1938
Colour variation
Price: $900 £600

MAN IN TUDOR COSTUME HN563
Designer: Unknown
Height: 3¾in., 9.5cm.
Issued: 1923–1938
Price: $1125 £750

MANDARIN (Style one) HN84
Designer: C. J. Noke
Height: 10¼in., 26cm.
Issued: 1918–1938
Price: $3000 £2000

MAGIC DRAGON HN2977

MAGPIE RING HN2978

MAM'SELLE HN724

MAJOR, 3rd NEW JERSEY REGIMENT 1776 HN2752

MAKE BELIEVE HN2225

MAKING FRIENDS HN3372

MANDARIN (Style one) HN316
Designer: C. J. Noke
Height: 10¹/₄in., 26cm.
Issued: 1918–1938
Colour variation
Price: $3000 £2000

MANDARIN (Style one) HN318
Designer: C. J. Noke
Height: 10in., 25.4cm.
Issued: 1918–1938
Colour variation
Price: $3000 £2000

MANDARIN (Style one) HN382
Designer: C. J. Noke
Height: 10in., 25.4cm.
Issued: 1920–1938
Colour variation
Price: $2400 £1600

MANDARIN (Style one) HN611
Designer: C. J. Noke
Height: 10in., 25.4cm.
Issued: 1924–1938
Colour variation
Price: $2400 £1600

MANDARIN (Style one) HN746
Designer: C. J. Noke
Height: 10in., 25.4cm.
Issued: 1925–1938
Colour variation
Price: $2400 £1600

MANDARIN (Style one) HN787
Designer: C. J. Noke
Height: 10in., 25.4cm.
Issued: 1926–1938
Colour variation
Price: $2400 £1600

MANDARIN (Style one) HN791
Designer: C. J. Noke
Height: 10in., 25.4cm.
Issued: 1926–1938
Colour variation
Price: $3000 £2000

MANDARIN (Style two) HN366
Designer: C. J. Noke
Height: 10in., 25.4cm.
Issued: 1920–1938
Price: $3750 £2500

MANDARIN (Style two) HN455
Designer: C. J. Noke
Height: 10in., 25.4cm.
Issued: 1921–1938
Price: $4500 £3000

MANDARIN (Style two) HN641
Designer: C. J. Noke
Height: 10in., 25.4cm.
Issued: 1924–1938
Colour variation
Price: $3750 £2500

MANDARIN (Style three) HN450
Designer: C. J. Noke
Height: Unknown
Issued: 1921–1938
Price: $3450 £2300

MANTILLA HN3192

MARCH HN2707

MANDARIN (Style three) HN460
Designer: C. J. Noke
Height: Unknown
Issued: 1921–1938
Colour variation
Price: $3750 £2500

MANDARIN (Style three) HN461
Designer: C. J. Noke
Height: Unknown
Issued: 1921–1938
Colour variation
Price: $4500 £3000

MANDARIN (Style three) HN601
Designer: C. J. Noke
Height: Unknown
Issued: 1924–1938
Colour variation
Price: $2400 £1600

MANDY HN2476
Designer: P. Davies
Height: 4¹/₂in., 11.5cm.
Issued: 1982–1992
Price: $100 £65

MANTILLA HN2712
Designer: E. J. Griffiths
Height: 11¹/₂in., 29.2cm.
Issued: 1974–1977
Price: $375 £250

MANTILLA HN3192
Designer: E. J. Griffiths
Height: 11¹/₂in., 29.2cm.
Issued: 1992 in a limited
edition of 1992 for
Expo 92
Price: $375 £250

MARCH HN2707
Designer: P. Davies
Height: 7³/₄in., 19.7cm.
Issued: 1987
Price: $165 £110

MARCH HN3332
Designer: P. Davies
Height: 7¹/₂in., 19cm.
Issued: 1991 U.S.A. only
Price: $165 £110

MARGARET HN1989
Designer: L. Harradine
Height: 7¹/₄in., 18.4cm.
Issued: 1947–1959
Price: $410 £275

MARGARET HN2397
Designer: P. Davies
Height: 7¹/₂in., 19cm.
Issued: 1982–
Price: R.R.P.

MARGARET HN3496
Designer: P. Davies
Height: 7¹/₂in., 19.1cm.
Issued: 1993
Colour variation
U.S.A. only
Price: R.R.P.

FIGURES

MARGARET OF ANJOU
HN2012
Designer: P. Davies
Height: 9¼in., 23.5cm.
Issued: 1949–1953
Price: $570 £350

MARGERY HN1413
Designer: L. Harradine
Height: 11in., 27.9cm.
Issued: 1930–1949
Price: $330 £220

MARGOT HN1628
Designer: L. Harradine
Height: 5½in., 14cm.
Issued: 1934–1938
Price: $675 £450

MARGOT HN1636
Designer: L. Harradine
Height: 5¾in., 14.6cm.
Issued: 1934–1938
Colour variation
Price: $675 £450

MARGOT HN1653
Designer: L. Harradine
Height: 5¾in., 14.6cm.
Issued: 1934–1938
Colour variation
Price: $675 £450

MARGUERITE HN1928
Designer: L. Harradine
Height: 8in., 20.3cm.
Issued: 1940–1959
Price: $330 £220

MARGUERITE HN1929
Designer: L. Harradine
Height: 8in., 20.3cm.
Issued: 1940–1949
Colour variation
Price: $330 £220

MARGUERITE HN1930
Designer: L. Harradine
Height: 8in., 20.3cm.
Issued: 1940–1949
Colour variation
Price: $525 £350

MARGUERITE HN1946
Designer: L. Harradine
Height: 8in., 20.3cm.
Issued: 1940–1949
Colour variation
Price: $450 £300

MARIA HN3381
Designer: Unknown
Height: 8½in., 22cm.
Issued: 1992 special edition
Price: $150 £100

MARIANNE HN2074
Designer: L. Harradine
Height: 7¼in., 18.4cm.
Issued: 1951–1953
Price: $525 £350

MARIE (Style one) HN401
Designer: L. Harradine
Height: 7in., 17.7cm.
Issued: 1920–1938
Price: $1200 £750

MARCH HN3332

MARGARET HN2397

MARIANNE HN2074

MARIA HN3381

MARGARET OF ANJOU HN2012

MARIE (Style one) HN434
Designer: L. Harradine
Height: 7in., 17.7cm.
Issued: 1921–1938
Colour variation
Price: $1200 £750

MARIE (Style one) HN502
Designer: L. Harradine
Height: 7in., 17.7cm.
Issued: 1921–1938
Colour variation
Price: $1200 £750

MARIE (Style one) HN504
Designer: L. Harradine
Height: 7in., 17.7cm.
Issued: 1921–1938
Colour variation
Price: $1200 £750

MARIE (Style one) HN505
Designer: L. Harradine
Height: 7in., 17.7cm.
Issued: 1921–1938
Colour variation
Price: $1200 £750

MARIE (Style one) HN506
Designer: L. Harradine
Height: 7in., 17.7cm.
Issued: 1921–1938
Colour variation
Price: $1200 £750

MARIE (Style two) HN1370
Designer: L. Harradine
Height: 4³/₄in., 12cm.
Issued: 1930–1988
Price: $140 £95

MARIE (Style two) HN1388
Designer: L. Harradine
Height: 4¹/₂in., 11.4cm.
Issued: 1930–1938
Colour variation
Price: $240 £160

MARIE (Style two) HN1417
Designer: L. Harradine
Height: 4³/₄in., 12cm.
Issued: 1930–1949
Colour variation
Price: $195 £130

MARIE (Style two) HN1489
Designer: L. Harradine
Height: 4¹/₂in., 11.4cm.
Issued: 1932–1949
Colour variation
Price: $195 £130

MARIE (Style two) HN1531
Designer: L. Harradine
Height: 4¹/₂in., 11.4cm.
Issued: 1932–1938
Colour variation
Price: $300 £200

MARIE (Style two) HN1635
Designer: L. Harradine
Height: 4³/₄in., 12cm.
Issued: 1934–1949
Colour variation
Price: $240 £160

MARIE (Style two) HN1370

MARIE HN3357

MARIETTA HN1341

MARIE (Style two) HN1655
Designer: L. Harradine
Height: 4¹/₂in., 11.4cm.
Issued: 1934–1938
Colour variation
Price: $300 £200

MARIE HN3357
Designer: P. Parsons
Height: 6in., 15.2cm.
Issued: 1992
Price: R.R.P.

MARIETTA HN1341
Designer: L. Harradine
Height: 8in., 20.3cm.
Issued: 1929–1949
Price: $675 £450

MARIETTA HN1446
Designer: L. Harradine
Height: 8in., 20.3cm.
Issued: 1931–1949
Colour variation
Price: $675 £450

MARIETTA HN1699
Designer: L. Harradine
Height: 8in., 20.3cm.
Issued: 1935–1949
Price: $750 £500

MARIGOLD HN1447
Designer: L. Harradine
Height: 6in., 15.2cm.
Issued: 1931–1949
Price: $340 £225

MARIGOLD HN1451
Designer: L. Harradine
Height: 6in., 15.2cm.
Issued: 1931–1938
Price: $340 £225

MARIGOLD HN1555
Designer: L. Harradine
Height: 6in., 15.2cm.
Issued: 1933–1949
Colour variation
Price: $340 £225

MARILYN HN3002
Designer: P. Gee
Height: 7¹/₄in., 18.5cm.
Issued: 1986
Price: R.R.P.

MARION HN1582
Designer: L. Harradine
Height: 6¹/₂in., 16.5cm.
Issued: 1933–1938
Price: $750 £500

MARION HN1583
Designer: L. Harradine
Height: 6¹/₂in., 16.5cm.
Issued: 1933–1938
Colour variation
Price: $750 £500

MARIQUITA HN1837
Designer: L. Harradine
Height: 8in., 20.3cm.
Issued: 1938–1949
Price: $1050 £700

MARJORIE HN2788
Designer: P. Davies
Height: 5¼in., 13.3cm.
Issued: 1980–1984
Price: $250 £165

MARKET DAY HN1991
Designer: L. Harradine
Height: 7¼in., 18.4cm.
Issued: 1975–1981
Price: $250 £165
Also called Country Lass

MARRIAGE OF ART AND INDUSTRY HN2261
Designer: P. Davies
Height: 19in., 48.3cm.
Issued: 1958 in a limited edition of 12
Price: $4000 £2500

MARY HN2374
Designer: J. Bromley
Height: 7¾in., 19.5cm.
Issued: 1984–1986
Price: $56 £35

MARY (White) HN3437
Designer: Alan Maslankowski
Height: 3¼in., 8cm.
Issued: 1993
U.S.A. only
Price: R.R.P.

MARY (Decorated) HN3485
Designer: Alan Maslankowski
Height: 3¼in., 8cm.
Issued: 1993
U.S.A. only
Price: R.R.P.

MARY, COUNTESS HOWE HN3007
Designer: P. Gee
Height: 9¼in., 23.5cm.
Issued: 1990 in a limited edition of 5000
Price: R.R.P.

MARY HAD A LITTLE LAMB HN2048
Designer: P. Davies
Height: 3½in., 8.9cm.
Issued: 1949–1988
Price: $250 £165

MARY JANE HN1990
Designer: L. Harradine
Height: 7½in., 19.1cm.
Issued: 1947–1959
Price: $340 £225

MARY, MARY HN2044
Designer: L. Harradine
Height: 5in., 12.7cm.
Issued: 1949–1973
Price: $220 £145

MARY QUEEN OF SCOTS HN2931 (Ship's figurehead)
Designer: S. Keenan
Height: 9½in., 24cm.
Issued: 1983 in a limited edition of 950
Price: $525 £350

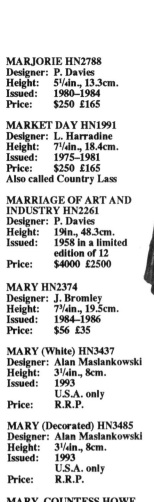

MARIGOLD HN1447

MARIQUITA HN1837

MARJORIE HN2788

MARY HN3485

MARY, COUNTESS HOWE HN3007

195

MARY QUEEN OF SCOTS
HN3142
Designer: P. Parsons
Height: 9in., 22.5cm.
Issued: 1990 in a limited
edition of 5000
Price: $450 £300

MASK HN656
Designer: L. Harradine
Height: 6³/₄in., 17.2cm.
Issued: 1924–1938
Price: $960 £600

MASK HN657
Designer: L. Harradine
Height: 6³/₄in., 17.2cm.
Issued: 1924–1938
Colour variation
Price: $960 £600

MASK HN729
Designer: L. Harradine
Height: 6³/₄in., 17.2cm.
Issued: 1925–1938
Colour variation
Price: $1050 £700

MASK HN733
Designer: L. Harradine
Height: 6³/₄in., 17.2cm.
Issued: 1925–1938
Colour variation
Price: $1050 £700

MASK HN785
Designer: L. Harradine
Height: 6³/₄in., 17.2cm.
Issued: 1926–1938
Colour variation
Price: $960 £600

MASK HN1271
Designer: L. Harradine
Height: 6³/₄in., 17.2cm.
Issued: 1928–1938
Colour variation
Price: $1200 £800

MASK SELLER HN1361
Designer: L. Harradine
Height: 8¹/₂in., 21.6cm.
Issued: 1929–1938
Price: $750 £500

MASK SELLER HN2103
Designer: L. Harradine
Height: 8¹/₂in., 21.6cm.
Issued: 1953–
Colour variation
Price: R.R.P.

MASQUE HN2554
Designer: D. V. Tootle
Height: 8¹/₂in., 21.6cm.
Issued: 1973–1982
Price: $260 £175

MASQUE HN2554A
Designer: D. V. Tootle
Height: 8¹/₂in., 21.6cm.
Issued: 1973–1982
Colour variation
Price: $260 £175

MARY QUEEN OF SCOTS
HN3142

MASQUE HN2554   MASK SELLER HN2103

MASQUERADE (Style one, man) HN599
Designer: L. Harradine
Height: 6³/₄in., 17.2cm.
Issued: 1924–1949
Price: $560 £350

MASQUERADE (Style one, man) HN636
Designer: L. Harradine
Height: 6³/₄in., 17.2cm.
Issued: 1924–1938
Colour variation
Price: $600 £400

MASQUERADE (Style one, man) HN683
Designer: L. Harradine
Height: 7¹/₄in., 18.4cm.
Issued: 1924–1938
Colour variation
Price: $600 £400

MASQUERADE (Style one, woman) HN600
Designer: L. Harradine
Height: 6³/₄in., 17.2cm.
Issued: 1924–1949
Price: $560 £350

MASQUERADE (Style one, woman) HN600A
Designer: L. Harradine
Height: 6in., 15.2cm.
Issued: 1924–1949
Colour variation
Price: $560 £350

MASQUERADE (Style one, woman) HN637
Designer: L. Harradine
Height: 6³/₄in., 17.2cm.
Issued: 1924–1938
Colour variation
Price: $600 £400

MASQUERADE (Style one, woman) HN674
Designer: L. Harradine
Height: 6³/₄in., 17.2cm.
Issued: 1924–1938
Colour variation
Price: $525 £350

MASQUERADE (Style two)
HN2251
Designer: P. Davies
Height: 8¹/₂in., 21.6cm.
Issued: 1960–1965
Price: $285 £190

MASQUERADE (Style two)
HN2259
Designer: P. Davies
Height: 8¹/₂in., 21.6cm.
Issued: 1960–1965
Colour variation
Price: $288 £180

MASTER HN2325
Designer: P. Davies
Height: 6¹/₄in., 15.9cm.
Issued: 1967–1992
Price: $200 £135

MASTER SWEEP HN2205
Designer: M. Nicoll
Height: 8¹/₂in., 21.6cm.
Issued: 1957–1962
Price: $490 £325

MATADOR AND BULL HN2324
Designer: P. Davies
Height: 16in., 40.6cm.
Issued: 1964–
Price: R.R.P.

MATILDA HN2011
Designer: P. Davies
Height: 9¹/₄in., 23.5cm.
Issued: 1949–1953
Price: $560 £350

MAUREEN HN1770
Designer: L. Harradine
Height: 7¹/₂in., 19.1cm.
Issued: 1936–1959
Price: $340 £225

MAUREEN HN1771
Designer: L. Harradine
Height: 7¹/₂in., 19.1cm.
Issued: 1936–1949
         Colour variation
Price: $450 £300

MAUREEN M84
Designer: L. Harradine
Height: 4in., 10.1cm.
Issued: 1939–1949
Price: $375 £250

MAUREEN M85
Designer: L. Harradine
Height: 4in., 10.1cm.
Issued: 1939–1949
         Colour variation
Price: $375 £250

MAUREEN HN2481
Designer: P. Davies
Height: 7¹/₂in., 19cm.
Issued: 1987–1992
Price: $165 £110

MAXINE HN3199
Designer: A. Hughes
Height: 9in., 23cm.
Issued: 1989
Price: R.R.P.

MAY HN2711
Designer: P. Davies
Height: 7³/₄in., 19.5cm.
Issued: 1987
Price: $165 £110

MAY HN2746
Designer: D. Tootle
Height: 8in., 20cm.
Issued: 1987–1992
Price: $220 £145

MAY HN3251
Designer: D. Tootle
Height: 8in., 20cm.
Issued: 1989 in a limited
         edition of 2000
Price: $220 £145

MASQUERADE (Style one, man) HN599

MAY HN2711

MASTER HN2325

MASK HN1271

MATILDA HN2011

MAY HN3334
U.S.A. edition
Price: R.R.P.

MAYOR HN2280
Designer: M. Nicholl
Height: 8¹/₄in., 21cm.
Issued: 1963–1971
Price: $370 £245

MAYTIME HN2113
Designer: L. Harradine
Height: 7in., 17.8cm.
Issued: 1953–1967
Price: $300 £200

MEDITATION HN2330
Designer: P. Davies
Height: 5³/₄in., 14.6cm.
Issued: 1971–1983
Price: $260 £175

MEG HN2743
Designer: D. Tootle
Height: 8¹/₂in., 22cm.
Issued: 1988–1991
Price: $165 £110

MEGAN HN3306
Designer: Peggy Davies
Height: 7¹/₂in., 19cm.
Issued: 1991
Price: R.R.P.

MELANIE HN2271
Designer: P. Davies
Height: 7³/₄in., 19.7cm.
Issued: 1965–1980
Price: $225 £150

MELISSA HN2467
Designer: P. Davies
Height: 6³/₄in., 17.2cm.
Issued: 1981–
Price: R.R.P.

MELODY HN2202
Designer: P. Davies
Height: 6¹/₄in., 15.9cm.
Issued: 1957–1962
Price: $250 £165

MEMORIES HN1855
Designer: L. Harradine
Height: 6in., 15.2cm.
Issued: 1938–1949
Price: $600 £400

MEMORIES HN1856
Designer: L. Harradine
Height: 6in., 15.2cm.
Issued: 1938–1949
           Colour variation
Price: $600 £400

MEMORIES HN1857
Designer: L. Harradine
Height: 6in., 15.2cm.
Issued: 1938–1949
           Colour variation
Price: $600 £400

MAY HN3334

MAYTIME HN2113

MEDITATION HN2330

MEGAN HN3306

MELISSA HN2467

MELANIE HN2271

FIGURES

MEMORIES HN2030
Designer: L. Harradine
Height: 6in., 15.2cm.
Issued: 1949–1959
Colour variation
Price: $340 £225

MENDICANT HN1355
Designer: L. Harradine
Height: 8¼in., 21cm.
Issued: 1929–1938
Price: $330 £220

MENDICANT HN1365
Designer: L. Harradine
Height: 8¼in., 21cm.
Issued: 1929–1969
Price: $270 £180

MEPHISTO HN722
Designer: L. Harradine
Height: 6½in., 16.5cm.
Issued: 1925–1938
Price: $1350 £900

MEPHISTO HN723
Designer: L. Harradine
Height: 6½in., 16.5cm.
Issued: 1925–1938
Colour variation
Price: $1350 £900

MEPHISTOPHELES AND MARGUERITE HN755
Designer: C. J. Noke
Height: 7¾in., 19.7cm.
Issued: 1925–1949
Price: $1200 £750

MEPHISTOPHELES AND MARGUERITE HN775
Designer: C. J. Noke
Height: 7¾in., 19.7cm.
Issued: 1925–1949
Colour variation
Price: $1200 £750

MERIEL HN1931
Designer: L. Harradine
Height: 7¼in., 18.4cm.
Issued: 1940–1949
Price: $640 £400

MERIEL HN1932
Designer: L. Harradine
Height: 7¼in., 18.4cm.
Issued: 1940–1949
Colour variation
Price: $640 £400

MERMAID HN97
Designer: H. Tittensor
Height: 7in., 17.8cm.
Issued: 1918–1936
Price: $450 £300

MERMAID HN300
Designer: H. Tittensor
Height: 7in., 17.8cm.
Issued: 1918–1936
Price: $450 £300

MEPHISTO HN723

MERMAID HN97

MENDICANT HN1365

MERIEL HN1932

FIGURES

MERRY CHRISTMAS HN3096
Designer: P. Parsons
Height: 8½in., 22cm.
Issued: 1987–1992
Price: $190 £125

MERYLL HN1917
Designer: L. Harradine
Height: 6¾in., 17.2cm.
Issued: 1939–1940
Price: $1200 £800
Also called Toinette

MEXICAN DANCER HN2866
Designer: P. Davies
Height: 8¼in., 21cm.
Issued: 1979 in a limited edition of 750
Price: $520 £325

MICHELLE HN2234
Designer: P. Davies
Height: 7in., 17.8cm.
Issued: 1967–1993
Price: $150 £100

MIDINETTE (Style one) HN1289
Designer: L. Harradine
Height: 9in., 22.9cm.
Issued: 1928–1938
Price: $1350 £900

MIDINETTE (Style one) HN1306
Designer: L. Harradine
Height: 9in., 22.9cm.
Issued: 1928–1938
Colour variation
Price: $1350 £900

MIDINETTE (Style two) HN2090
Designer: L. Harradine
Height: 7¼in., 18.4cm.
Issued: 1952–1965
Price: $340 £225

MIDSUMMER NOON HN1899
Designer: L. Harradine
Height: 4¾in., 12cm.
Issued: 1939–1949
Price: $560 £350

MIDSUMMER NOON HN1900
Designer: L. Harradine
Height: 4¾in., 12cm.
Issued: 1939–1949
Colour variation
Price: $560 £350

MIDSUMMER NOON HN2033
Designer: L. Harradine
Height: 4¾in., 12cm.
Issued: 1949–1955
Colour variation
Price: $560 £350

MILADY HN1970
Designer: L. Harradine
Height: 6½in., 16.5cm.
Issued: 1941–1949
Price: $480 £300

MIRANDA HN1818

MILESTONE HN3297

MILESTONE HN3297
Designer: Adrian Hughes
Height: 7¼in., 18.5cm.
Issued: 1990
Price: R.R.P.

MILKING TIME HN3
Designer: P. Stabler
Height: Unknown
Issued: 1913–1938
Price: $2400 £1600

MILKING TIME HN306
Designer: P. Stabler
Height: Unknown
Issued: 1913–1938
Colour variation
Price: $2400 £1600

MILKMAID HN2057
Designer: L. Harradine
Height: 6½in., 16.5cm.
Issued: 1975–1982
Price: $220 £145
Also called The Jersey Milkmaid

MILLICENT HN1714
Designer: L. Harradine
Height: 8in., 20.3cm.
Issued: 1935–1949
Price: $825 £550

MILLICENT HN1715
Designer: L. Harradine
Height: 8in., 20.3cm.
Issued: 1935–1949
Colour variation
Price: $825 £550

MILLICENT HN1860
Designer: L. Harradine
Height: 8in., 20.3cm.
Issued: 1938–1949
Colour variation
Price: $825 £550

MINUET HN2019
Designer: P. Davies
Height: 7¼in., 18.4cm.
Issued: 1949–1971
Price: $260 £175

MINUET HN2066
Designer: P. Davies
Height: 7¼in., 18.4cm.
Issued: 1950–1955
Colour variation
Price: $410 £275

MIRABEL HN1743
Designer: L. Harradine
Height: 7¾in., 19.7cm.
Issued: 1935–1949
Price: $750 £500

MIRABEL HN1744
Designer: L. Harradine
Height: 7¾in., 19.7cm.
Issued: 1935–1949
Colour variation
Price: $750 £500

MIRABEL M68
Designer: L. Harradine
Height: 4in., 10.1cm.
Issued: 1936–1949
Price: $450 £300

MIRABEL M74
Designer: L. Harradine
Height: 4in., 10.1cm.
Issued: 1936–1949
Colour variation
Price: $450 £300

MIRANDA HN1818
Designer: L. Harradine
Height: 8½in., 21.6cm.
Issued: 1937–1949
Price: $825 £550

MIRANDA HN1819
Designer: L. Harradine
Height: 8½in., 21.6cm.
Issued: 1937–1949
Colour variation
Price: $825 £550

MIRANDA HN3037
Designer: A. Hughes
Height: 8½in., 21cm.
Issued: 1987–1990
Price: $190 £125

MIRROR HN1852
Designer: L. Harradine
Height: 7½in., 18.4cm.
Issued: 1938–1949
Price: $1125 £750

MIRROR HN1853
Designer: L. Harradine
Height: 7½in., 18.4cm.
Issued: 1938–1949
Colour variation
Price: $1500 £1000

MISS DEMURE HN1402
Designer: L. Harradine
Height: 7½in., 19.1cm.
Issued: 1930–1975
Price: $260 £175

MISS DEMURE HN1440
Designer: L. Harradine
Height: 7in., 17.8cm.
Issued: 1930–1949
Colour variation
Price: $340 £225

MISS DEMURE HN1463
Designer: L. Harradine
Height: 7in., 17.8cm.
Issued: 1931–1949
Colour variation
Price: $340 £225

MISS DEMURE HN1499
Designer: L. Harradine
Height: 7in., 17.8cm.
Issued: 1932–1938
Colour variation
Price: $340 £225

MISS DEMURE HN1560
Designer: L. Harradine
Height: 7in., 17.7cm.
Issued: 1933–1949
Price: $375 £250

MINUET HN2019

MISS DEMURE HN1463

MILKMAID HN2057

MEXICAN DANCER HN2866

MIDINETTE (Style two)
HN2090

201

MISS FORTUNE HN1897
Designer: L. Harradine
Height: 6in., 15.2cm.
Issued: 1938–1949
Price: $525 £350

MISS FORTUNE HN1898
Designer: L. Harradine
Height: 5³/₄in., 14.6cm.
Issued: 1938–1949
Colour variation
Price: $675 £450

MISS MUFFET HN1936
Designer: L. Harradine
Height: 5¹/₂in., 13.3cm.
Issued: 1940–1967
Price: $225 £150

MISS MUFFET HN1937
Designer: L. Harradine
Height: 5¹/₂in., 13.3cm.
Issued: 1940–1952
Colour variation
Price: $225 £150

MISS 1926 HN1205
Designer: L. Harradine
Height: 7¹/₄in., 18.4cm.
Issued: 1926–1938
Price: $1280 £800

MISS 1926 HN1207
Designer: L. Harradine
Height: 7¹/₄in., 18.4cm.
Issued: 1926–1938
Colour variation
Price: $1280 £800

MISS WINSOME HN1665
Designer: L. Harradine
Height: 6³/₄in., 17.2cm.
Issued: 1934–1949
Price: $1425 £950

MISS WINSOME HN1666
Designer: L. Harradine
Height: 6³/₄in., 17.2cm.
Issued: 1934–1938
Colour variation
Price: $450 £300

M'LADY'S MAID HN1795
Designer: L. Harradine
Height: 9in., 22.9cm.
Issued: 1936–1949
Price: $1050 £700

M'LADY'S MAID HN1822
Designer: L. Harradine
Height: 9in., 22.9cm.
Issued: 1937–1949
Colour variation
Price: $1050 £700

MODENA HN1845
Designer: L. Harradine
Height: 7¹/₄in., 18.4cm.
Issued: 1938–1949
Price: $975 £650

MODENA HN1846
Designer: L. Harradine
Height: 7¹/₄in., 18.4cm.
Issued: 1938–1949
Colour variation
Price: $975 £650

MISS 1926 HN1205

MOLLY MALONE HN1455

MOIRA HN1347

MODERN PIPER HN756
Designer: L. Harradine
Height: 8¹/₂in., 21.6cm.
Issued: 1925–1938
Price: $1500 £1000

MODESTY HN2744
Designer: D. Tootle
Height: 8¹/₄in., 21cm.
Issued: 1988–1991
Price: $140 £95

MOIRA HN1347
Designer: L. Harradine
Height: 6¹/₂in., 16.5cm.
Issued: 1929–1938
Price: $1360 £850

MOLLY MALONE HN1455
Designer: L. Harradine
Height: 7in., 17.8cm.
Issued: 1931–1938
Price: $1425 £950

MONICA HN1458
Designer: L. Harradine
Height: 4in., 10.1cm.
Issued: 1931–1949
Price: $260 £175

MONICA HN1459
Designer: L. Harradine
Height: 4in., 10.1cm.
Issued: 1931–1949
Price: $260 £175

MONICA HN1467
Designer: L. Harradine
Height: 4in., 10.1cm.
Issued: 1931–
Colour variation
Price: R.R.P.

MONICA M66
Designer: L. Harradine
Height: 3in., 7.6cm.
Issued: 1935–1949
Price: $300 £200

MONICA M72
Designer: L. Harradine
Height: 3in., 7.6cm.
Issued: 1936–1949
Colour variation
Price: $192 £120

MONICA HN3617
Designer: L. Harradine
Height: 4in., 10.1cm.
Issued: 1994
Colour variation
Price: R.R.P.

MONTE CARLO HN2332
Designer: P. Davies
Height: 8¹/₄in., 20.9cm.
Issued: 1982 in a limited
edition of 1500
Price: $225 £150

MOON DANCER HN3181
Designer: D. Tootle
Height: 11³/₄in., 30cm.
Issued: 1988–1990
Price: $165 £110

FIGURES

MOONLIGHT ROSE HN3483
Designer: P. Davies
Height: 7in., 18cm.
Issued: 1993–
Price: R.R.P.

MOOR HN1308
Designer: C. J. Noke
Height: 16¹/₂in., 41.9cm.
Issued: 1929–1938
Price: $1350 £900

MOOR HN1366
Designer: C. J. Noke
Height: 16¹/₂in., 41.9cm.
Issued: 1930–1949
        Colour variation
Price: $1200 £800

MOOR HN1425
Designer: C. J. Noke
Height: 16¹/₂in., 41.9cm.
Issued: 1930–1949
        Colour variation
Price: $1350 £900

MOOR HN1657
Designer: C. J. Noke
Height: 16¹/₂in., 41.9cm.
Issued: 1934–1949
        Colour variation
Price: $1350 £900

MOOR HN2082
Designer: C. J. Noke
Height: 16¹/₄in., 41.2cm.
Issued: 1952–
        Colour variation
Price: R.R.P.
Also called "An Arab"

MOORISH MINSTREL HN34
Designer: C. J. Noke
Height: 13¹/₂in., 34.3cm.
Issued: 1913–1938
        Colour variation
Price: $1125 £750

MOORISH MINSTREL HN364
Designer: C. J. Noke
Height: 13¹/₂in., 34.3cm.
Issued: 1920–1938
        Colour variation
Price: $1425 £950

MOORISH MINSTREL HN415
Designer: C. J. Noke
Height: 13¹/₂in., 34.3cm.
Issued: 1920–1938
        Colour variation
Price: $1425 £950

MOORISH MINSTREL HN797
Designer: C. J. Noke
Height: 13¹/₂in., 34.3cm.
Issued: 1926–1949
        Colour variation
Price: $1425 £950

MOORISH PIPER MINSTREL HN301
Designer: C. J. Noke
Height: 13¹/₂in., 34.3cm.
Issued: 1918–1938
Price: $1425 £950

MONICA HN3617

MOORISH MINSTREL HN34

MOONLIGHT ROSE HN3483

MODERN PIPER HN756

MONTE CARLO HN2332

FIGURES

**MOORISH PIPER MINSTREL
HN328**
Designer: C. J. Noke
Height: 13¹/₂in., 34.3cm.
Issued: 1918–1938
Colour variation
Price: $1425 £950

**MOORISH PIPER MINSTREL
HN416**
Designer: C. J. Noke
Height: 13¹/₂in., 34.3cm.
Issued: 1920–1938
Colour variation
Price: $1425 £950

MORNING BREEZE HN3313
Designer: Peter Gee
Height: 8¹/₂in., 21.5cm.
Issued: 1990
Price: R.R.P.

MORNING GLORY HN3093
Designer: P. Parsons
Height: 12³/₄in., 32cm.
Issued: 1987–1989
Price: $150 £100

MORNING MA'AM HN2895
Designer: W. K. Harper
Height: 9in., 23cm.
Issued: 1986–1989
Price: $180 £120

**MOTHER AND CHILD
HN3235 (Blue)**
Designer: Pauline Parsons
Height: 7¹/₂in., 19cm.
Issued: 1991
Price: R.R.P.

**MOTHER AND CHILD
HN3348 (Pink)**
Designer: Pauline Parsons
Height: 7¹/₂in., 19cm.
Issued: 1991
Price: R.R.P.

**MOTHER AND CHILD
HN3353 (White)**
Designer: Pauline Parsons
Height: 7¹/₂in., 19cm.
Issued: 1992
Price: R.R.P.

**MOTHER AND DAUGHTER
HN2843 (Black)**
Designer: E. Griffiths
Height: 8¹/₂in., 21.5cm.
Issued: 1981
Price: R.R.P.

**MOTHER AND DAUGHTER
HN2841 (White)**
Designer: E. Griffiths
Height: 8¹/₂in., 21.5cm.
Issued: 1981
Price: R.R.P.

MOTHER'S HELP HN2151
Designer: P. Davies
Height: 5in., 12.7cm.
Issued: 1962–1969
Price: $165 £110

MY BEST FRIEND HN3011

**MOTHER AND CHILD
HN3348 (Pink)**

MORNING BREEZE HN3313

MOTHERHOOD HN28
Designer: P. Stabler
Height: 8in., 20.3cm.
Issued: 1913–1938
Price: $1875 £1250

MOTHERHOOD HN30
Designer: P. Stabler
Height: 8in., 20.3cm.
Issued: 1913–1938
Colour variation
Price: $1875 £1250

MOTHERHOOD HN303
Designer: P. Stabler
Height: 8in., 20.3cm.
Issued: 1918–1938
Colour variation
Price: $1800 £1200

MOTHERLY LOVE HN3545
Designer: Adrian Hughes
Height: 6in., 15cm.
Issued: 1990
Price: R.R.P.

**MR MICAWBER (Style one)
HN532**
Designer: L. Harradine
Height: 3¹/₂in., 8.9cm.
Issued: 1922–1932
Price: $70 £45

**MR MICAWBER (Style two)
HN557**
Designer: L. Harradine
Height: 7in., 17.8cm.
Issued: 1923–1939
Price: $300 £200

**MR MICAWBER (Style two)
HN1895**
Designer: L. Harradine
Height: 7in., 17.8cm.
Issued: 1938–1952
Colour variation
Price: $300 £200

**MR MICAWBER (Style three)
HN2097**
Designer: L. Harradine
Height: 7¹/₂in., 19.1cm.
Issued: 1952–1967
Price: $285 £190

MR MICAWBER M42
Designer: L. Harradine
Height: 4in., 10.1cm.
Issued: 1932–1982
Price: $60 £40

**MR PICKWICK (Style one)
HN529**
Designer: L. Harradine
Height: 3³/₄in., 9.5cm.
Issued: 1922–1932
Price: $70 £45

**MR PICKWICK (Style two)
HN556**
Designer: L. Harradine
Height: 7in., 17.8cm.
Issued: 1923–1939
Price: $300 £200

MR PICKWICK (Style two)
HN1894
Designer: L. Harradine
Height: 7in., 17.8cm.
Issued: 1938–1952
Colour variation
Price: $300 £200

MR PICKWICK (Style three)
HN2099
Designer: L. Harradine
Height: 7¹/₂in., 19.1cm.
Issued: 1952–1967
Price: $285 £190

MR PICKWICK M41
Designer: L. Harradine
Height: 4in., 10.1cm.
Issued: 1932–1982
Colour variation
Price: $60 £40

MRS BARDELL M86
Designer: L. Harradine
Height: 4¹/₄in., 10.1cm.
Issued: 1949–1982
Price: $60 £40

MRS FITZHERBERT HN2007
Designer: P. Davies
Height: 9¹/₄in., 23.5cm.
Issued: 1948–1953
Price: $600 £375

MRS HUGH BONFOY HN3319
Designer: Peter Gee
Height: 9¹/₂in., 24cm.
Issued: 1992 in a limited
edition of 5000
Price: R.R.P.

MUSICALE HN2756
Designer: E. Griffiths
Height: 9in., 23cm.
Issued: 1983–1986
Price: $250 £165

MY BEST FRIEND HN3011
Designer: Peter Gee
Height: 8in., 20cm.
Issued: 1990
Price: R.R.P.

MY FIRST FIGURINE HN3424
Designer: Nada Pedley
Height: 4¹/₄in., 11cm.
Issued: 1993
Price: R.R.P.

MY FIRST PET HN3122
Designer: Alan Maslankowski
Height: 4¹/₂in., 11.5cm.
Issued: 1991
Price: R.R.P.

MY LOVE HN2339
Designer: P. Davies
Height: 6¹/₄in., 15.9cm.
Issued: 1969–
Price: R.R.P.

MY PET HN2238
Designer: P. Davies
Height: 2³/₄in., 7cm.
Issued: 1962–1975
Price: $180 £120

MOTHER AND CHILD
HN3235 (Blue)

MY FIRST PET HN3122

MY FIRST
FIGURINE HN3424

MRS HUGH
BONFOY HN3319

MUSICALE HN2756

MORNING MA'AM HN2895

MYFANWY JONES HN39
Designer: E. W. Light
Height: 12in., 30.5cm.
Issued: 1914–1938
Price: $2250 £1500
See Welsh Girl

MYFANWY JONES HN92
Designer: E. W. Light
Height: 12in., 30.5cm.
Issued: 1918–1938
         Colour variation
Price: $2625 £1750
See Welsh Girl

MYFANWY JONES HN456
Designer: E. W. Light
Height: 12in., 30.5cm.
Issued: 1921–1938
         Colour variation
Price: $2250 £1500
See Welsh Girl

MYFANWY JONES HN514
Designer: E. W. Light
Height: 12in., 30.5cm.
Issued: 1921–1938
         Colour variation
Price: $3000 £2000
See Welsh Girl

MYFANWY JONES HN516
Designer: E. W. Light
Height: 12in., 30.5cm.
Issued: 1921–1938
         Colour variation
Price: $3000 £2000
See Welsh Girl

MYFANWY JONES HN519
Designer: E. W. Light
Height: 12in., 30.5cm.
Issued: 1921–1938
         Colour variation
Price: $3000 £2000
See Welsh Girl

MYFANWY JONES HN520
Designer: E. W. Light
Height: 12in., 30.5cm.
Issued: 1921–1938
         Colour variation
Price: $3000 £2000
See Welsh Girl

MYFANWY JONES HN660
Designer: E. W. Light
Height: 12in., 30.5cm.
Issued: 1924–1938
         Colour variation
Price: $1875 £1250
See Welsh Girl

MY PRETTY MAID HN2064
Designer: L. Harradine
Height: 5¹/₂in., 14cm.
Issued: 1950–1954
Price: $375 £250

MY TEDDY HN2177
Designer: P. Davies
Height: 3¹/₄in., 8.3cm.
Issued: 1962–1967
Price: $410 £275

MYFANWY JONES HN39

NANNY HN2221

MYFANWY JONES HN668
Designer: E. W. Light
Height: 12in., 30.5cm.
Issued: 1924–1938
         Colour variation
Price: $2100 £1400
See Welsh Girl

MYFANWY JONES HN669
Designer: E. W. Light
Height: 12in., 30.5cm.
Issued: 1924–1938
         Colour variation
Price: $1875 £1250
See Welsh Girl

MYFANWY JONES HN701
Designer: E. W. Light
Height: 12in., 30.5cm.
Issued: 1925–1938
         Colour variation
Price: $1875 £1250
See Welsh Girl

MYFANWY JONES HN792
Designer: E. W. Light
Height: 12in., 30.5cm.
Issued: 1926–1938
         Colour variation
Price: $1875 £1250
See Welsh Girl

N

NADINE HN1885
Designer: L. Harradine
Height: 7³/₄in., 19.7cm.
Issued: 1938–1949
Price: $480 £300

NADINE HN1886
Designer: L. Harradine
Height: 7³/₄in., 19.7cm.
Issued: 1938–1949
         Colour variation
Price: $480 £300

NANA HN1766
Designer: L. Harradine
Height: 4³/₄in., 12cm.
Issued: 1936–1949
Price: $300 £200

NANA HN1767
Designer: L. Harradine
Height: 4³/₄in., 12cm.
Issued: 1936–1949
         Colour variation
Price: $300 £200

NANCY HN2955
Designer: P. Parsons
Height: 7¹/₂in., 19cm.
Issued: 1982–
Price: R.R.P.

NANNY HN2221
Designer: P. Davies
Height: 6in., 15.2cm.
Issued: 1958–1991
Price: $220 £145

FIGURES

NAPOLEON AT WATERLOO
HN3429
Designer: Alan Maslankowski
Height: 11½in., 29cm.
Issued: 1992 in a limited
edition of 1500
Price: R.R.P.

NATALIE HN3173
Designer: P. Davies
Height: 8in., 20cm.
Issued: 1988
Price: R.R.P.

NATALIE HN3498
Designer: P. Davies
Height: 8in., 20.3cm.
Issued: 1993
Colour variation
U.S.A. only
Price: R.R.P.

NEGLIGEE HN1219
Designer: L. Harradine
Height: 5in., 12.7cm.
Issued: 1927–1938
Price: $720 £450

NEGLIGEE HN1228
Designer: L. Harradine
Height: 5in., 12.7cm.
Issued: 1927–1938
Colour variation
Price: $720 £450

NEGLIGEE HN1272
Designer: L. Harradine
Height: 5in., 12.7cm.
Issued: 1928–1938
Colour variation
Price: $720 £450

NEGLIGEE HN1273
Designer: L. Harradine
Height: 5in., 12.7cm.
Issued: 1928–1938
Colour variation
Price: $720 £450

NEGLIGEE HN1454
Designer: L. Harradine
Height: 5in., 12.7cm.
Issued: 1931–1938
Colour variation
Price: $720 £450

NELL HN3014
Designer: P. Parsons
Height: 4in., 10cm.
Issued: 1983–1989
Price: $190 £125

NELL GWYNN HN1882
Designer: L. Harradine
Height: 6¾in., 17.2cm.
Issued: 1938–1949
Price: $750 £500

NELL GWYNN HN1887
Designer: L. Harradine
Height: 6¾in., 17.2cm.
Issued: 1938–1949
Colour variation
Price: $750 £500

NATALIE HN3173

NAPOLEON AT WATERLOO
HN3429

NATALIE HN3498

NEGLIGEE HN1228

207

FIGURES

NELSON HN2928 (Ship's figurehead)
Designer: S. Keenan
Height: 8³/₄in., 22.2cm.
Issued: 1981 in a limited edition of 950
Price: $450 £300

NESTLING DOWN HN3531
Designer: A. Hughes
Height: 13in., 33cm.
Issued: 1986
Price: R.R.P.

NEW BONNET HN1728
Designer: L. Harradine
Height: 7in., 17.8cm.
Issued: 1935–1949
Price: $450 £300

NEW BONNET HN1957
Designer: L. Harradine
Height: 7in., 17.8cm.
Issued: 1940–1949
Colour variation
Price: $450 £300

NEW COMPANIONS HN2770
Designer: W. K. Harper
Height: 7³/₄in., 19.5cm.
Issued: 1982–1986
Price: $180 £120

NEWHAVEN FISHWIFE HN1480
Designer: H. Fenton
Height: 7³/₄in., 19.7cm.
Issued: 1931–1938
Price: $1875 £1250

NEWSBOY HN2244
Designer: P. Davies
Height: 8¹/₂in., 21.6cm.
Issued: 1959–1965
Price: $450 £300

NEWS VENDOR HN2891
Designer: W. Harper
Height: 7in., 17.8cm.
Issued: 1986 in a limited edition of 2500
Price: $300 £200

NICOLA HN2839
Designer: P. Davies
Height: 7in., 17.8cm.
Issued: 1978–
Price: R.R.P.

NICOLA HN2804
Designer: P. Davies
Height: 7¹/₂in., 19.1cm.
Issued: 1987
Price: $190 £125

NICOLE HN3421
Designer: Nada Pedley
Height: 7¹/₂in., 19.1cm.
Issued: 1993
Price: R.R.P.

NINA HN2347
Designer: P. Davies
Height: 7¹/₂in., 19.1cm.
Issued: 1969–1976
Price: $220 £145

NOVEMBER HN2695

NICOLE HN3421

NEW BONNET HN1728

NEW COMPANIONS HN2770

NINETTE HN2379
Designer: P. Davies
Height: 7¹/₂in., 19.1cm.
Issued: 1971–
Price: R.R.P.

NINETTE HN3215
Designer: P. Davies
Height: 3¹/₂in., 9cm.
Issued: 1988
Price: R.R.P.

NINETTE HN3417
Designer: P. Davies
Height: 7¹/₂in., 19.1cm.
Issued: 1992
Price: $225 £150

NOELLE HN2179
Designer: P. Davies
Height: 6³/₄in., 17.2cm.
Issued: 1957–1967
Price: $330 £220

NORMA M36
Designer: Unknown
Height: 4¹/₂in., 11.4cm.
Issued: 1933–1945
Price: $375 £250

NORMA M37
Designer: Unknown
Height: 4¹/₂in., 11.4cm.
Issued: 1933–1945
Colour variation
Price: $375 £250

NORTH AMERICAN INDIAN DANCER HN2809
Designer: P. Davies
Height: 8¹/₂in., 21.5cm.
Issued: 1982 in a limited edition of 750
Price: $520 £325

NOVEMBER HN2695
Designer: P. Davies
Height: 7³/₄in., 19.5cm.
Issued: 1987
Price: $165 £110

NOVEMBER HN3328
Designer: P. Davies
Height: 7¹/₂in., 19.1cm.
Issued: 1991–
U.S.A. only
Price: $165 £110

NUDE ON ROCK HN593
Designer: Unknown
Height: Unknown
Issued: 1924–1938
Price: $1125 £750

O

OCTOBER HN2693
Designer: P. Davies
Height: 7³/₄in., 19.5cm.
Issued: 1987
Price: $165 £110

FIGURES

NINETTE HN3417

NICOLA HN2839

NINETTE HN2379

NOVEMBER HN3328

NORTH AMERICAN INDIAN
DANCER HN2809

NINA HN2347

NEWS VENDOR HN2891

209

OCTOBER HN3327
Designer: P. Davies
Height: 7½in., 19.1cm.
Issued: 1991–
U.S.A. only
Price: $165 £110

OCTOBER HN3410
Designer: P. Davies
Height: 7½in., 19.1cm.
Issued: 1991–
Canada only
Price: $165 £110

ODDS AND ENDS HN1844
Designer: L. Harradine
Height: 7¾in., 19.6cm.
Issued: 1938–1949
Price: $900 £600

OFFICER OF THE LINE HN2733
Designer: W. K. Harper
Height: 9in., 23cm.
Issued: 1983–1986
Price: $255 £170

OLD BALLOON SELLER HN1315
Designer: L. Harradine
Height: 7½in., 19.1cm.
Issued: 1929–
Price: R.R.P.

OLD BALLOON SELLER HN2129
Designer: L. Harradine
Height: 3½in., 9cm.
Issued: 1989–1991
Price: $110 £75

OLD BALLOON SELLER AND BULLDOG HN1791
Designer: L. Harradine
Height: 7in., 17.8cm.
Issued: 1932–1938
Price: $592 £370

OLD BALLOON SELLER AND BULLDOG HN1912
Designer: L. Harradine
Height: 7in., 17.8cm.
Issued: 1939–1949
Price: $560 £350

OLD BEN HN3190
Designer: E. Griffiths
Height: 6½in., 16.5cm.
Issued: 1991 in a limited
edition of 1500
Price: $145 £95

OLD COUNTRY ROSES HN3483
Designer: P. Davies
Height: 7in., 19cm.
Issued: 1993
Price: R.R.P.

OLD KING HN358
Designer: C. J. Noke
Height: 9¾in., 24.7cm.
Issued: 1919–1938
Price: $900 £600

OCTOBER HN3327

OLD COUNTRY ROSES
HN3482

OFFICER OF THE LINE
HN2733

OLD BALLOON SELLER
HN1315

OLD BEN HN3190

OLD KING HN623
Designer: C. J. Noke
Height: 9³/₄in., 24.7cm.
Issued: 1924–1938
Colour variation
Price: $900 £600

OLD KING HN1801
Designer: C. J. Noke
Height: 9³/₄in., 24.7cm.
Issued: 1937–1954
Price: $1425 £950

OLD KING HN2134
Designer: C. J. Noke
Height: 10³/₄in., 27.3cm.
Issued: 1954–1992
Colour variation
Price: $525 £350

OLD KING COLE HN2217
Designer: P. Davies
Height: 6¹/₂in., 16.5cm.
Issued: 1963–1967
Price: $480 £320

OLD LAVENDER SELLER HN1492
Designer: L. Harradine
Height: 6in., 15.2cm.
Issued: 1932–1949
Price: $490 £325

OLD LAVENDER SELLER HN1571
Designer: L. Harradine
Height: 6¹/₂in., 16.5cm.
Issued: 1933–1949
Price: $495 £325

OLD MAN HN451
Designer: Unknown
Height: Unknown
Issued: 1921–1938
Price: $1875 £1250

OLD MEG HN2494
Designer: M. Nicoll
Height: 8¹/₄in., 21cm.
Issued: 1974–1976
Price: $210 £140

OLD MOTHER HUBBARD HN2314
Designer: M. Nicoll
Height: 8in., 20.3cm.
Issued: 1964–1975
Price: $330 £220

OLGA HN2463
Designer: J. Bromley
Height: 8¹/₄in., 21cm.
Issued: 1972–1975
Price: $180 £120

OLGA HN2463

OLD MEG HN2494

OLD MOTHER HUBBARD
HN2314

OLD KING HN2134

OLIVER HARDY HN2775
Designer: W.K. Harper
Height: 10in., 25cm.
Issued: 1992
Price: R.R.P.

OLIVER TWIST M89
Designer: L. Harradine
Height: 4¼in., 10.8cm.
Issued: 1949–1982
Price: $60 £40

OLIVIA HN1995
Designer: L. Harradine
Height: 7½in., 19.1cm.
Issued: 1947–1951
Price: $410 £275

OLIVIA HN3339
U.S.A. edition
Price: R.R.P.

OMAR KHAYYAM (Style one)
HN408
Designer: C. J. Noke
Height: 6in., 15.2cm.
Issued: 1920–1938
Price: $2250 £1500

OMAR KHAYYAM (Style one)
HN409
Designer: C. J. Noke
Height: 6in., 15.2cm.
Issued: 1920–1938
Colour variation
Price: $3000 £2000

OMAR KHAYYAM (Style two)
HN2247
Designer: M. Nicoll
Height: 6¼in., 15.9cm.
Issued: 1965–1983
Price: $250 £165

OMAR KHAYYAM AND THE
BELOVED HN407
Designer: C. J. Noke
Height: 10in., 25.4cm.
Issued: 1920–1938
Price: $2700 £1800

OMAR KHAYYAM AND THE
BELOVED HN419
Designer: C. J. Noke
Height: 6in., 15.2cm.
Issued: 1920–1938
Price: $2700 £1800

OMAR KHAYYAM AND THE
BELOVED HN459
Designer: C. J. Noke
Height: 10in., 25.4cm.
Issued: 1921–1938
Price: $2700 £1800

OMAR KHAYYAM AND THE
BELOVED HN598
Designer: C. J. Noke
Height: 10in., 25.4cm.
Issued: 1924–1938
Price: $3000 £2000

ONCE UPON A TIME HN2047
Designer: L. Harradine
Height: 4¼in., 10.8cm.
Issued: 1949–1955
Price: $410 £275

OLIVER HARDY HN2775

OLIVIA HN3339

OMAR KHAYYAM (Style two)
HN2247

ONE OF THE FORTY
(Style one) HN417
Designer: H. Tittensor
Height: 8¼in., 21cm.
Issued: 1920–1938
Price: $768 £480

ONE OF THE FORTY
(Style one) HN490
Designer: H. Tittensor
Height: 8¼in., 21cm.
Issued: 1921–1938
Colour variation
Price: $768 £480

ONE OF THE FORTY
(Style one) HN495
Designer: H. Tittensor
Height: 8¼in., 21cm.
Issued: 1921–1938
Colour variation
Price: $768 £480

ONE OF THE FORTY
(Style one) HN501
Designer: H. Tittensor
Height: 8¼in., 21cm.
Issued: 1921–1938
Colour variation
Price: $768 £480

ONE OF THE FORTY
(Style one) HN648
Designer: H. Tittensor
Height: 8¼in., 21cm.
Issued: 1924–1938
Colour variation
Price: $768 £480

ONE OF THE FORTY
(Style one) HN528
Designer: H. Tittensor
Height: 8¼in., 21cm.
Issued: 1921–1938
Colour variation
Price: $768 £480

ONE OF THE FORTY
(Style one) HN1351
Designer: H. Tittensor
Height: 8¼in., 21cm.
Issued: 1920–1949
Colour variation
Price: $768 £480

ONE OF THE FORTY
(Style one) HN1352
Designer: H. Tittensor
Height: 8¼in., 21cm.
Issued: 1929–1949
Colour variation
Price: $768 £480

ONE OF THE FORTY
(Style two) HN418
Designer: H. Tittensor
Height: 7¼in., 18.4cm.
Issued: 1920–1938
Price: $768 £480

ONE OF THE FORTY
(Style two) HN498
Designer: H. Tittensor
Height: 7¼in., 18.4cm.
Issued: 1921–1938
Colour variation
Price: $768 £480

ONE OF THE FORTY
(Style two) HN647
Designer: H. Tittensor
Height: 7¹/₄in., 18.4cm.
Issued: 1924–1938
Colour variation
Price: $768 £480

ONE OF THE FORTY
(Style two) HN666
Designer: H. Tittensor
Height: 7¹/₄in., 18.4cm.
Issued: 1924–1938
Colour variation
Price: $768 £480

ONE OF THE FORTY
(Style two) HN704
Designer: H. Tittensor
Height: 7¹/₄in., 18.4cm.
Issued: 1925–1938
Colour variation
Price: $768 £480

ONE OF THE FORTY
(Style two) HN1353
Designer: H. Tittensor
Height: 7¹/₄in., 18.4cm.
Issued: 1929–1949
Colour variation
Price: $768 £480

ONE OF THE FORTY
(Style four) HN423A
Designer: H. Tittensor
Height: 3in., 7.6cm.
Issued: 1921–1938
Price: $400 £250

ONE OF THE FORTY
(Style five) HN423B
Designer: H. Tittensor
Height: 2³/₄in., 6.9cm.
Issued: 1921–1938
Price: $400 £250

ONE OF THE FORTY
(Style six) HN423C
Designer: H. Tittensor
Height: 2³/₄in., 6.9cm.
Issued: 1921–1938
Price: $400 £250

ONE OF THE FORTY
(Style seven) HN423D
Designer: H. Tittensor
Height: 2³/₄in., 6.9cm.
Issued: 1921–1938
Price: $400 £250

ONE OF THE FORTY
(Style eight) HN423E
Designer: H. Tittensor
Height: 3in., 7.6cm.
Issued: 1921–1938
Price: $400 £250

ONE OF THE FORTY
(Style nine) HN427
Designer: H. Tittensor
Height: Unknown
Issued: 1921–1938
Price: $768 £480

ONE OF THE FORTY
(Style thirteen) HN665

ONE OF THE FORTY
(Style eleven) HN483

ONE OF THE FORTY
(Style ten) HN480
Designer: H. Tittensor
Height: 7in., 17.8cm.
Issued: 1921–1938
Price: $768 £480

ONE OF THE FORTY
(Style ten) HN493
Designer: H. Tittensor
Height: 6³/₄in., 17.1cm.
Issued: 1921–1938
Price: $768 £480

ONE OF THE FORTY
(Style ten) HN499
Designer: H. Tittensor
Height: 6³/₄in., 17.1cm.
Issued: 1921–1938
Colour variation
Price: $768 £480

ONE OF THE FORTY
(Style ten) HN664
Designer: H. Tittensor
Height: 7³/₄in., 19.7cm.
Issued: 1924–1938
Colour variation
Price: $768 £480

ONE OF THE FORTY
(Style eleven) HN483
Designer: H. Tittensor
Height: Unknown
Issued: 1921–1938
Colour variation
Price: $768 £480

ONE OF THE FORTY
(Style thirteen) HN665
Designer: H. Tittensor
Height: 7³/₄in., 19.7cm.
Issued: 1924–1938
Colour variation
Price: $768 £480

ONE OF THE FORTY
(Style ten) HN714
Designer: H. Tittensor
Height: 6³/₄in., 17.1cm.
Issued: 1925–1938
Colour variation
Price: $768 £480

ONE OF THE FORTY
(Style eleven) HN481
Designer: H. Tittensor
Height: Unknown
Issued: 1921–1938
Price: $768 £480

ONE OF THE FORTY
(Style eleven) HN491
Designer: H. Tittensor
Height: Unknown
Issued: 1921–1938
Colour variation
Price: $768 £480

ONE OF THE FORTY
(Style eleven) HN646
Designer: H. Tittensor
Height: Unknown
Issued: 1924–1938
Colour variation
Price: $768 £480

ONE OF THE FORTY
(Style one) HN677
Designer: H. Tittensor
Height: 8¼in., 21cm.
Issued: 1924–1938
Colour variation
Price: $768 £480

ONE OF THE FORTY
(Style two) HN494
Designer: H. Tittensor
Height: 7¼in., 18.4cm.
Issued: 1921–1938
Colour variation
Price: $768 £480

ONE OF THE FORTY
(Style three) HN423
Designer: H. Tittensor
Height: 3in., 7.6cm.
Issued: 1921–1938
Price: $400 £250

ONE OF THE FORTY
(Style ten) HN497
Designer: H. Tittensor
Height: 6¾in., 17.1cm.
Issued: 1921–1938
Colour variation
Price: $768 £480

ONE OF THE FORTY
(Style eleven) HN667
Designer: H. Tittensor
Height: Unknown
Issued: 1924–1938
Colour variation
Price: $768 £480

ONE OF THE FORTY
(Style eleven) HN712
Designer: H. Tittensor
Height: Unknown
Issued: 1925–1938
Colour variation
Price: $768 £480

ONE OF THE FORTY
(Style eleven) HN1336
Designer: H. Tittensor
Height: Unknown
Issued: 1929–1938
Colour variation
Price: $768 £480

ONE OF THE FORTY
(Style eleven) HN1350
Designer: H. Tittensor
Height: Unknown
Issued: 1929–1949
Colour variation
Price: $768 £480

ONE OF THE FORTY
(Style twelve) HN482
Designer: H. Tittensor
Height: 6in., 15.2cm.
Issued: 1921–1938
Price: $768 £480

ONE OF THE FORTY
(Style twelve) HN484
Designer: H. Tittensor
Height: 6in., 15.2cm.
Issued: 1921–1938
Colour variation
Price: $768 £480

ONE OF THE FORTY
(Style three) HN423

ONE OF THE FORTY
(Style twelve) HN492

ONE OF THE FORTY
(Style ten) HN497

ONE OF THE FORTY
(Style one) HN677

ONE OF THE FORTY
(Style twelve) HN492
Designer: H. Tittensor
Height: 6in., 15.2cm.
Issued: 1921–1938
Colour variation
Price: $768 £480

ONE OF THE FORTY
(Style twelve) HN645
Designer: H. Tittensor
Height: 6in., 15.2cm.
Issued: 1924–1938
Colour variation
Price: $768 £480

ONE OF THE FORTY
(Style twelve) HN663
Designer: H. Tittensor
Height: 6in., 15.2cm.
Issued: 1924–1938
Colour variation
Price: $768 £480

ONE OF THE FORTY
(Style twelve) HN713
Designer: H. Tittensor
Height: 6in., 15.2cm.
Issued: 1925–1938
Colour variation
Price: $768 £480

ONE OF THE FORTY
(Style thirteen) HN496
Designer: H. Tittensor
Height: 7¾in., 19.7cm.
Issued: 1921–1938
Price: $768 £480

ONE OF THE FORTY
(Style thirteen) HN500
Designer: H. Tittensor
Height: 7¾in., 19.7cm.
Issued: 1921–1938
Colour variation
Price: $768 £480

ONE OF THE FORTY
(Style thirteen) HN649
Designer: H. Tittensor
Height: 7¾in., 19.7cm.
Issued: 1924–1938
Colour variation
Price: $768 £480

ONE OF THE FORTY
(Style thirteen) HN1354
Designer: H. Tittensor
Height: 7¾in., 19.7cm.
Issued: 1929–1949
Colour variation
Price: $768 £480

ONE THAT GOT AWAY
HN2153
Designer: P. Davies
Height: 6¼in., 15.9cm.
Issued: 1955–1959
Price: $290 £195

ORANGE LADY HN1759
Designer: L. Harradine
Height: 8¾in., 22.2cm.
Issued: 1936–1975
Price: $255 £170

FIGURES

ORANGE LADY HN1953
Designer: L. Harradine
Height: 8½in., 21.6cm.
Issued: 1940–1975
Colour variation
Price: $255 £170

ORANGE SELLER HN1325
Designer: L. Harradine
Height: 7in., 17.8cm.
Issued: 1929–1949
Price: $675 £450

ORANGE VENDOR HN72
Designer: C. J. Noke
Height: 6¼in., 15.8cm.
Issued: 1917–1938
Price: $720 £450

ORANGE VENDOR HN508
Designer: C. J. Noke
Height: 6¼in., 15.8cm.
Issued: 1921–1938
Price: $720 £450

ORANGE VENDOR HN521
Designer: C. J. Noke
Height: 6¼in., 15.8cm.
Issued: 1921–1938
Colour variation
Price: $720 £450

ORANGE VENDOR HN1966
Designer: C. J. Noke
Height: 6¼in., 15.8cm.
Issued: 1941–1949
Colour variation
Price: $450 £300

ORGAN GRINDER HN2173
Designer: M. Nicoll
Height: 8¾in., 22.2cm.
Issued: 1956–1965
Price: $525 £350

OUR FIRST CHRISTMAS HN3452
Designer: Pauline Parsons
Height: 11½in., 29cm.
Issued: 1993
Price: R.R.P.

OUT FOR A WALK HN86
Designer: H. Tittensor
Height: Unknown
Issued: 1918–1936
Price: $2025 £1350

OUT FOR A WALK HN443
Designer: H. Tittensor
Height: Unknown
Issued: 1921–1936
Price: $2025 £1350

OUT FOR A WALK HN748
Designer: H. Tittensor
Height: 10in., 25.4cm.
Issued: 1925–1936
Price: $2025 £1350

OVER THE THRESHOLD HN3274
Designer: R. Tabbenor
Height: 12in., 30.5cm.
Issued: 1989
Price: R.R.P.

ONE THAT GOT AWAY HN2153

ORANGE SELLER HN1325

ORANGE LADY HN1953

ORANGE VENDOR HN508

ORGAN GRINDER HN2173

215

OWD WILLUM HN2042
Designer: H. Tittensor
Height: 6³/₄in., 17.2cm.
Issued: 1949–1973
Price: $290 £195

P

PAINTING HN3012
Designer: P. Parsons
Height: 6in., 15cm.
Issued: 1988 in a limited
edition of 750
Price: $750 £500

PAISLEY SHAWL (Style one) HN1392
Designer: L. Harradine
Height: 8¹/₄in., 21cm.
Issued: 1930–1949
Price: $330 £220

PAISLEY SHAWL (Style one) HN1460
Designer: L. Harradine
Height: 8¹/₄in., 21cm.
Issued: 1931–1949
Colour variation
Price: $340 £225

PAISLEY SHAWL (Style one) HN1707
Designer: L. Harradine
Height: 8¹/₄in., 21cm.
Issued: 1935–1949
Colour variation
Price: $340 £275

PAISLEY SHAWL (Style one) HN1739
Designer: L. Harradine
Height: 8¹/₄in., 21cm.
Issued: 1935–1949
Colour variation
Price: $375 £250

PAISLEY SHAWL (Style one) HN1987
Designer: L. Harradine
Height: 8¹/₄in., 21cm.
Issued: 1946–1949
Colour variation
Price: $300 £200

PAISLEY SHAWL (Style two) HN1914
Designer: L. Harradine
Height: 6¹/₄in., 16.5cm.
Issued: 1939–1949
Price: $240 £160

PAISLEY SHAWL (Style two) HN1988
Designer: L. Harradine
Height: 6¹/₄in., 15.9cm.
Issued: 1946–1975
Colour variation
Price: $300 £200

PAISLEY SHAWL M3
Designer: L. Harradine
Height: 4in., 10.1cm.
Issued: 1932–1938
Price: $300 £200

OWD WILLUM HN2042

PAISLEY SHAWL (Style two) HN1988

PAINTING HN3012

PAISLEY SHAWL M4
Designer: L. Harradine
Height: 4in., 10.1cm.
Issued: 1932–1945
        Colour variation
Price: $300 £200

PAISLEY SHAWL M26
Designer: L. Harradine
Height: 3³/₄in., 9.5cm.
Issued: 1932–1945
        Colour variation
Price: $300 £200

PALIO HN2428
Designer: P. Davies
Height: 17¹/₂in., 44.5cm.
Issued: 1971 in a limited
        edition of 500
Price: $4500 £3000

PAMELA HN1468
Designer: L. Harradine
Height: 7¹/₂in., 19.1cm.
Issued: 1931–1938
Price: $600 £400

PAMELA HN1469
Designer: L. Harradine
Height: 7¹/₂in., 19.1cm.
Issued: 1931–1938
        Colour variation
Price: $450 £300

PAMELA HN1564
Designer: L. Harradine
Height: 8in., 20.3cm.
Issued: 1933–1938
        Colour variation
Price: $600 £400

PAMELA HN3223
Designer: P. Davies
Height: 7in., 18cm.
Issued: 1989
Price: $180 £120

PAMELA HN2479
Designer: P. Davies
Height: 7in., 17.5cm.
Issued: 1986
Price: R.R.P.

PAN ON ROCK HN621
Designer: Unknown
Height: 5³/₄in., 13.3cm.
Issued: 1924–1938
Price: $1500 £1000

PAN ON ROCK HN622
Designer: Unknown
Height: 5³/₄in., 13.3cm.
Issued: 1924–1938
Price: $1500 £1000

PANORAMA HN3028
Designer: R. Jefferson
Height: 12¹/₄in., 31cm.
Issued: 1987–1989
Price: $150 £100

PANTALETTES HN1362
Designer: L. Harradine
Height: 7³/₄in., 19.7cm.
Issued: 1929–1938
Price: $420 £275

PAMELA HN1469

PANTALETTES HN1362

PARISIAN HN2445

PANTALETTES HN1412
Designer: L. Harradine
Height: 7³/₄in., 19.7cm.
Issued: 1930–1949
        Colour variation
Price: $450 £300

PANTALETTES HN1507
Designer: L. Harradine
Height: 7³/₄in., 19.7cm.
Issued: 1932–1949
        Colour variation
Price: $450 £300

PANTALETTES HN1709
Designer: L. Harradine
Height: 8in., 20.3cm.
Issued: 1935–1938
        Colour variation
Price: $450 £300

PANTALETTES M15
Designer: L. Harradine
Height: 3³/₄in., 9.5cm.
Issued: 1932–1945
Price: $340 £225

PANTALETTES M16
Designer: L. Harradine
Height: 3³/₄in., 9.5cm.
Issued: 1932–1945
        Colour variation
Price: $340 £225

PANTALETTES M31
Designer: L. Harradine
Height: 4in., 10.1cm.
Issued: 1932–1945
        Colour variation
Price: $340 £225

PARADISE HN3074
Designer: A. Hughes
Height: 13¹/₂in., 34.5cm.
Issued: 1985–1992
Price: $150 £100

PARISIAN HN2445
Designer: M. Nicoll
Height: 8in., 20.3cm.
Issued: 1972–1975
Price: $220 £145

PARK PARADE HN3116
Designer: A. Maslankowski
Height: 11³/₄in., 30cm.
Issued: 1987
Price: R.R.P.

PARSON'S DAUGHTER HN337
Designer: H. Tittensor
Height: 10in., 25.4cm.
Issued: 1919–1938
Price: $525 £350

PARSON'S DAUGHTER HN338
Designer: H. Tittensor
Height: 10in., 25.4cm.
Issued: 1919–1938
        Colour variation
Price: $525 £350

PARSON'S DAUGHTER
HN441
Designer: H. Tittensor
Height: 10in., 25.4cm.
Issued: 1921–1938
        Colour variation
Price: $525 £350

PARSON'S DAUGHTER
HN564
Designer: H. Tittensor
Height: 9¹/₂in., 24.1cm.
Issued: 1923–1949
        Colour variation
Price: $300 £200

PARSON'S DAUGHTER
HN790
Designer: H. Tittensor
Height: 10in., 25.4cm.
Issued: 1926–1938
        Colour variation
Price: $375 £250

PARSON'S DAUGHTER
HN1242
Designer: H. Tittensor
Height: 10in., 25.4cm.
Issued: 1927–1938
        Colour variation
Price: $525 £350

PARSON'S DAUGHTER
HN1356
Designer: H. Tittensor
Height: 9¹/₄in., 23.5cm.
Issued: 1929–1938
        Colour variation
Price: $375 £250

PARSON'S DAUGHTER
HN2018
Designer: H. Tittensor
Height: 9³/₄in., 24.7cm.
Issued: 1949–1953
        Colour variation
Price: $340 £225

PARTNERS HN3119
Designer: A. Maslankowski
Height: 6³/₄in., 17.2cm.
Issued: 1990–1992
Price: $200 £135

PAST GLORY HN2484
Designer: M. Nicoll
Height: 7¹/₂in., 19.1cm.
Issued: 1973–1978
Price: $420 £275

PATCHWORK QUILT HN1984
Designer: L. Harradine
Height: 6in., 15.2cm.
Issued: 1945–1959
Price: $375 £250

PATIENCE HN3533
Designer: Peter Gee
Height: 12¹/₄in., 31cm.
Issued: 1987
Price: R.R.P.

PARSON'S DAUGHTER
HN441

PARTNERS HN3119

PATRICIA HN1414
Designer: L. Harradine
Height: 8¹/₂in., 21.6cm.
Issued: 1930–1949
Price: $375 £250

PATRICIA HN1431
Designer: L. Harradine
Height: 8¹/₂in., 21.6cm.
Issued: 1930–1949
        Colour variation
Price: $375 £250

PATRICIA HN1462
Designer: L. Harradine
Height: 8in., 20.3cm.
Issued: 1931–1938
        Colour variation
Price: $450 £300

PATRICIA HN1567
Designer: L. Harradine
Height: 8¹/₂in., 21.6cm.
Issued: 1933–1949
        Colour variation
Price: $450 £300

PATRICIA M7
Designer: L. Harradine
Height: 4in., 10.1cm.
Issued: 1932–1945
Price: $330 £220

PATRICIA M8
Designer: L. Harradine
Height: 4in., 10.1cm.
Issued: 1932–1938
        Colour variation
Price: $330 £220

PATRICIA M28
Designer: L. Harradine
Height: 4in., 10.1cm.
Issued: 1932–1945
        Colour variation
Price: $330 £220

PATRICIA HN2715
Designer: E. Griffiths
Height: 7¹/₂in., 19cm.
Issued: 1982–1985
Price: $240 £160

PATRICIA HN3365
Designer: Valerie Annand
Height: 8¹/₂in., 21.5cm.
Issued: 1993
Price: R.R.P.

PAULA HN2906
Designer: P. Parsons
Height: 7in., 17.8cm.
Issued: 1980–1986
Price: $200 £135

PAULA HN3234
Designer: Pauline Parsons
Height: 7¹/₂in., 19cm.
Issued: 1990
Price: R.R.P.

PAULINE HN1444
Designer: L. Harradine
Height: 6in., 15.2cm.
Issued: 1931–1938
Price: $340 £225

PAULINE HN2441
Designer: P. Davies
Height: 5in., 12.5cm.
Issued: 1984–1989
Price: $260 £175

PAULINE HN3643
Designer: Nada Pedley
Height: Unknown
Issued: 1994 special
commission
Price: R.R.P.

PAVLOVA HN487
Designer: C. J. Noke
Height: 4¼in., 10.8cm.
Issued: 1921–1938
Price: $3750 £2500

PAVLOVA HN676
Designer: Unknown
Height: 4¼in., 10.8cm.
Issued: 1924–1938
Colour variation
Price: $3750 £2500

PEACE HN2433 (Black)
Designer: P. Davies
Height: 8in., 20.3cm.
Issued: 1981
Price: R.R.P.

PEACE HN2470 (White)
Designer: P. Davies
Height: 8in., 20.3cm.
Issued: 1981
Price: R.R.P.

PEARLY BOY (Style one) HN1482
Designer: W. K. Harper
Height: 5½in., 14cm.
Issued: 1931–1949
Price: $260 £175

PEARLY BOY (Style one) HN1547
Designer: W. K. Harper
Height: 5½in., 14cm.
Issued: 1933–1949
Colour variation
Price: $260 £175

PEARLY BOY (Style two) HN2035
Designer: W. K. Harper
Height: 5½in., 14cm.
Issued: 1949–1959
Price: $225 £150

PEARLY BOY HN2767
Designer: W. K. Harper
Height: 8in., 20.3cm.
Issued: 1989–1992
Price: $190 £125

PEARLY GIRL (Style one) HN1483
Designer: W. K. Harper
Height: 5½in., 14cm.
Issued: 1931–1949
Price: $260 £175

PAULA HN3234

PATRICIA HN3365

PAULA HN2906

PAST GLORY HN2484

PATRICIA HN1567

PEARLY GIRL (Style one)
HN1548
Designer: W. K. Harper
Height: 5¹/₂in., 14cm.
Issued: 1933–1949
Colour variation
Price: $260 £175

PEARLY GIRL (Style two)
HN2036
Designer: W. K. Harper
Height: 5¹/₂in., 14cm.
Issued: 1949–1959
Price: $260 £175

PEARLY GIRL HN2769
Designer: W. K. Harper
Height: 8in., 20.3cm.
Issued: 1989–1992
Price: $190 £125

PECKSNIFF (Style one) HN535
Designer: L. Harradine
Height: 3³/₄in., 9.5cm.
Issued: 1922–1932
Price: $70 £45

PECKSNIFF (Style two) HN553
Designer: L. Harradine
Height: 7in., 17.8cm.
Issued: 1923–1939
Price: $300 £200

PECKSNIFF (Style two)
HN1891
Designer: L. Harradine
Height: 7in., 17.8cm.
Issued: 1938–1952
Price: $300 £200

PECKSNIFF (Style three)
HN2098
Designer: L. Harradine
Height: 7¹/₄in., 18.4cm.
Issued: 1952–1967
Price: $270 £180

PECKSNIFF, MR M43
Designer: L. Harradine
Height: 4¹/₄in., 10.8cm.
Issued: 1932–1982
Price: $60 £40

PEDLAR WOLF HN7
Designer: C. J. Noke
Height: 5¹/₂in., 14cm.
Issued: 1913–1938
Price: $2250 £1500

PEEK-A-BOO HN3363
Designer: Valerie Annand
Height: 2¹/₂in., 6.4cm.
Issued: 1992
Price: R.R.P.

PEGGY HN1941
Designer: L. Harradine
Height: 5in., 12.7cm.
Issued: 1940–1949
Price: $190 £125

PEGGY HN2038
Designer: L. Harradine
Height: 5in., 12.7cm.
Issued: 1949–1978
Price: $165 £110

PERFECT PAIR HN581

PEEK-A-BOO HN3363

PENSIVE MOMENTS HN2704

PENELOPE HN1901
Designer: L. Harradine
Height: 7in., 17.8cm.
Issued: 1939–1975
Price: $370 £245

PENELOPE HN1902
Designer: L. Harradine
Height: 7in., 17.8cm.
Issued: 1939–1949
Colour variation
Price: $450 £300

PENNY HN2338
Designer: P. Davies
Height: 4³/₄in., 12cm.
Issued: 1968–
Price: R.R.P.

PENNY HN2424
Designer: P. Davies
Height: 4³/₄in., 12cm.
Issued: 1983–1992
Price: $75 £50

PENSIVE HN3109
Designer: R. Jefferson
Height: 13in., 33cm.
Issued: 1987–1989
Price: $135 £90

PENSIVE MOMENTS HN2704
Designer: P. Davies
Height: 5in., 12.7cm.
Issued: 1975–1982
Price: $225 £150

PERFECT PAIR HN581
Designer: L. Harradine
Height: 6³/₄in., 17.2cm.
Issued: 1923–1938
Price: $720 £450

PHILIPPA OF HAINAULT
HN2008
Designer: P. Davies
Height: 9³/₄in., 24.7cm.
Issued: 1948–1953
Price: $560 £350

PHILIPPINE DANCER HN2439
Designer: P. Davies
Height: 9¹/₂in., 24.1cm.
Issued: 1978 in a limited
edition of 750
Price: $520 £325

PHYLLIS HN1420
Designer: L. Harradine
Height: 9in., 22.9cm.
Issued: 1930–1949
Price: $450 £300

PHYLLIS HN1430
Designer: L. Harradine
Height: 9in., 22.9cm.
Issued: 1930–1938
Colour variation
Price: $450 £300

PHYLLIS HN1486
Designer: L. Harradine
Height: 9in., 22.9cm.
Issued: 1931–1949
Colour variation
Price: $450 £300

PHYLLIS HN1698
Designer: L. Harradine
Height: 9in., 22.9cm.
Issued: 1935–1949
Colour variation
Price: $450 £300

PHYLLIS HN3180
Designer: D. Tootle
Height: 7¼in., 18.5cm.
Issued: 1988–1991
Price: $180 £120

PICARDY PEASANT (Man) HN13
Designer: P. Stabler
Height: 9in., 22.9cm.
Issued: 1913–1938
Price: $1500 £1000

PICARDY PEASANT (Man) HN17
Designer: P. Stabler
Height: 9½in., 24cm.
Issued: 1913–1938
Colour variation
Price: $1500 £1000

PICARDY PEASANT (Man) HN19
Designer: P. Stabler
Height: 9½in., 24cm.
Issued: 1913–1938
Colour variation
Price: $1500 £1000

PICARDY PEASANT (Woman) HN4
Designer: P. Stabler
Height: 9¼in., 23.5cm.
Issued: 1913–1938
Price: $800 £500

PICARDY PEASANT (Woman) HN5
Designer: P. Stabler
Height: 9¼in., 23.5cm.
Issued: 1913–1938
Colour variation
Price: $1200 £800

PICARDY PEASANT (Woman) HN17A
Designer: P. Stabler
Height: 9½in., 24cm.
Issued: 1913–1938
Colour variation
Price: $1275 £850

PICARDY PEASANT (Woman) HN351
Designer: P. Stabler
Height: 9½in., 24cm.
Issued: 1919–1938
Colour variation
Price: $975 £650

PICARDY PEASANT (Woman) HN513
Designer: P. Stabler
Height: 9½in., 24cm.
Issued: 1921–1938
Colour variation
Price: $1500 £1000

PICNIC HN2308
Designer: P. Davies
Height: 3¾in., 9.5cm.
Issued: 1965–1988
Price: $165 £110

PHILIPPINE DANCER HN2439

PHILIPPA OF HAINAULT HN2008

PHYLLIS HN1420

PICNIC HN2308

FIGURES

PIED PIPER HN1215
Designer: L. Harradine
Height: 8¼in., 21cm.
Issued: 1926–1938
Price: $750 £500

PIED PIPER HN2102
Designer: L. Harradine
Height: 8½in., 21.6cm.
Issued: 1953–1976
Colour variation
Price: $300 £200

PIERRETTE (Style one) HN642
Designer: L. Harradine
Height: 7¼in., 18.4cm.
Issued: 1924–1938
Price: $900 £600

PIERRETTE (Style one) HN643
Designer: L. Harradine
Height: 7¼in., 18.4cm.
Issued: 1924–1938
Colour variation
Price: $900 £600

PIERRETTE (Style one) HN644
Designer: L. Harradine
Height: 7¼in., 18.4cm.
Issued: 1924–1938
Colour variation
Price: $600 £400

PIERRETTE (Style one) HN691
Designer: L. Harradine
Height: 7¼in., 18.4cm.
Issued: 1925–1938
Colour variation
Price: $720 £450

PIERRETTE (Style one) HN721
Designer: L. Harradine
Height: 7¼in., 18.4cm.
Issued: 1925–1938
Colour variation
Price: $900 £600

PIERRETTE (Style one) HN731
Designer: L. Harradine
Height: 7¼in., 18.4cm.
Issued: 1925–1938
Colour variation
Price: $900 £600

PIERRETTE (Style one) HN732
Designer: L. Harradine
Height: 7¼in., 18.4cm.
Issued: 1925–1938
Colour variation
Price: $900 £600

PIERRETTE (Style one) HN784
Designer: L. Harradine
Height: 7¼in., 18.4cm.
Issued: 1926–1938
Colour variation
Price: $900 £600

PIERRETTE (Style two) HN795
Designer: L. Harradine
Height: 3½in., 8.9cm.
Issued: 1926–1938
Price: $900 £600

PIED PIPER HN1215

PIERRETTE (Style one) HN643

PIERRETTE (Style three)
HN1391

PIERRETTE (Style one) HN644

FIGURES

PIERRETTE (Style two) HN796
Designer: L. Harradine
Height: 3½in., 8.9cm.
Issued: 1926–1938
Price: $825 £550

PIERRETTE (Style three)
HN1391
Designer: L. Harradine
Height: 8½in., 21.6cm.
Issued: 1930–1938
Price: $900 £600

PIERRETTE (Style three)
HN1749
Designer: L. Harradine
Height: 8½in., 21.6cm.
Issued: 1936–1949
Colour variation
Price: $750 £500

PILLOW FIGHT HN2270
Designer: P. Davies
Height: 5in., 12.7cm.
Issued: 1965–1969
Price: $225 £170

PINKIE HN1552
Designer: L. Harradine
Height: 5in., 12.7cm.
Issued: 1933–1938
Price: $525 £350

PINKIE HN1553
Designer: L. Harradine
Height: 5in., 12.7cm.
Issued: 1933–1938
Colour variation
Price: $525 £350

PIPER HN2907
Designer: M. Abberley
Height: 8in., 20.3cm.
Issued: 1980–1992
Price: $250 £165

PIPER HN3444
Designer: Peter Gee
Height: 10in., 25.5cm.
Issued: 1993
Price: R.R.P.

PIRATE KING HN2901
Designer: W. K. Harper
Height: 10in., 25.4cm.
Issued: 1981–1986
Price: $450 £300

PIROUETTE HN2216
Designer: P. Davies
Height: 5¾in., 14.6cm.
Issued: 1959–1967
Price: $250 £165

PLAYFUL HN3534
Designer: Adrian Hughes
Height: 7½in., 19.5cm.
Issued: 1987
Price: R.R.P.

PLAYMATES HN3127
Designer: P. Parsons
Height: 8½in., 22cm.
Issued: 1988–1992
Price: $135 £90

PIERRETTE (Style three)
HN1749

PIPER HN2907

PIPER HN3444

PIRATE KING HN2901

PIROUETTE HN2216

223

FIGURES

PLEASE KEEP STILL HN2967
Designer: P. Parsons
Height: 4¹/₂in., 11.5cm.
Issued: 1982–1985
Price: $190 £125

POACHER HN2043
Designer: L. Harradine
Height: 6in., 15.2cm.
Issued: 1949–1959
Price: $290 £195

POCAHONTAS HN2930
(Ship's figurehead)
Designer: S. Keenan
Height: 8in., 20.3cm.
Issued: 1982 in a limited
edition of 950
Price: $450 £300

POKE BONNET HN362
Designer: C. J. Noke
Height: 8³/₄in., 22.2cm.
Issued: 1919–1938
Price: $900 £600

POKE BONNET HN612
Designer: C. J. Noke
Height: 9¹/₂in., 24.1cm.
Issued: 1924–1938
Colour variation
Price: $900 £600

POKE BONNET HN765
Designer: C. J. Noke
Height: 8³/₄in., 22.2cm.
Issued: 1925–1938
Colour variation
Price: $900 £600
Also called 'In Grandma's Days'
and Lilac Shawl

POLISH DANCER HN2836
Designer: P. Davies
Height: 9¹/₂in., 24.1cm.
Issued: 1980 in a limited
edition of 750
Price: $520 £325

POLKA HN2156
Designer: P. Davies
Height: 7¹/₂in., 19.1cm.
Issued: 1955–1969
Price: $290 £195

POLLY HN3178
Designer: D. Tootle
Height: 8¹/₄in., 21cm.
Issued: 1988
Price: $180 £120

POLLY PEACHUM M23
Designer: L. Harradine
Height: 2¹/₄in., 5.7cm.
Issued: 1932–1938
Colour variation
Price: $300 £200

**POLLY PEACHUM (Style one)
HN463**
Designer: L. Harradine
Height: 6¹/₄in., 15.9cm.
Issued: 1921–1949
Price: $450 £300

POACHER HN2043

**POLISH
DANCER HN2836**

**POLLY PEACHUM (Style one)
HN550**

**POLLY PEACHUM (Style one)
HN465**
Designer: L. Harradine
Height: 6¹/₂in., 16.5cm.
Issued: 1921–1949
Colour variation
Price: $450 £300

**POLLY PEACHUM (Style one)
HN550**
Designer: L. Harradine
Height: 6¹/₂in., 16.5cm.
Issued: 1922–1949
Colour variation
Price: $450 £300

**POLLY PEACHUM (Style one)
HN589**
Designer: L. Harradine
Height: 6¹/₂in., 16.5cm.
Issued: 1924–1949
Colour variation
Price: $450 £300

**POLLY PEACHUM (Style one)
HN614**
Designer: L. Harradine
Height: 6¹/₂in., 16.5cm.
Issued: 1924–1949
Colour variation
Price: $420 £275

**POLLY PEACHUM (Style one)
HN680**
Designer: L. Harradine
Height: 6¹/₂in., 16.5cm.
Issued: 1924–1949
Colour variation
Price: $450 £300

**POLLY PEACHUM (Style one)
HN693**
Designer: L. Harradine
Height: 6¹/₂in., 16.5cm.
Issued: 1925–1949
Colour variation
Price: $420 £275

**POLLY PEACHUM (Style two)
HN489**
Designer: L. Harradine
Height: 4¹/₄in., 10.8cm.
Issued: 1921–1938
Price: $420 £275

**POLLY PEACHUM (Style two)
HN549**
Designer: L. Harradine
Height: 4¹/₄in., 10.8cm.
Issued: 1922–1949
Colour variation
Price: $450 £300

**POLLY PEACHUM (Style two)
HN620**
Designer: L. Harradine
Height: 4¹/₄in., 10.8cm.
Issued: 1924–1938
Colour variation
Price: $420 £275

**POLLY PEACHUM (Style two)
HN694**
Designer: L. Harradine
Height: 4¹/₄in., 10.8cm.
Issued: 1925–1949
Colour variation
Price: $525 £350

POLLY PEACHUM (Style two)
HN734
Designer: L. Harradine
Height: 4¹/₄in., 10.8cm.
Issued: 1925–1949
     Colour variation
Price: $525 £350

POLLY PEACHUM
(Style three) HN698
Designer: L. Harradine
Height: 2¹/₄in., 5.7cm.
Issued: 1925–1949
Price: $525 £350

POLLY PEACHUM
(Style three) HN699
Designer: L. Harradine
Height: 2¹/₄in., 5.7cm.
Issued: 1925–1949
     Colour variation
Price: $290 £195

POLLY PEACHUM
(Style three) HN757
Designer: L. Harradine
Height: 2¹/₄in., 5.7cm.
Issued: 1925–1949
     Colour variation
Price: $525 £350

POLLY PEACHUM
(Style three) HN758
Designer: L. Harradine
Height: 2¹/₄in., 5.7cm.
Issued: 1925–1949
     Colour variation
Price: $525 £350

POLLY PEACHUM
(Style three) HN759
Designer: L. Harradine
Height: 2¹/₄in., 5.7cm.
Issued: 1925–1949
     Colour variation
Price: $525 £350

POLLY PEACHUM
(Style three) HN760
Designer: L. Harradine
Height: 2¹/₄in., 5.7cm.
Issued: 1925–1949
     Colour variation
Price: $525 £350

POLLY PEACHUM
(Style three) HN761
Designer: L. Harradine
Height: 2¹/₄in., 5.7cm.
Issued: 1925–1949
     Colour variation
Price: $525 £350

POLLY PEACHUM
(Style three) HN762
Designer: L. Harradine
Height: 2¹/₄in., 5.7cm.
Issued: 1925–1949
     Colour variation
Price: $525 £350

POLLY PEACHUM M21
Designer: L. Harradine
Height: 2¹/₄in., 5.7cm.
Issued: 1932–1945
Price: $330 £220

POLLYANNA HN2965

POPE JOHN PAUL II HN2888

POLLY PEACHUM M22
Designer: L. Harradine
Height: 2¹/₄in., 5.7cm.
Issued: 1932–1938
     Colour variation
Price: $420 £275

POLLY PUT THE KETTLE ON
HN3021
Designer: P. Parsons
Height: 8in., 20cm.
Issued: 1984–1987
Price: $165 £110

POLLYANNA HN2965
Designer: P. Parsons
Height: 6³/₄in., 17cm.
Issued: 1982–1985
Price: $165 £110

POPE JOHN PAUL II HN2888
Designer: E. Griffiths
Height: 10in., 25.4cm.
Issued: 1982–1992
Price: $165 £110

POSY FOR YOU, A, HN3606
Designer: Nada Pedley
Height: 4³/₄in., 12cm.
Issued: 1994
Price: R.R.P.

POTTER HN1493
Designer: C. J. Noke
Height: 7in., 17.8cm.
Issued: 1932–
Price: $340 £225

POTTER HN1518
Designer: C. J. Noke
Height: 6³/₄in., 17.2cm.
Issued: 1932–1949
     Colour variation
Price: $450 £300

POTTER HN1522
Designer: C. J. Noke
Height: 6³/₄in., 17.2cm.
Issued: 1932–1949
     Colour variation
Price: $525 £350

PREMIERE HN2343
Designer: P. Davies
Height: 7¹/₂in., 19.1cm.
Issued: 1969–1978
Price: $240 £160

PRETTY LADY HN69
Designer: H. Tittensor
Height: 9¹/₂in., 24.1cm.
Issued: 1916–1938
Price: $900 £600

PRETTY LADY HN70
Designer: H. Tittensor
Height: 9¹/₂in., 24.1cm.
Issued: 1916–1938
     Colour variation
Price: $525 £350

PRETTY LADY HN302
Designer: H. Tittensor
Height: 9¹/₂in., 24.1cm.
Issued: 1918–1938
     Colour variation
Price: $720 £450

PRETTY LADY HN330
Designer: H. Tittensor
Height: 9¹/₂in., 24.1cm.
Issued: 1918–1938
Colour variation
Price: $720 £450

PRETTY LADY HN361
Designer: H. Tittensor
Height: 9¹/₂in., 24.1cm.
Issued: 1919–1938
Colour variation
Price: $720 £450

PRETTY LADY HN384
Designer: H. Tittensor
Height: 9¹/₂in., 24.1cm.
Issued: 1920–1938
Colour variation
Price: $720 £450

PRETTY LADY HN565
Designer: H. Tittensor
Height: 10in., 25.4cm.
Issued: 1923–1938
Colour variation
Price: $720 £450

PRETTY LADY HN700
Designer: H. Tittensor
Height: 9¹/₂in., 24.1cm.
Issued: 1925–1938
Colour variation
Price: $720 £450

PRETTY LADY HN763
Designer: H. Tittensor
Height: 9¹/₂in., 24.1cm.
Issued: 1925–1938
Colour variation
Price: $720 £450

PRETTY LADY HN783
Designer: H. Tittensor
Height: 9¹/₂in., 24.1cm.
Issued: 1926–1938
Colour variation
Price: $720 £450

PRETTY POLLY HN2768
Designer: W. K. Harper
Height: 6in., 15cm.
Issued: 1984–1988
Price: $250 £165

PRIDE AND JOY HN2945
Designer: R. Tabbenor
Height: 7in., 17.8cm.
Issued: 1984
Price: $370 £245

PRIMROSES HN1617
Designer: L. Harradine
Height: 6¹/₂in., 16.5cm.
Issued: 1934–1949
Price: $525 £350

PRINCE OF WALES HN1217
Designer: L. Harradine
Height: 7¹/₂in., 19.1cm.
Issued: 1926–1938
Price: $1050 £700

PRINCE OF WALES HN2883
Designer: E. Griffiths
Height: 8in., 20.3cm.
Issued: 1981 in a limited
edition of 1500
Price: $450 £300

PRETTY POLLY HN2768

PRINCE OF WALES HN2884

PRIDE AND JOY HN2945

PRINCE OF WALES HN2884
Designer: E. Griffiths
Height: 8in., 20.3cm.
Issued: 1981 in a limited
edition of 1500
Price: $720 £450

PRINCESS HN391
Designer: Unknown
Height: 9¼in., 23.5cm.
Issued: 1920–1938
Price: $2250 £1500

PRINCESS HN392
Designer: Unknown
Height: 9¼in., 23.5cm.
Issued: 1920–1938
Colour variation
Price: $2250 £1500

PRINCESS HN420
Designer: Unknown
Height: 9¼in., 23.5cm.
Issued: 1920–1938
Colour variation
Price: $2250 £1500

PRINCESS HN430
Designer: Unknown
Height: 9¼in., 23.5cm.
Issued: 1921–1938
Colour variation
Price: $2250 £1500

PRINCESS HN431
Designer: Unknown
Height: 9¼in., 23.5cm.
Issued: 1921–1938
Colour variation
Price: $2250 £1500

PRINCESS HN633
Designer: Unknown
Height: 9¼in., 23.5cm.
Issued: 1924–1938
Colour variation
Price: $2250 £1500

PRINCESS BADOURA HN2081
Designer: H. Tittensor, H. E.
Stanton and F. Van
Allen Phillips
Height: 20in., 50.8cm.
Issued: 1952–
Price: R.R.P.

**PRINCESS OF WALES
HN2887**
Designer: E Griffiths
Height: 7¾in., 19.6cm.
Issued: 1982 in a limited
edition of 1500
Price: $825 £550

PRINTEMPS HN3066
Designer: R. Jefferson
Height: 11½in., 29cm.
Issued: 1987 in a limited
edition of 300
Price: $800 £500

PRISCILLA HN1340
Designer: L. Harradine
Height: 8in., 20.3cm.
Issued: 1929–1949
Colour variation
Price: $260 £175

PRISCILLA HN1340

PRINCE OF WALES HN2883

PRINCESS OF WALES
HN2887

227

PRISCILLA HN1337
Designer: L. Harradine
Height: 8in., 20.3cm.
Issued: 1929–1938
Price: $375 £250

PRISCILLA HN1495
Designer: L. Harradine
Height: 8in., 20.3cm.
Issued: 1932–1949
Colour variation
Price: $375 £250

PRISCILLA HN1501
Designer: L. Harradine
Height: 8in., 20.3cm.
Issued: 1932–1938
Colour variation
Price: $375 £250

PRISCILLA HN1559
Designer: L. Harradine
Height: 8in., 20.3cm.
Issued: 1933–1949
Colour variation
Price: $375 £250

PRISCILLA M13
Designer: L. Harradine
Height: 4in., 10.1cm.
Issued: 1932–1938
Price: $300 £200

PRISCILLA M14
Designer: L. Harradine
Height: 3³/₄in., 9.5cm.
Issued: 1932–1945
Colour variation
Price: $300 £200

PRISCILLA M24
Designer: L. Harradine
Height: 3³/₄in., 9.5cm.
Issued: 1932–1945
Colour variation
Price: $300 £200

PRIVATE, CONNECTICUT
REGIMENT 1777 HN2845
Designer: E. J. Griffiths
Height: 11¹/₄in., 28.5cm.
Issued: 1978 in a limited
edition of 350
Price: $825 £550

PRIVATE, DELAWARE
REGIMENT 1776 HN2761
Designer: E. J. Griffiths
Height: 12in., 30.5cm.
Issued: 1977 in a limited
edition of 350
Price: $825 £550

PRIVATE, 1ST GEORGIA
REGIMENT 1777 HN2779
Designer: E. J. Griffiths
Height: 11in., 27.9cm.
Issued: 1975 in a limited
edition of 350
Price: $825 £550

PRIVATE, MASSACHUSETTS
REGIMENT 1778 HN2760
Designer: E. J. Griffiths
Height: 12¹/₂in., 31.7cm.
Issued: 1977 in a limited
edition of 350
Price: $825 £550

PRIZED POSSESSIONS
HN2942

PROFESSOR HN2281

PRIVATE, PENNSYLVANIA
RIFLE BATTALION 1776
HN2846
Designer: E. J. Griffiths
Height: 11¹/₄in., 28.5cm.
Issued: 1978 in a limited
edition of 350
Price: $825 £550

PRIVATE, RHODE ISLAND
REGIMENT 1781 HN2759
Designer: E. J. Griffiths
Height: 11³/₄in., 29.8cm.
Issued: 1977 in a limited
edition of 350
Price: $825 £550

PRIVATE, 2ND SOUTH
CAROLINA REGIMENT 1781
HN2717
Designer: E. J. Griffiths
Height: 11¹/₂in., 29.2cm.
Issued: 1975 in a limited
edition of 350
Price: $825 £550

PRIVATE, 3RD NORTH
CAROLINA REGIMENT 1778
HN2754
Designer: E. J. Griffiths
Height: 11in., 27.9cm.
Issued: 1976 in a limited
edition of 350
Price: $825 £550

PRIZED POSSESSIONS
HN2942
Designer: R. Tabbenor
Height: 7in., 17.8cm.
Issued: 1982
Price: $525 £350

PROFESSOR HN2281
Designer: M. Nicoll
Height: 7¹/₄in., 18.4cm.
Issued: 1965–1980
Price: $250 £165

PROMENADE HN2076
Designer: P. Davies
Height: 8in., 20.3cm.
Issued: 1951–1953
Price: $1500 £1000

PROMENADE HN3072
Designer: A. Hughes
Height: 13in., 33cm.
Issued: 1987
Price: R.R.P.

PROPOSAL (Man) HN725
Designer: Unknown
Height: 5¹/₂in., 14cm.
Issued: 1925–1938
Price: $720 £450

PROPOSAL (Man) HN1209
Designer: Unknown
Height: 5¹/₂in., 14cm.
Issued: 1926–1938
Colour variation
Price: $720 £450

PROPOSAL (Woman) HN715
Designer: Unknown
Height: 5³/₄in., 14.6cm.
Issued: 1925–1938
Price: $720 £450

PROPOSAL (Woman) HN716
Designer: Unknown
Height: 5³/₄in., 14.6cm.
Issued: 1925–1938
　　　　Colour variation
Price: $720 £450

PROPOSAL (Woman) HN788
Designer: Unknown
Height: 5³/₄in., 14.6cm.
Issued: 1926–1938
　　　　Colour variation
Price: $720 £450

PRUDENCE HN1883
Designer: L. Harradine
Height: 6³/₄in., 17.2cm.
Issued: 1938–1949
Price: $450 £300

PRUDENCE HN1884
Designer: L. Harradine
Height: 6³/₄in., 17.2cm.
Issued: 1938–1949
　　　　Colour variation
Price: $450 £300

PRUE HN1996
Designer: L. Harradine
Height: 6³/₄in., 17.2cm.
Issued: 1947–1955
Price: $410 £275

PUFF AND POWDER HN397
Designer: L. Harradine
Height: 6¹/₂in., 16.4cm.
Issued: 1920–1938
Price: $1875 £1250

PUFF AND POWDER HN398
Designer: L. Harradine
Height: 6¹/₂in., 16.4cm.
Issued: 1920–1938
　　　　Colour variation
Price: $1875 £1250

PUFF AND POWDER HN400
Designer: L. Harradine
Height: 6¹/₂in., 16.4cm.
Issued: 1920–1938
　　　　Colour variation
Price: $1875 £1250

PUFF AND POWDER HN432
Designer: L. Harradine
Height: 6¹/₂in., 16.4cm.
Issued: 1921–1938
　　　　Colour variation
Price: $1875 £1250

PUFF AND POWDER HN433
Designer: L. Harradine
Height: 6¹/₂in., 16.4cm.
Issued: 1921–1938
　　　　Colour variation
Price: $1875 £1250

PROPOSAL (Woman) HN715

PROPOSAL (Man) HN725

PRUDENCE HN1883

PROMENADE HN2076

PUNCH AND JUDY MAN
HN2765
Designer: W. K. Harper
Height: 9in., 22.9cm.
Issued: 1981–
Price: $260 £175

PUPPETMAKER HN2253
Designer: M. Nicoll
Height: 8in., 20.3cm.
Issued: 1962–1973
Price: $420 £275

PUPPY LOVE HN3371
Designer: Nada Pedley
Height: 7¼in., 18.5cm.
Issued: 1991 in a limited
edition of 9500
Price: R.R.P.

PUSSY HN18
Designer: F. C. Stone
Height: 7¾in., 19.7cm.
Issued: 1913–1938
Price: $1875 £1250

PUSSY HN325
Designer: F. C. Stone
Height: 7½in., 19.1cm.
Issued: 1918–1938
Colour variation
Price: $1875 £1250

PUSSY HN507
Designer: F. C. Stone
Height: 7½in., 19.1cm.
Issued: 1921–1938
Colour variation
Price: $2250 £1500

PYJAMAS HN1942
Designer: L. Harradine
Height: 5¼in., 13.3cm.
Issued: 1940–1949
Price: $330 £220

Q

QUALITY STREET HN1211
Designer: Unknown
Height: 7¼in., 18.4cm.
Issued: 1926–1938
Price: $750 £500

QUALITY STREET HN1211A
Designer: Unknown
Height: 7¼in., 18.4cm.
Issued: 1926–1938
Colour variation
Price: $750 £500

QUEEN ANNE HN3141
Designer: P. Parsons
Height: 9½in., 24cm.
Issued: 1989 in a limited
edition of 5000
Price: $300 £200

QUEEN ELIZABETH I HN3099
Designer: P. Parsons
Height: 9in., 22.5cm.
Issued: 1987 in a limited
edition of 5000
Price: $375 £250

PUPPY LOVE HN3371

PUNCH AND JUDY MAN
HN2765

QUEEN ELIZABETH II
HN2502

QUEEN ANNE HN3141

QUEEN ELIZABETH II
HN2502
Designer: P. Davies
Height: 7³/₄in., 19.7cm.
Issued: 1973 in a limited
edition of 750
Price: $975 £650

QUEEN ELIZABETH II
HN3436
Designer: Alan Maslankowski
Height: 8¹/₄in., 21cm.
Issued: 1992 in a limed
edition of 5000
Price: R.R.P.

QUEEN ELIZABETH II
HN3440
Designer: P. Gee
Height: 4¹/₂in., 19cm.
Issued: 1992 in a limited
edition of 3500
Price: $375 £250

QUEEN MOTHER HN2882
Designer: E. Griffiths
Height: 8in., 20.3cm.
Issued: 1980 in a limited
edition of 1500
Price: $825 £550

QUEEN MOTHER AS THE
DUCHESS OF YORK HN3230
Designer: P. Parsons
Height: 9in., 22.5cm.
Issued: 1989 in a limited
edition of 9500
Price: $560 £375

QUEEN OF SHEBA HN2328
Designer: P. Davies
Height: 9in., 22.8cm.
Issued: 1982 in a limited
edition of 750
Price: $1360 £850

QUEEN OF THE DAWN
HN2437
Designer: P. Davies
Height: 8¹/₂in., 21.5cm.
Issued: 1983–1986
Price: $250 £165

QUEEN OF THE ICE HN2435
Designer: P. Davies
Height: 8in., 20cm.
Issued: 1983–1986
Price: $250 £165

QUEEN VICTORIA HN3125
Designer: P. Parsons
Height: 8in., 20cm.
Issued: 1988 in a limited
edition of 5000
Price: $975 £650

R

RACHEL HN2919
Designer: P. Gee
Height: 7¹/₂in., 19.1cm.
Issued: 1980–1984
Price: $225 £150

QUEEN MOTHER HN2882

QUEEN VICTORIA HN3125

QUEEN MOTHER AS THE
DUCHESS OF YORK HN3230

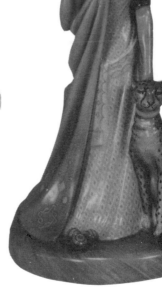

QUEEN OF SHEBA HN2328

FIGURES

RACHEL HN2936
Designer: P. Gee
Height: 7³/₄in., 19.5cm.
Issued: 1985–
Colour variation
Price: R.R.P.

RAG DOLL HN2142
Designer: P. Davies
Height: 4³/₄in., 12cm.
Issued: 1954–1986
Price: $140 £95

RAG DOLL SELLER HN2944
Designer: R. Tabbenor
Height: 7in., 17.5cm.
Issued: 1984–
Price: R.R.P.

REBECCA HN2805
Designer: P. Davies
Height: 7¹/₄in., 18.4cm.
Issued: 1980–
Price: R.R.P.

REBECCA HN3414
Designer: Peggy Davies
Height: 3¹/₂in., 9cm.
Issued: 1992
Price: R.R.P.

REFLECTION HN3039
Designer: A. Hughes
Height: 8in., 22cm.
Issued: 1988–1989
Price: $150 £100

REFLECTIONS HN1820
Designer: L. Harradine
Height: 5in., 12.7cm.
Issued: 1937–1938
Price: $900 £600

REFLECTIONS HN1821
Designer: L. Harradine
Height: 5in., 12.7cm.
Issued: 1937–1938
Colour variation
Price: $900 £600

REFLECTIONS HN1847
Designer: L. Harradine
Height: 4¹/₂in., 11.4cm.
Issued: 1938–1949
Colour variation
Price: $900 £600

REFLECTIONS HN1848
Designer: L. Harradine
Height: 5in., 12.7cm.
Issued: 1938–1949
Colour variation
Price: $900 £600

REGAL LADY HN2709
Designer: P. Davies
Height: 7¹/₂in., 19.1cm.
Issued: 1975–1984
Price: $200 £135

REGENCY HN1752
Designer: L. Harradine
Height: 8in., 20.3cm.
Issued: 1936–1949
Price: $600 £400

REBECCA HN3414

RACHEL HN2919

RAG DOLL SELLER HN2944

REGENCY HN1752

232

FIGURES

REGENCY BEAU HN1972
Designer: H. Fenton
Height: 8in., 20.3cm.
Issued: 1941–1949
Price: $975 £650

RENDEZVOUS HN2212
Designer: P. Davies
Height: 7¼in., 18.4cm.
Issued: 1962–1971
Price: $330 £220

REPOSE HN2272
Designer: P. Davies
Height: 5¼in., 13.3cm.
Issued: 1972–1978
Price: $340 £225

REST AWHILE HN2728
Designer: W. K. Harper
Height: 8in., 20.3cm.
Issued: 1981–1984
Price: $220 £145

RETURN OF PERSEPHONE HN31
Designer: C. Vyse
Height: 16in., 40.6cm.
Issued: 1913–1938
Price: $3000 £2000

REVERIE HN2306
Designer: P. Davies
Height: 6½in., 16.5cm.
Issued: 1964–1982
Price: $340 £225

REWARD HN3391
Designer: Alan Maslankowski
Height: 4½in., 11.5cm.
Issued: 1992
Price: R.R.P.

RHAPSODY HN2267
Designer: P. Davies
Height: 6¾in., 17.2cm.
Issued: 1961–1973
Price: $225 £150

RHODA HN1573
Designer: L. Harradine
Height: 10¼in., 26.7cm.
Issued: 1933–1949
Price: $450 £300

RHODA HN1574
Designer: L. Harradine
Height: 10¼in., 26.7cm.
Issued: 1933–1938
Colour variation
Price: $450 £300

RHODA HN1688
Designer: L. Harradine
Height: 10¼in., 26.7cm.
Issued: 1935–1949
Colour variation
Price: $450 £300

RHYTHM HN1903
Designer: L. Harradine
Height: 6¾in., 17.2cm.
Issued: 1939–1949
Price: $1275 £850

REWARD HN3391

REST AWHILE HN2728

REBECCA HN2805

REVERIE HN2306

RHYTHM HN1904
Designer: L. Harradine
Height: 6³/₄in., 17.2cm.
Issued: 1939–1949
Colour variation
Price: $1275 £850

RITA HN1448
Designer: L. Harradine
Height: 7in., 17.8cm.
Issued: 1931–1938
Price: $750 £500

RITA HN1450
Designer: L. Harradine
Height: 7in., 17.8cm.
Issued: 1931–1938
Colour variation
Price: $750 £500

RITZ BELL BOY HN2772
Designer: W. Harper
Height: 8in., 20cm.
Issued: 1989–1993
Price: $140 £95

RIVER BOY HN2128
Designer: P. Davies
Height: 4in., 10.1cm.
Issued: 1962–1975
Price: $225 £150

ROBERT BURNS HN42
Designer: E. W. Light
Height: 18in., 45.7cm.
Issued: 1914–1938
Price: $2400 £1500

ROBERT E. LEE, GEN. HN3404
Designer: Robert Tabbenor
Height: 11¹/₂in., 29cm.
Issued: 1993 in a limited
edition of 5000
Price: R.R.P.

ROBIN M38
Designer: Unknown
Height: 2¹/₂in., 6.4cm.
Issued: 1933–1945
Price: $375 £250

ROBIN M39
Designer: L. Harradine
Height: 2¹/₂in., 6.4cm.
Issued: 1933–1945
Colour variation
Price: $375 £250

ROBIN HOOD HN2773
Designer: W. K. Harper
Height: 8in., 20cm.
Issued: 1985–1990
Price: $210 £140

ROBIN HOOD AND MAID MARIAN HN3111
Designer: Robert Jefferson
Height: 12in., 30.5cm.
Issued: 1994 in a limited
edition of 150
Price: R.R.P.

ROCKING HORSE HN2072
Designer: L. Harradine
Height: 7in., 17.8cm.
Issued: 1951–1953
Price: $1500 £1000

RHYTHM HN1904

ROBIN HOOD AND MAID
MARIAN HN3111

ROBERT E. LEE, GEN.
HN3404

ROMANCE HN2430
Designer: P. Davies
Height: 5¹/in., 13.3cm.
Issued: 1972–1980
Price: $260 £175

ROMANY SUE HN1757
Designer: L. Harradine
Height: 9¹/₄in., 23.5cm.
Issued: 1936–1949
Price: $600 £400

ROMANY SUE HN1758
Designer: L. Harradine
Height: 9¹/₂in., 24.1cm.
Issued: 1936–1949
Colour variation
Price: $600 £400

ROMEO AND JULIET HN3113
Designer: Robert Jefferson
Height: 12in., 30.5cm.
Issued: 1993 in a limited
edition of 150
Price: R.R.P.

ROSABELL HN1620
Designer: L. Harradine
Height: 6³/₄in., 17.1cm.
Issued: 1934–1938
Price: $675 £450

ROSALIND HN2393
Designer: P. Davies
Height: 5¹/₂in., 14cm.
Issued: 1970–1975
Price: $220 £145

ROSAMUND (Style one) HN1320
Designer: L. Harradine
Height: 7¹/₄in., 18.4cm.
Issued: 1929–1938
Price: $1500 £1000

ROSAMUND (Style two) HN1497
Designer: L. Harradine
Height: 8¹/₂in., 21.6cm.
Issued: 1932–1938
Price: $750 £500

ROSAMUND (Style two) HN1551
Designer: L. Harradine
Height: 8¹/₂in., 21.6cm.
Issued: 1933–1938
Colour variation
Price: $900 £600

ROSAMUND M32
Designer: L. Harradine
Height: 4¹/₄in., 10.8cm.
Issued: 1932–1945
Price: $410 £275

ROSAMUND M33
Designer: L. Harradine
Height: 4in., 10.1cm.
Issued: 1932–1945
Colour variation
Price: $410 £275

ROSE HN1387
Designer: L. Harradine
Height: 4¹/₂in., 11.4cm.
Issued: 1930–1938
Colour variation
Price: $285 £190

ROMEO AND JULIET HN3113

RITZ BELL BOY HN2772

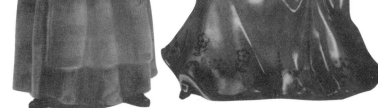

ROMANY SUE HN1758   ROMANCE HN2430

ROSE HN1368
Designer: L. Harradine
Height: 4¹/₂in., 11.4cm.
Issued: 1930–
Price: R.R.P.

ROSE HN1416
Designer: L. Harradine
Height: 4¹/₂in., 11.4cm.
Issued: 1930–1949
Colour variation
Price: $210 £140

ROSE HN1506
Designer: L. Harradine
Height: 4¹/₂in., 11.4cm.
Issued: 1932–1938
Colour variation
Price: $270 £180

ROSE HN1654
Designer: L. Harradine
Height: 4¹/₂in., 11.4cm.
Issued: 1934–1938
Colour variation
Price: $300 £200

ROSE HN2123
Designer: L. Harradine
Height: 4¹/₂in., 11.4cm.
Issued: 1983–
Price: R.R.P.

ROSE ARBOUR HN3145
Designer: D. Brindley
Height: 12in., 30.5cm.
Issued: 1987–1990
Price: $150 £100

ROSEANNA HN1921
Designer: L. Harradine
Height: 8in., 20.3cm.
Issued: 1940–1949
Price: $600 £400

ROSEANNA HN1926
Designer: L. Harradine
Height: 8in., 20.3cm.
Issued: 1940–1959
Colour variation
Price: $330 £220

ROSEBUD (Style one) HN1580
Designer: L. Harradine
Height: 3in., 7.6cm.
Issued: 1933–1938
Price: $450 £300

ROSEBUD (Style one) HN1581
Designer: L. Harradine
Height: 3in., 7.6cm.
Issued: 1933–1938
Colour variation
Price: $450 £300

ROSEBUD (Style two) HN1983
Designer: L. Harradine
Height: 7¹/₂in., 19.1cm.
Issued: 1945–1952
Price: $420 £275

ROSEMARY HN2091
Designer: L. Harradine
Height: 7in., 17.8cm.
Issued: 1952–1959
Price: $440 £295

ROSEANNA
HN1926

ROSE HN1368

ROYAL GOVERNOR'S COOK HN2233

ROSEMARY HN3143
Designer: P. Parsons
Height: 7¹/₂in., 19cm.
Issued: 1988–1991
Price: $180 £120

ROSINA HN1358
Designer: L. Harradine
Height: 5³/₄in., 14.6cm.
Issued: 1929–1938
Price: $560 £375

ROSINA HN1364
Designer: L. Harradine
Height: 5¹/₄in., 13.3cm.
Issued: 1929–1938
Colour variation
Price: $560 £375

ROSINA HN1556
Designer: L. Harradine
Height: 5³/₄in., 14.6cm.
Issued: 1933–1938
Colour variation
Price: $560 £375

ROWENA HN2077
Designer: L. Harradine
Height: 7¹/₄in., 18.4cm.
Issued: 1951–1955
Price: $490 £325

**ROYAL CANADIAN
MOUNTED POLICE 1873
(BUST.) HN2555**
Designer: D. Tootle
Height: 8¹/₄in., 21cm.
Issued: 1973 in a limited
edition of 1500
Price: $450 £300

**ROYAL CANADIAN
MOUNTED POLICE 1973
HN2547**
Designer: D. Tootle
Height: 8in., 20.3cm.
Issued: 1973 in a limited
edition of 1500
Price: $675 £450

**ROYAL GOVERNOR'S COOK
HN2233**
Designer: P. Davies
Height: 6in., 15.2cm.
Issued: 1960–1984
Price: $375 £250

RUBY HN1724
Designer: L. Harradine
Height: 5¹/₄in., 13.3cm.
Issued: 1935–1949
Price: $360 £240

RUBY HN1725
Designer: L. Harradine
Height: 5¹/₄in., 13.3cm.
Issued: 1935–1949
Colour variation
Price: $360 £240

RUMPELSTILTSKIN HN3025
Designer: R. Jefferson
Height: 8in., 20cm.
Issued: 1983–1986
Price: $260 £175

RUSTIC SWAIN HN1745
Designer: L. Harradine
Height: 5¼in., 13.3cm.
Issued: 1935–1949
Price: $1200 £750

RUSTIC SWAIN HN1746
Designer: L. Harradine
Height: 5¼in., 13.3cm.
Issued: 1935–1949
      Colour variation
Price: $1200 £750

RUTH HN2799
Designer: P. Davies
Height: 6in., 15.2cm.
Issued: 1976–1982
Price: $250 £165

RUTH THE PIRATE MAID
HN2900
Designer: W. K. Harper
Height: 11¾in., 29.8cm.
Issued: 1981–1986
Price: $450 £300

S

SABBATH MORN HN1982
Designer: L. Harradine
Height: 7¼in., 18.4cm.
Issued: 1945–1959
Price: $280 £175

SAILOR'S HOLIDAY HN2442
Designer: M. Nicoll
Height: 6¼in., 15.9cm.
Issued: 1972–1978
Price: $260 £175

SAIREY GAMP M46
Designer: L. Harradine
Height: 4in., 10.1cm.
Issued: 1932–1982
Price: $60 £40

SAIREY GAMP (Style one)
HN533
Designer: L. Harradine
Height: 4in., 10.1cm.
Issued: 1922–1932
Price: $70 £45

SAIREY GAMP (Style two)
HN1896
Designer: L. Harradine
Height: 7in., 17.8cm.
Issued: 1938–1952
      Colour variation
Price: $300 £200

SAIREY GAMP (Style three)
HN2100
Designer: L. Harradine
Height: 7¼in., 18.4cm.
Issued: 1952–1967
Price: $270 £180

RUSTIC SWAIN HN1745

RUMPELSTILTSKIN HN3025

RUTH THE PIRATE MAID
HN2900

SAILOR'S HOLIDAY HN2442

237

FIGURES

SAIREY GAMP (Style two)
HN558
Designer: L. Harradine
Height: 7in., 17.8cm.
Issued: 1923–1939
Price: $300 £200

SALLY HN2741
Designer: D. Tootle
Height: 5½in., 13.5cm.
Issued: 1988–1991
Price: $140 £95

SALOME HN1775
Designer: R. Garbe
Height: 8in., 24.4cm.
Issued: 1933 in a limited
edition of 100
Price: $3000 £2000

SALOME HN1828
Designer: R. Garbe
Height: 8in., 24.4cm.
Issued: 1937–1949
Colour variation
Price: $2250 £1500

SALOME HN3267
Designer: P. Davies
Height: 9½in., 24.1cm.
Issued: 1990 in a limited
edition of 1000
Price: $600 £400

SAM WELLER HN531
Designer: L. Harradine
Height: 4in., 10.1cm.
Issued: 1922–1932
Price: $60 £40

SAM WELLER M48
Designer: L. Harradine
Height: 4in., 10.1cm.
Issued: 1932–1982
Price: $60 £40

SAMANTHA HN2954
Designer: P. Parsons
Height: 7in., 17.5cm.
Issued: 1982–1984
Price: $250 £165

SAMANTHA HN3304
Designer: Peggy Davies
Height: 7¼in., 18.5cm.
Issued: 1990
Price: R.R.P.

SAMURAI WARRIOR HN3402
Designer: R. Tabbenor
Height: 9in., 22.7cm.
Issued: 1992 in a limited
edition of 950
Price: $340 £225

SAMWISE HN2925
Designer: D. Lyttleton
Height: 4½in., 11.5cm.
Issued: 1982–1984
Price: $360 £240

SANDRA HN2275
Designer: P. Davies
Height: 7¾in., 19.7cm.
Issued: 1969–
Price: R.R.P.

SAMANTHA HN3304

SAMURAI WARRIOR HN3402

SAIREY GAMP (Style two)
HN558

SAMWISE HN2925

SALOME HN3267

SANDRA HN2401
Designer: P. Davies
Height: 8in., 20cm.
Issued: 1983–
Price: $180 £120

SANTA CLAUS HN2725
Designer: W. K. Harper
Height: 9¹/₂in., 24cm.
Issued: 1982–1992
Price: $260 £175

SANTA'S HELPER HN3301
Designer: A. Hughes
Height: 6¹/₂in., 16.5cm.
Issued: 1991
Price: R.R.P.

SARA HN2265
Designer: P. Davies
Height: 7¹/₂in., 19.1cm.
Issued: 1981–
Price: R.R.P.

SARA HN3219
Designer: P. Davies
Height: 3³/₄in., 9.5cm.
Issued: 1988
Price: R.R.P.

SARA (Blue/crimson) HN3308
Designer: Peggy Davies
Height: 7³/₄in., 19.5cm.
Issued: 1981
Price: R.R.P.

SAUCY NYMPH HN1539
Designer: Unknown
Height: 4¹/₂in., 11.4cm.
Issued: 1933–1949
Price: $330 £220

SAVE SOME FOR ME HN2959
Designer: P. Parsons
Height: 7¹/₄in., 18cm.
Issued: 1982–1985
Price: $165 £110

SCHOOLMARM HN2223
Designer: P. Davies
Height: 6³/₄in., 17.2cm.
Issued: 1958–1980
Price: $290 £195

SCOTCH GIRL HN1269
Designer: L. Harradine
Height: 7¹/₂in., 19.1cm.
Issued: 1928–1938
Price: $1425 £950

SCOTTIES HN1281
Designer: L. Harradine
Height: 5¹/₂in., 14cm.
Issued: 1928–1938
Price: $800 £500

SCOTTIES HN1349
Designer: L. Harradine
Height: 5¹/₄in., 13.3cm.
Issued: 1929–1949
        Colour variation
Price: $900 £600

SANTA'S HELPER HN3301

SAVE SOME FOR ME HN2959

SANTA CLAUS HN2725

SANDRA HN2275

SCHOOLMARM HN2223

239

FIGURES

SCOTTISH HIGHLAND DANCER HN2436
Designer: P. Davies
Height: 9½in., 24.1cm.
Issued: 1978 in a limited edition of 750
Price: $520 £325

SCRIBE HN305
Designer: C. J. Noke
Height: 6in., 15.2cm.
Issued: 1918–1936
Price: $800 £500

SCRIBE HN324
Designer: C. J. Noke
Height: 6in., 15.2cm.
Issued: 1918–1938
Colour variation
Price: $800 £500

SCRIBE HN1235
Designer: C. J. Noke
Height: 6in., 15.2cm.
Issued: 1927–1938
Colour variation
Price: $800 £500

SCROOGE M87
Designer: L. Harradine
Height: 4in., 10.1cm.
Issued: 1949–1982
Price: $60 £40

SEA HARVEST HN2257
Designer: M. Nicoll
Height: 7½in., 19.1cm.
Issued: 1969–1976
Price: $290 £195

SEA SHORE HN2263
Designer: P. Davies
Height: 3½in., 8.9cm.
Issued: 1961–1965
Price: $270 £180

SEA SPRITE (Style one) HN1261
Designer: L. Harradine
Height: 5in., 12.7cm.
Issued: 1927–1938
Price: $480 £320

SEA SPRITE (Style two) HN2191
Designer: P. Davies
Height: 7in., 17.8cm.
Issued: 1958–1962
Price: $300 £200

SEAFARER HN2455
Designer: M. Nicoll
Height: 8½in., 21.6cm.
Issued: 1972–1976
Price: $250 £165

SECRET MOMENT HN3106
Designer: R. Jefferson
Height: 12¼in., 31cm.
Issued: 1987–1989
Price: $150 £100

SECRET THOUGHTS HN2382
Designer: P. Davies
Height: 6¼in., 15.9cm.
Issued: 1971–1988
Price: $240 £160

SEPTEMBER HN3326

SEA HARVEST HN2257

SEAFARER HN2455

SCOTTISH HIGHLAND DANCER HN2436

FIGURES

SENTIMENTAL PIERROT
HN36
Designer: C. J. Noke
Height: 5¹/₂in., 14cm.
Issued: 1914–1938
Price: $2100 £1400

SENTIMENTAL PIERROT
HN307
Designer: C. J. Noke
Height: 5¹/₂in., 14cm.
Issued: 1918–1938
Price: $1500 £1000

SENTINEL HN523
Designer: Unknown
Height: 17¹/₂in., 44.4cm.
Issued: 1921–1938
Price: $2880 £1800

SEPTEMBER HN3166
Designer: P. Davies
Height: 7³/₄in., 19.7cm.
Issued: 1987
Price: $165 £110

SEPTEMBER HN3326
Designer: P. Davies
Height: 7¹/₂in., 19.1cm.
Issued: 1991
    U.S.A. only
Price: $165 £110

SEPTEMBER HN3409
Designer: P. Davies
Height: 7¹/₂in., 19.1cm.
Issued: 1991
    Canada only
Price: $165 £110

SERENA HN1868
Designer: L. Harradine
Height: 11in., 27.9cm.
Issued: 1938–1949
Price: $525 £350

SERENADE HN2753
Designer: E. Griffiths
Height: 9in., 23cm.
Issued: 1983–1986
Price: $190 £125

SERENITY HN3542
Designer: John Ablitt
Height: 11in., 28cm.
Issued: 1990
Price: R.R.P.

SERGEANT, 6TH MARYLAND
REGIMENT 1777 HN2815
Designer: E. J. Griffiths
Height: 13³/₄in., 34.9cm.
Issued: 1976 in a limited
    edition of 350
Price: $825 £550

SERGEANT, VIRGINIA 1ST
REGIMENT CONTINENTAL
LIGHT DRAGOONS, 1777
HN2844
Designer: E. J. Griffiths
Height: 14¹/₄in., 36.1cm.
Issued: 1978 in a limited
    edition of 350
Price: $1275 £850

SEPTEMBER HN3409

SERENADE HN2753

SEPTEMBER HN3166

SECRET THOUGHTS HN2382

241

SHADOW PLAY HN3526
Designer: Russell Willis
Height: 10in., 25.5cm.
Issued: 1982
Price: R.R.P.

SHARON HN3047
Designer: P. Parsons
Height: 5¹/₂in., 14cm.
Issued: 1984–1993
Price: $130 £85

SHARON HN3455
Designer: P. Parsons
Height: 5¹/₂in., 14cm.
Issued: 1994
        Colour variation
Price: R.R.P.

SHE LOVES ME NOT HN2045
Designer: L. Harradine
Height: 5¹/₂in., 14cm.
Issued: 1949–1962
Price: $220 £145

SHEIKH HN3083
Designer: E. J. Griffiths
Height: 9³/₄in., 25cm.
Issued: 1988–1989
Price: $150 £100

SHEILA HN2742
Designer: D. Tootle
Height: 8¹/₄in., 21cm.
Issued: 1984–1991
Price: $180 £120

SHEPHERD (Style one) HN81
Designer: C. J. Noke
Height: 13¹/₄in., 33.6cm.
Issued: 1918–1938
Price: $2250 £1700

SHEPHERD (Style one) HN617
Designer: C. J. Noke
Height: 13¹/₄in., 33.6cm.
Issued: 1924–1938
        Colour variation
Price: $3000 £2000

SHEPHERD (Style one) HN632
Designer: C. J. Noke
Height: 13¹/₄in., 33.6cm.
Issued: 1924–1938
        Colour variation
Price: $3000 £2000

SHEPHERD (Style two) HN709
Designer: Unknown
Height: 3¹/₂in., 8.8cm.
Issued: 1925–1938
Price: $900 £600

SHEPHERD (Style three) HN751
Designer: Unknown
Height: 7¹/₂in., 19.1cm.
Issued: 1925–1938
Price: $1050 £700

SHEPHERD (Style four) HN1975
Designer: H. Fenton
Height: 8¹/₂in., 21.6cm.
Issued: 1945–1975
Price: $240 £160

SHEILA HN2742

SHEPHERD (Style four)
HN1975

SHEPHERD HN3160
Designer: A. Hughes
Height: 8¹/₂in., 22cm.
Issued: 1988–1989
Price: $150 £100

SHEPHERD M17
Designer: Unknown
Height: 3³/₄in., 9.5cm.
Issued: 1932–1938
Price: $600 £400

SHEPHERD M19
Designer: Unknown
Height: 3³/₄in., 9.5cm.
Issued: 1932–1938
        Colour variation
Price: $600 £400

SHEPHERDESS (Style one) HN708
Designer: Unknown
Height: 3¹/₂in., 8.8cm.
Issued: 1925–1948
Price: $600 £400

SHEPHERDESS (Style two) HN735
Designer: Unknown
Height: 7in., 17.8cm.
Issued: 1925–1938
Price: $900 £600

SHEPHERDESS (Style two) HN750
Designer: Unknown
Height: 7in., 17.8cm.
Issued: 1925–1938
        Colour variation
Price: $900 £600

SHEPHERDESS HN2990
Designer: R. Tabbenor
Height: 8in., 20.3cm.
Issued: 1988–1989
Price: $150 £100

SHEPHERDESS M18
Designer: Unknown
Height: 3¹/₂in., 8.9cm.
Issued: 1932–1938
Price: $600 £400

SHEPHERDESS M20
Designer: Unknown
Height: 3³/₄in., 9.5cm.
Issued: 1932–1938
        Colour variation
Price: $600 £400

SHEPHERDESS HN2420
Designer: J. Bromley
Height: 9in., 22.9cm.
Issued: 1991 in a limited
        edition of 12500
Price: R.R.P.

SHIRLEY HN2702
Designer: P. Davies
Height: 7¹/₄in., 18cm.
Issued: 1985–
Price: R.R.P.

FIGURES

SHORE LEAVE HN2254
Designer: M. Nicoll
Height: 7¹/₂in., 19.1cm.
Issued: 1965–1978
Price: $220 £145

SHY ANNE HN60
Designer: L. Perugini
Height: 7³/₄in., 19.7cm.
Issued: 1916–1938
Price: $1875 £1250

SHY ANNE HN64
Designer: L. Perugini
Height: 7³/₄in., 19.7cm.
Issued: 1916–1938
      Colour variation
Price: $1875 £1250

SHY ANNE HN65
Designer: L. Perugini
Height: 7³/₄in., 19.7cm.
Issued: 1916–1938
      Colour variation
Price: $1875 £1250

SHY ANNE HN568
Designer: L. Perugini
Height: 7¹/₂in., 19.1cm.
Issued: 1923–1938
      Colour variation
Price: $1875 £1250

SHYLOCK HN79
Designer: C. J. Noke
Height: Unknown
Issued: 1917–1938
Price: $2250 £1500

SHYLOCK HN317
Designer: C. J. Noke
Height: Unknown
Issued: 1918–1938
      Colour variation
Price: $1875 £1250

SIBELL HN1668
Designer: L. Harradine
Height: 6¹/₂in., 16.5cm.
Issued: 1934–1949
Price: $450 £300

SIBELL HN1695
Designer: L. Harradine
Height: 6¹/₂in., 16.5cm.
Issued: 1935–1949
      Colour variation
Price: $450 £300

SIBELL HN1735
Designer: L. Harradine
Height: 6¹/₂in., 16.5cm.
Issued: 1935–1949
      Colour variation
Price: $450 £300

SIESTA HN1305
Designer: L. Harradine
Height: 4³/₄in., 12cm.
Issued: 1928–1938
Price: $1425 £950

SIBELL HN1695

SHORE LEAVE HN2254

SHEPHERDESS HN2420

SIESTA HN1305

243

SILKS AND RIBBONS HN2017
Designer: L. Harradine
Height: 6in., 15.2cm.
Issued: 1949–
Price: R.R.P.

SILVERSMITH OF WILLIAMSBURG HN2208
Designer: P. Davies
Height: 6¼in., 15.9cm.
Issued: 1960–1983
Price: $220 £145

SIMONE HN2378
Designer: P. Davies
Height: 7¼in., 18.4cm.
Issued: 1971–1982
Price: $190 £125

SINGLE RED ROSE HN3376
Designer: Nada Pedley
Height: 8in., 20cm.
Issued: 1992
Price: R.R.P.

SIR EDWARD HN2370
Designer: J. Bromley
Height: 11in., 27.9cm.
Issued: 1979 in a limited
edition of 500
Price: $410 £275

SIR RALPH HN2371
Designer: J. Bromley
Height: 7½in., 19.1cm.
Issued: 1979 in a limited
edition of 500
Price: $410 £275

SIR THOMAS HN2372
Designer: J. Bromley
Height: 11in., 27.9cm.
Issued: 1979 in a limited
edition of 500
Price: $410 £275

SIR THOMAS LOVELL HN356
Designer: C. J. Noke
Height: 7¾in., 19.7cm.
Issued: 1919–1938
Price: $1275 £850

SIR WALTER RALEIGH HN1742
Designer: L. Harradine
Height: 10½in., 26.7cm.
Issued: 1935–1949
Price: $975 £650

SIR WALTER RALEIGH HN1751
Designer: L. Harradine
Height: 11½in., 29.2cm.
Issued: 1936–1949
Colour variation
Price: $600 £400

SIR WALTER RALEIGH HN2015
Designer: L. Harradine
Height: 11½in., 29.2cm.
Issued: 1948–1955
Colour variation
Price: $525 £350

SIR WINSTON CHURCHILL HN3057
Designer: A. Hughes
Height: 10½in., 26.5cm.
Issued: 1985–
Price: R.R.P.

SINGLE RED ROSE HN3376

SIR EDWARD HN2370

SIR THOMAS HN2372

SILVERSMITH OF
WILLIAMSBURG HN2208

SILKS AND RIBBONS HN2017

SIMONE HN2378

SIR WINSTON CHURCHILL
HN3057

SIR WALTER RALEIGH
HN2015

SIR RALPH HN2371

SISTERLY LOVE HN3031
Designer: P. Parsons
Height: 8¹/₂in., 21.5cm.
Issued: 1987
Price: R.R.P.

SISTERS HN3018
Designer: P. Parsons
Height: 8¹/₂in., 21.5cm.
Issued: 1983–
Price: R.R.P.

SISTERS HN3019
Designer: P. Parsons
Height: 8¹/₂in., 21.5cm.
Issued: 1983–
Colour variation
Price: R.R.P.

SIT HN3123
Designer: Alan Maslankowski
Height: 4¹/₂in., 11.5cm.
Issued: 1991
Price: R.R.P.

SKATER HN2117
Designer: P. Davies
Height: 7¹/₄in., 18.4cm.
Issued: 1953–1971
Price: $290 £195

THE SKATER HN3439
Designer: Peter Gee
Height: 8in., 20cm.
Issued: 1992
Price: R.R.P.

SKETCH GIRL Model 444
Designer: L. Harradine
Height: 7in., 17.7cm.
Issued: 1924–1938
Price: $1125 £750

SLAPDASH HN2277
Designer: Mary Nicoll
Height: 10in., 25.5cm.
Issued: 1990
Price: R.R.P.

SLEEP HN24
Designer: P. Stabler
Height: 8¹/₄in., 21cm.
Issued: 1913–1938
Price: $900 £600

SLEEP HN24A
Designer: P. Stabler
Height: 8¹/₄in., 21cm.
Issued: 1913–1938
Colour variation
Price: $900 £600

SLEEP HN25
Designer: P. Stabler
Height: 8¹/₄in., 21cm.
Issued: 1913–1938
Colour variation
Price: $900 £600

SLEEP HN25A
Designer: P. Stabler
Height: 8¹/₄in., 21cm.
Issued: 1913–1938
Colour variation
Price: $900 £600

SIT HN3123

SLAPDASH HN2277

THE SKATER HN3439

SKATER HN2117

SLEEP HN424
Designer: P. Stabler
Height: 6in., 15.2cm.
Issued: 1921–1938
Colour variation
Price: $900 £600

SLEEP HN692
Designer: P. Stabler
Height: 8¹/₄in., 21cm.
Issued: 1925–1938
Colour variation
Price: $900 £600

SLEEP HN710
Designer: P. Stabler
Height: 8¹/₄in., 21cm.
Issued: 1925–1938
Colour variation
Price: $900 £600

SLEEPING BEAUTY HN3079
Designer: A. Hughes
Height: 4¹/₂in. x 8in.,
11cm. x 22cm.
Issued: 1987–1989
Price: $250 £165

SLEEPY DARLING HN2953
Designer: P. Parsons
Height: 7¹/₄in., 18.4cm.
Issued: Only available in
1981
Price: $290 £195
(Collectors Club Issue)

SLEEPY SCHOLAR HN15
Designer: W. White
Height: 6³/₄in., 17.2cm.
Issued: 1913–1938
Price: $1875 £1250

SLEEPY SCHOLAR HN16
Designer: W. White
Height: 6³/₄in., 17.2cm.
Issued: 1913–1938
Colour variation
Price: $1800 £1200

SLEEPY SCHOLAR HN29
Designer: W. White
Height: 6³/₄in., 17.2cm.
Issued: 1913–1938
Colour variation
Price: $1875 £1250

SLEEPYHEAD HN2114
Designer: P. Davies
Height: 5in., 12.7cm.
Issued: 1953–1955
Price: $975 £650

SMILING BUDDHA HN454
Designer: C. J. Noke
Height: 6¹/₄in., 15.9cm.
Issued: 1921–1938
Price: $1500 £1000

SNAKE CHARMER HN1317
Designer: Unknown
Height: 4in., 10.1cm.
Issued: 1929–1938
Price: $900 £600

SOIRÉE HN2312
Designer: P. Davies
Height: 7¹/₂in., 19.1cm.
Issued: 1967–1984
Price: $200 £135

SOLITUDE HN2810
Designer: P. Davies
Height: 5¹/₂in., 14cm.
Issued: 1977–1983
Price: $340 £225

SONATA HN2438
Designer: P. Davies
Height: 6¹/₂in., 16.5cm.
Issued: 1983–1986
Price: $190 £125

SONG OF THE SEA HN2729
Designer: W. K. Harper
Height: 7¹/₄in., 18cm.
Issued: 1983–1991
Price: $250 £165

SONIA HN1692
Designer: L. Harradine
Height: 6¹/₄in., 15.9cm.
Issued: 1935–1949
Price: $600 £400

SONIA HN1738
Designer: L. Harradine
Height: 6¹/₂in., 16.5cm.
Issued: 1935–1949
Colour variation
Price: $600 £400

SONNY HN1313
Designer: L. Harradine
Height: 3¹/₂in., 8.9cm.
Issued: 1929–1938
Price: $600 £400

SONNY HN1314
Designer: L. Harradine
Height: 3¹/₂in., 8.9cm.
Issued: 1929–1938
Colour variation
Price: $600 £400

SOPHIA CHARLOTTE, LADY SHEFFIELD HN3008
Designer: Peter Gee
Height: 10in., 24.5cm.
Issued: 1991 in a limited
edition of 5000
Price: R.R.P.

SOPHIE HN2833
Designer: P. Davies
Height: 6in., 15.2cm.
Issued: 1977–1987
Price: $165 £110

SOPHISTICATION HN3059
Designer: A. Hughes
Height: 11¹/₂in., 29cm.
Issued: 1988–1990
Price: $150 £100

SONATA HN2438

SOPHIA CHARLOTTE, LADY SHEFFIELD HN3008

SOLITUDE HN2810

SLEEPY DARLING HN2953

SONG OF THE SEA HN2729

247

SOUTHERN BELLE HN2229
Designer: P. Davies
Height: 7½in., 19.1cm.
Issued: 1958–
Price: R.R.P.

SOUTHERN BELLE HN2425
Designer: P. Davies
Height: 7½in., 19.1cm.
Issued: 1983–
    Colour variation
Price: R.R.P.

SOUTHERN BELLE HN3174
Designer: P. Davies
Height: 4in., 10cm.
Issued: 1988
Price: R.R.P.

**SPANISH FLAMENCO
DANCER HN2831**
Designer: P. Davies
Height: 7¼in., 18.4cm.
Issued: 1977 in a limited
    edition of 750
Price: $560 £350

SPANISH LADY HN1262
Designer: L. Harradine
Height: 8½in., 21.6cm.
Issued: 1927–1938
Price: $675 £450

SPANISH LADY HN1290
Designer: L. Harradine
Height: 8¼in., 21cm.
Issued: 1928–1938
    Colour variation
Price: $675 £450

SPANISH LADY HN1293
Designer: L. Harradine
Height: 8¼in., 21cm.
Issued: 1928–1938
    Colour variation
Price: $675 £450

SPANISH LADY HN1294
Designer: L. Harradine
Height: 8¼in., 21cm.
Issued: 1928–1938
    Colour variation
Price: $675 £450

SPANISH LADY HN1309
Designer: L. Harradine
Height: 8¼in., 21cm.
Issued: 1929–1938
    Colour variation
Price: $675 £450

SPINNING HN2390
Designer: P. Davies
Height: 7½in., 19cm.
Issued: 1984 in a limited
    edition of 750
Price: $825 £550

SPIRIT OF THE WIND HN1777
Designer: R. Garbe
Height: Unknown
Issued: 1933 in a limited
    edition of 50
Price: $3750 £2500

SOUTHERN BELLE HN2229

SPANISH FLAMENCO
DANCER HN2831

SPIRIT OF THE WIND HN1825
Designer: R. Garbe
Height: Unknown
Issued: 1937–1949
    Colour variation
Price: $3000 £2000

SPOOK HN50
Designer: H. Tittensor
Height: 7in., 17.8cm.
Issued: 1916–1938
Price: $1200 £800

SPOOK HN51
Designer: H. Tittensor
Height: 7in., 17.8cm.
Issued: 1916–1938
    Colour variation
Price: $1500 £1000

SPOOK HN51A
Designer: H. Tittensor
Height: 7in., 17.8cm.
Issued: 1916–1938
    Colour variation
Price: $1650 £1100

SPOOK HN51B
Designer: H. Tittensor
Height: 7in., 17.8cm.
Issued: 1916–1938
    Colour variation
Price: $1650 £1100

SPOOK HN58
Designer: H. Tittensor
Height: 7in., 17.8cm.
Issued: 1916–1938
    Colour variation
Price: $1500 £1000

SPOOK HN512
Designer: H. Tittensor
Height: 7in., 17.8cm.
Issued: 1921–1938
    Colour variation
Price: $2250 £1500

SPOOK HN625
Designer: H. Tittensor
Height: 7in., 17.8cm.
Issued: 1924–1938
    Colour variation
Price: $1200 £800

SPOOK HN1218
Designer: H. Tittensor
Height: 7in., 17.8cm.
Issued: 1926–1938
    Colour variation
Price: $1050 £700

SPOOKS HN88
Designer: C. J. Noke
Height: 7¼in., 18.4cm.
Issued: 1918–1936
Price: $1875 £1250

SPOOKS HN89
Designer: C. J. Noke
Height: 7¼in., 18.4cm.
Issued: 1918–1936
    Colour variation
Price: $2175 £1450

FIGURES

SPOOKS HN372
Designer: C. J. Noke
Height: 7¼in., 18.4cm.
Issued: 1920–1936
Colour variation
Price: $1800 £1200

SPRING (Style one) HN312
Designer: Unknown
Height: 7½in., 19.1cm.
Issued: 1918–1938
Price: $750 £500

SPRING (Style one) HN472
Designer: Unknown
Height: 7½in., 19.1cm.
Issued: 1921–1938
Colour variation
Price: $750 £500

SPRING (Style two) HN1774
Designer: R. Garbe
Height: 21in., 53.3cm.
Issued: 1933 in a limited
edition of 100
Price: $975 £650

SPRING (Style two) HN1827
Designer: R. Garbe
Height: 21in., 53.3cm.
Issued: 1937–1949
Colour variation
Price: $1125 £750

SPRING (Style three) HN2085
Designer: P. Davies
Height: 7¾in., 19.6cm.
Issued: 1952–1959
Price: $440 £295

SPRING FLOWERS HN1807
Designer: L. Harradine
Height: 7¼in., 18.4cm.
Issued: 1937–1959
Price: $330 £220

SPRING FLOWERS HN1945
Designer: L. Harradine
Height: 7¼in., 18.4cm.
Issued: 1940–1949
Colour variation
Price: $525 £350

SPRING MORNING HN1922
Designer: L. Harradine
Height: 7½in., 19.1cm.
Issued: 1940–1973
Price: $240 £160

SPRING MORNING HN1923
Designer: L. Harradine
Height: 7½in., 19.1cm.
Issued: 1940–1949
Colour variation
Price: $410 £275

SPRING SONG HN3446
Designer: P. Gee
Height: 7in., 17.8cm.
Issued: 1993
Special colourway
yellow
Price: R.R.P.

SPRING FLOWERS HN1945

SPRING FLOWERS HN1807

SPRING SONG HN3446

SPINNING HN2390

249

FIGURES

SPRING WALK HN3120
Designer: A. Maslankowski
Height: 13in., 32.9cm.
Issued: 1990–1992

Price: $210 £140

SPRINGTIME HN1971
Designer: L. Harradine
Height: 6in., 15.2cm.
Issued: 1941–1949
Price: $825 £550

SPRINGTIME HN3033
Designer: A. Hughes
Height: 8in., 20cm.
Issued: 1983
Price: $370 £245

SPRINGTIME HN3477
Designer: V. Annand
Height: Unknown
Issued: 1993
Price: R.R.P.

SQUIRE HN1814
Designer: Unknown
Height: 9³/₄in., 24.7cm.
Issued: 1937–1949
Price: $1875 £1250
Also called 'Hunting Squire'

ST. GEORGE (Style one) HN385
Designer: S. Thorogood
Height: 16in., 40.6cm.
Issued: 1920–1938
Price: $1875 £1250

ST. GEORGE (Style one) HN386
Designer: S. Thorogood
Height: 16in., 40.6cm.
Issued: 1920–1938
Colour variation
Price: $1875 £1250

ST. GEORGE (Style one) HN1800
Designer: S. Thorogood
Height: 16in., 40.6cm.
Issued: 1934–1950
Colour variation
Price: $1875 £1250

ST. GEORGE (Style one) HN2067
Designer: S. Thorogood
Height: 15³/₄in., 40cm.
Issued: 1950–1976
Colour variation
Price: $1875 £1250

ST. GEORGE (Style two) HN2051
Designer: P. Davies
Height: 7¹/₂in., 19.1cm.
Issued: 1950–1986
Price: $440 £295

ST. GEORGE AND THE DRAGON (Style three) HN2856
Designer: W. K. Harper
Height: 16in., 40.6cm.
Issued: 1978–
Price: R.R.P.

SPRINGTIME HN3033

SPRING WALK HN3120

SPRINGTIME HN3477

ST. GEORGE (Style two) HN2051

STAN LAUREL HN2774
Designer: W.K. Harper
Height: 10in., 25.5cm.
Issued: 1992
Price: R.R.P.

STAR GAZER HN3182
Designer: D. V. Tootle
Height: 10¹/₂in., 26.5cm.
Issued: 1988–1990
Price: $150 £100

STATESMAN HN2859
Designer: W. Harper
Height: 9¹/₄in., 23.5cm.
Issued: 1988–1990
Price: $190 £125

STAYED AT HOME HN2207
Designer: P. Davies
Height: 5in., 12.7cm.
Issued: 1958–1969
Price: $150 £100

STEPHANIE HN2807
Designer: P. Davies
Height: 7¹/₄in., 18.4cm.
Issued: 1977–1982
Price: $220 £145

STEPHANIE HN2811
Designer: P. Davies
Height: 7¹/₂in., 19cm.
Issued: 1983–
Price: R.R.P.

STICK 'EM UP HN2981
Designer: A. Hughes
Height: 7in., 17.5cm.
Issued: 1984–1985
Price: $130 £85

STIGGINS HN536
Designer: L. Harradine
Height: 3³/₄in., 9.5cm.
Issued: 1922–1932
Price: $70 £45

STIGGINS M50
Designer: L. Harradine
Height: 4in., 10.1cm.
Issued: 1932–1982
Price: $60 £40

STITCH IN TIME HN2352
Designer: M. Nicoll
Height: 6¹/₄in., 15.9cm.
Issued: 1966–1980
Price: $255 £170

STOP PRESS HN2683
Designer: M. Nicoll
Height: 7¹/₂in., 19.1cm.
Issued: 1977–1980
Price: $240 £160

STORYTIME HN3126
Designer: P. Parsons
Height: 6in., 15.2cm.
Issued: 1987–1992
Price: $150 £100

STROLLING HN3073
Designer: A. Hughes
Height: 13¹/₂in., 34.5cm.
Issued: 1985
Price: R.R.P.

STITCH IN TIME HN2352

STEPHANIE HN2807

STAN LAUREL HN2774

STOP PRESS HN2683

SUITOR HN2132
Designer: P. Davies
Height: 7¼in., 18.4cm.
Issued: 1962–1971
Price: $370 £245

SUMMER (Style one) HN313
Designer: Unknown
Height: 7½in., 19.1cm.
Issued: 1918–1938
Price: $750 £500

SUMMER (Style one) HN473
Designer: Unknown
Height: 7½in., 19.1cm.
Issued: 1921–1938
Price: $750 £500

SUMMER (Style two) HN2086
Designer: P. Davies
Height: 7¼in., 18.4cm.
Issued: 1952–1959
Price: $410 £275

SUMMER ROSE HN3085
Designer: E. Griffiths
Height: 8½in., 21.5cm.
Issued: 1987–1992
Price: $165 £110

SUMMER ROSE HN3309
Designer: Peggy Davies
Height: 7¾in., 19.5cm.
Issued: 1991
Price: R.R.P.

SUMMER SERENADE HN3610
Designer: P. Davies
Height: 7in., 17.8cm.
Issued: 1993
Special colourway
blue
Price: R.R.P.

SUMMER'S DARLING HN3091
Designer: P. Parsons
Height: 11¼in., 28cm.
Issued: 1986
Price: R.R.P.

SUMMER'S DAY HN2181
Designer: P. Davies
Height: 5¾in., 14.6cm.
Issued: 1957–1962
Price: $290 £195

SUMMER'S DAY HN3378
Designer: Tim Potts
Height: 8½in., 22cm.
Issued: 1991
Price: R.R.P.

SUMMERTIME HN3137
Designer: P. Parsons
Height: 8in., 20cm.
Issued: 1987
Price: $210 £140

SUNDAY BEST HN3218
Designer: P. Davies
Height: 3¾in., 9.5cm.
Issued: 1988–1993
Price: $80 £55

SUMMER ROSE HN3309

SUMMER SERENADE HN3610

SUMMERTIME HN3137

SUNDAY BEST HN2206

SUNDAY BEST HN2206
Designer: P. Davies
Height: 7¹/₂in., 19.1cm.
Issued: 1979–1984
Price: $220 £145

SUNDAY BEST HN2698
Designer: P. Davies
Height: 7¹/₂in., 19.1cm.
Issued: 1985–
Price: R.R.P.

SUNDAY MORNING HN2184
Designer: P. Davies
Height: 7¹/₂in., 19.1cm.
Issued: 1963–1969
Price: $340 £225

SUNSHINE GIRL HN1344
Designer: L. Harradine
Height: 5in., 12.7cm.
Issued: 1929–1938
Price: $1800 £1200

SUNSHINE GIRL HN1348
Designer: L. Harradine
Height: 5in., 12.7cm.
Issued: 1929–1938
          Colour variation
Price: $1800 £1200

SUSAN HN2056
Designer: L. Harradine
Height: 7in., 17.8cm.
Issued: 1950–1959
Price: $375 £250

SUSAN HN2952
Designer: P. Parsons
Height: 8¹/₂in., 21.5cm.
Issued: 1982–
Price: $250 £165

SUSAN (Red) HN3050
Designer: P. Parsons
Height: 8¹/₂in., 21.5cm.
Issued: 1986
Price: R.R.P.

SUSANNA HN1233
Designer: L. Harradine
Height: 6in., 15.2cm.
Issued: 1927–1938
Price: $750 £500

SUSANNA HN1288
Designer: L. Harradine
Height: 6in., 15.2cm.
Issued: 1928–1938
Price: $750 £500

SUSANNA HN1299
Designer: L. Harradine
Height: 6in., 15.2cm.
Issued: 1928–1938
          Colour variation
Price: $750 £500

SUZETTE HN1487
Designer: L. Harradine
Height: 7¹/₂in., 19.1cm.
Issued: 1931–1950
Price: $370 £245

SUMMER'S DAY HN3378

SUSAN HN2952

SUZETTE HN1487

SUNSHINE GIRL HN1344

SUZETTE HN1577
Designer: L. Harradine
Height: 7¹/₂in., 19.1cm.
Issued: 1933–1949
Colour variation
Price: $410 £275

SUZETTE HN1585
Designer: L. Harradine
Height: 7¹/₂in., 19.1cm.
Issued: 1933–1938
Colour variation
Price: $410 £275

SUZETTE HN1696
Designer: L. Harradine
Height: 7¹/₂in., 19.1cm.
Issued: 1935–1949
Colour variation
Price: $410 £275

SUZETTE HN2026
Designer: L. Harradine
Height: 7¹/₄in., 18.4cm.
Issued: 1949–1959
Colour variation
Price: $410 £275

SWEET AND FAIR HN1864
Designer: L. Harradine
Height: 7¹/₂in., 19.1cm.
Issued: 1938–1949
Price: $975 £650

SWEET AND FAIR HN1865
Designer: L. Harradine
Height: 7¹/₄in., 18.4cm.
Issued: 1938–1949
Colour variation
Price: $975 £650

SWEET AND TWENTY
(Style one) HN1298
Designer: L. Harradine
Height: 5³/₄in., 14.6cm.
Issued: 1928–1969
Price: $340 £225

SWEET AND TWENTY
(Style one) HN1360
Designer: L. Harradine
Height: 6in., 15.2cm.
Issued: 1929–1938
Colour variation
Price: $520 £345

SWEET AND TWENTY
(Style one) HN1437
Designer: L. Harradine
Height: 6in., 15.2cm.
Issued: 1930–1938
Colour variation
Price: $520 £345

SWEET AND TWENTY
(Style one) HN1438
Designer: L. Harradine
Height: 6in., 15.2cm.
Issued: 1930–1938
Colour variation
Price: $520 £345

SWEET ANNE HN1496

SWEET LAVENDER HN1373

SWEET AND TWENTY (Style one) HN1298

SWEET AND TWENTY
(Style one) HN1549
Designer: L. Harradine
Height: 6in., 15.2cm.
Issued: 1933–1949
Colour variation
Price: $440 £295

SWEET AND TWENTY
(Style one) HN1563
Designer: L. Harradine
Height: 6in., 15.2cm.
Issued: 1933–1938
Colour variation
Price: $590 £395

SWEET AND TWENTY
(Style one) HN1649
Designer: L. Harradine
Height: 6in., 15.2cm.
Issued: 1934–1949
Colour variation
Price: $590 £395

SWEET AND TWENTY
(Style two) HN1589
Designer: L. Harradine
Height: 3¹/₂in., 8.9cm.
Issued: 1933–1949
Price: $340 £225

SWEET AND TWENTY
(Style two) HN1610
Designer: L. Harradine
Height: 3¹/₂in., 8.9cm.
Issued: 1933–1938
Colour variation
Price: $420 £280

SWEET ANNE HN1318
Designer: L. Harradine
Height: 7¹/₂in., 19.1cm.
Issued: 1929–1949
Price: $260 £175

SWEET ANNE HN1330
Designer: L. Harradine
Height: 7¹/₄in., 18.4cm.
Issued: 1929–1949
Colour variation
Price: $260 £175

SWEET ANNE HN1331
Designer: L. Harradine
Height: 7¹/₄in., 18.4cm.
Issued: 1929–1949
Colour variation
Price: $260 £175

SWEET ANNE HN1453
Designer: L. Harradine
Height: 7in., 17.8cm.
Issued: 1931–1949
Colour variation
Price: $330 £220

SWEET ANNE HN1496
Designer: L. Harradine
Height: 7in., 17.8cm.
Issued: 1932–1967
Colour variation
Price: $260 £175

SWEET DREAMS HN2380

SWEET DREAMS
HN3394

SWEET MAID (Style one)
HN1505

SWEET ANNE HN1631
Designer: L. Harradine
Height: 7in., 17.8cm.
Issued: 1934–1938
Colour variation
Price: $410 £275

SWEET ANNE HN1701
Designer: L. Harradine
Height: 7in., 17.8cm.
Issued: 1935–1938
Colour variation
Price: $410 £275

SWEET ANNE M5
Designer: L. Harradine
Height: 4in., 10.1cm.
Issued: 1932–1945
Price: $300 £200

SWEET ANNE M6
Designer: L. Harradine
Height: 4in., 10.1cm.
Issued: 1932–1945
Colour variation
Price: $300 £200

SWEET ANNE M27
Designer: L. Harradine
Height: 4in., 10.1cm.
Issued: 1932–1945
Colour variation
Price: $300 £200

SWEET APRIL HN2215
Designer: P. Davies
Height: 7¹/₄in., 18.4cm.
Issued: 1965–1967
Price: $290 £195

SWEET DREAMS HN2380
Designer: P. Davies
Height: 5in., 12.7cm.
Issued: 1971–1990
Price: $190 £125

SWEET DREAMS HN3394
Designer: Alan Maslankowski
Height: 6in., 15cm.
Issued: 1992
Price: R.R.P.

SWEET LAVENDER HN1373
Designer: L. Harradine
Height: 9in., 22.8cm.
Issued: 1930–1949
Price: $525 £350

SWEET MAID (Style one)
HN1504
Designer: L. Harradine
Height: 8in., 20.3cm.
Issued: 1932–1938
Price: $675 £450

SWEET MAID (Style one)
HN1505
Designer: L. Harradine
Height: 8in., 20.3cm.
Issued: 1932–1938
Colour variation
Price: $675 £450

SWEET MAID (Style two)
HN2092
Designer: L. Harradine
Height: 7in., 17.8cm.
Issued: 1952–1955
Price: $410 £275

SWEET PERFUME HN3094
Designer: P. Parsons
Height: 13in., 33cm.
Issued: 1986
Price: R.R.P.

SWEET SEVENTEEN HN2734
Designer: D. V. Tootle
Height: 7¹/₂in., 19.1cm.
Issued: 1975–1993
Price: $220 £145

SWEET SIXTEEN HN2231
Designer: P. Davies
Height: 7¹/₄in., 18.4cm.
Issued: 1958–1965
Price: $240 £160

SWEET SUZY HN1918
Designer: L. Harradine
Height: 6¹/₂in., 16.5cm.
Issued: 1939–1949
Price: $525 £350

SWEET VIOLETS HN3175
Designer: D. Tootle
Height: 10¹/₄in., 26cm.
Issued: 1988–1989
Price: $150 £100

SWEETING HN1935
Designer: L. Harradine
Height: 6in., 15.2cm.
Issued: 1940–1973
Price: $200 £135

SWEETING HN1938
Designer: L. Harradine
Height: 6in., 15.2cm.
Issued: 1940–1949
        Colour variation
Price: $200 £135

SWIMMER HN1270
Designer: L. Harradine
Height: 7¹/₄in., 18.4cm.
Issued: 1928–1938
Price: $1050 £700

SWIMMER HN1326
Designer: L. Harradine
Height: 7¹/₂in., 19.1cm.
Issued: 1929–1938
        Colour variation
Price: $1050 £700

SWIMMER HN1329
Designer: L. Harradine
Height: 7¹/₂in., 19.1cm.
Issued: 1929–1938
        Colour variation
Price: $1050 £700

SYLVIA HN1478
Designer: L. Harradine
Height: 10¹/₂in., 26.7cm.
Issued: 1931–1938
Price: $450 £300

SWEET SEVENTEEN HN2734

TAPESTRY WEAVING
HN3048

FIGURES

SYMPATHY HN2838 (Black)
Designer: P. Davies
Height: 11³/₄in., 29.8cm.
Issued: 1981–1986
Price: $150 £100

SYMPATHY HN2876 (White)
Designer: P. Davies
Height: 11³/₄in., 29.8cm.
Issued: 1981–1986
Price: $150 £100

SYMPHONY HN2287
Designer: D. B. Lovegrove
Height: 5¹/₄in., 13.3cm.
Issued: 1961–1965
Price: $290 £195

T

TAILOR HN2174
Designer: M. Nicoll
Height: 5in., 12.7cm.
Issued: 1956–1959
Price: $750 £500

TAKING THINGS EASY HN2677
Designer: M. Nicoll
Height: 6³/₄in., 17.2cm.
Issued: 1975–1987
Price: $220 £145

TAKING THINGS EASY HN2680
Designer: M. Nicoll
Height: 7¹/₂in., 19.5cm.
Issued: 1987
Price: R.R.P.

TALL STORY HN2248
Designer: M. Nicoll
Height: 6¹/₂in., 16.5cm.
Issued: 1968–1975
Price: $250 £165

TANGO HN3075
Designer: A. Hughes
Height: 13in., 33cm.
Issued: 1985–1992
Price: $165 £110

TAPESTRY WEAVING HN3048
Designer: P. Parsons
Height: 7¹/₂in., 19cm.
Issued: 1985 in a limited edition of 750
Price: $825 £550

TEATIME HN2255
Designer: M. Nicoll
Height: 7¹/₄in., 18.4cm.
Issued: 1972–
Price: R.R.P.

TEEING OFF HN3276
Designer: Robert Tabbenor
Height: 8¹/₂in., 21.5cm.
Issued: 1990
Price: R.R.P.

TEATIME HN2255

TEEING OFF HN3276

SWIMMER HN1270

TAKING THINGS EASY HN2677

257

TEENAGER HN2203
Designer: P. Davies
Height: 7¼in., 18.4cm.
Issued: 1957–1962
Price: $288 £180

TENDER MOMENT HN3303
Designer: Peggy Davies
Height: 7in., 17.5cm.
Issued: 1990
Price: R.R.P.

TENDERNESS HN2713
Designer: E. Griffiths
Height: 11¾in., 29.5cm.
Issued: 1982–
Colour variation White
Price: R.R.P.

TENDERNESS HN2714
Designer: E. Griffiths
Height: 11¾in., 29.5cm.
Issued: 1982–1992
Colour variation Black
Price: $120 £80

TERESA HN1682
Designer: L. Harradine
Height: 5¾in., 14.6cm.
Issued: 1935–1949
Price: $825 £550

TERESA HN1683
Designer: L. Harradine
Height: 5¾in., 14.6cm.
Issued: 1935–1938
       Colour variation
Price: $825 £550

TERESA HN3206
Designer: A. Hughes
Height: 7¾in., 19.6cm.
Issued: 1989–1992
Price: $165 £110

TESS HN2865
Designer: P. Davies
Height: 5¾in., 14.6cm.
Issued: 1978–1983
Price: $250 £165

TÊTE-À-TÊTE (Style one) HN798
Designer: L. Harradine
Height: 5¾in., 14.6cm.
Issued: 1926–1938
Price: $900 £600

TÊTE-À-TÊTE (Style one) HN799
Designer: L. Harradine
Height: 5¾in., 14.6cm.
Issued: 1926–1938
       Colour variation
Price: $900 £600

TÊTE-À-TÊTE (Style two) HN1236
Designer: C. J. Noke
Height: 3in., 7.6cm.
Issued: 1927–1938
Price: $825 £550

THIS LITTLE PIG HN1793

TERESA HN3206

TÊTE-À-TÊTE (Style one)
HN799

THANK YOU HN2732

TENDER MOMENT HN3303

TÊTE-À-TÊTE HN1237
Designer: C. J. Noke
Height: 3in., 7.6cm.
Issued: 1927–1938
          Colour variation
Price: $825 £550

THANK YOU HN2732
Designer: W. K. Harper
Height: 8¼in., 21cm.
Issued: 1983–1986
Price: $220 £145

THANK YOU HN3390
Designer: Alan Maslankowski
Height: 6¼in., 16cm.
Issued: 1991
Price: R.R.P.

THANKFUL (White) HN3129
Designer: P. Parsons
Height: 8½in., 21.5cm.
Issued: 1987
Price: R.R.P.

THANKFUL (Black) HN3135
Designer: P. Parsons
Height: 8½in., 21.5cm.
Issued: 1987
Price: R.R.P.

THANKS DOC HN2731
Designer: W. K. Harper
Height: 8¾in., 22.2cm.
Issued: 1975–1990
Price: $250 £165

THANKSGIVING HN2446
Designer: M. Nicoll
Height: 8in., 20.3cm.
Issued: 1972–1976
Price: $240 £160

THINKING OF YOU HN3124
Designer: Alan Maslankowski
Height: 6¾in., 17cm.
Issued: 1991
Price: R.R.P.

THINKING OF YOU HN3490
Designer: Alan Maslankowski
Height: 6¾in., 17cm.
Issued: 1993
          Colour variation
Price: R.R.P.

THIS LITTLE PIG HN1793
Designer: L. Harradine
Height: 4in., 10.1cm.
Issued: 1936–
Price: R.R.P.

THIS LITTLE PIG HN1794
Designer: L. Harradine
Height: 4in., 10.1cm.
Issued: 1936–1949
          Colour variation
Price: $375 £250

THANK YOU HN3390

THANKS DOC HN2731

THINKING OF YOU HN3124

THANKSGIVING HN2446

259

FIGURES

THIS LITTLE PIG HN2125
Designer: L. Harradine
Height: 4in., 10.1cm.
Issued: 1984–
Colour variation
Price: R.R.P.

TILDY HN1576
Designer: L. Harradine
Height: 5in., 12.7cm.
Issued: 1933–1938
Price: $750 £500

TILDY HN1859
Designer: L. Harradine
Height: 5¹/₂in., 14cm.
Issued: 1938–1949
Colour variation
Price: $750 £500

TINA HN3494
Designer: P. Davies
Height: 7¹/₂in., 19.1cm.
Issued: 1993
Colour variation
U.K. only
Price: $150 £100

TINKLE BELL HN1677
Designer: L. Harradine
Height: 4³/₄in., 12cm.
Issued: 1935–1988
Price: $90 £60

TINSMITH HN2146
Designer: M. Nicoll
Height: 6¹/₂in., 16.5cm.
Issued: 1962–1967
Price: $340 £225

TINY TIM HN539
Designer: L. Harradine
Height: 3¹/₂in., 8.9cm.
Issued: 1922–1932
Price: $70 £45

TINY TIM M56
Designer: L. Harradine
Height: 3³/₄in., 9.5cm.
Issued: 1932–1983
Price: $60 £40

TIPTOE HN3293
Designer: Adrian Hughes
Height: 9in., 23cm.
Issued: 1990
Price: R.R.P.

TO BED HN1805
Designer: L. Harradine
Height: 6in., 15.2cm.
Issued: 1937–1959
Price: $195 £130

TO BED HN1806
Designer: L. Harradine
Height: 6in., 15.2cm.
Issued: 1937–1949
Colour variation
Price: $320 £210

TOINETTE HN1940
Designer: L. Harradine
Height: 6³/₄in., 17.1cm.
Issued: 1940–1949
Price: $825 £550
Also called 'Meryll'

TOP O' THE HILL HN3499

TOWN CRIER HN3261

TINA HN3494

TOM BOMBADIL HN2924

TOP O' THE HILL HN2126

TIPTOE HN3293

TOM HN2864
Designer: P. Davies
Height: 5³/₄in., 14.6cm.
Issued: 1978–1982
Price: $280 £185

TOM BOMBADIL HN2924
Designer: D. Lyttleton
Height: 5³/₄in., 14.6cm.
Issued: 1982–1984
Price: $70 £45

TOM BROWN HN2941
Designer: R. Tabbenor
Height: 6³/₄in., 17cm.
Issued: 1983–1985
Price: $165 £110

TOM SAWYER HN2926
Designer: D. Lyttleton
Height: 5¹/₄in., 13cm.
Issued: 1982–1985
Price: $165 £110

TOM, TOM THE PIPER'S SON HN3032
Designer: A. Hughes
Height: 7in., 17.5cm.
Issued: 1984–1987
Price: $110 £75

TOMORROW'S DREAMS HN3128
Designer: P. Parsons
Height: 6¹/₂in., 16.5cm.
Issued: 1988–1992
Price: $135 £90

TONY WELLER (Style one) HN346
Designer: C. J. Noke
Height: 10¹/₂in., 26.7cm.
Issued: 1919–1938
Price: $1275 £850

TONY WELLER (Style one) HN368
Designer: C. J. Noke
Height: 10¹/₂in., 26.7cm.
Issued: 1920–1938
Colour variation
Price: $900 £600

TONY WELLER (Style one) HN684
Designer: C. J. Noke
Height: 10¹/₄in., 26cm.
Issued: 1924–1938
Colour variation
Price: $900 £600

TONY WELLER (Style two) HN544
Designer: L. Harradine
Height: 3¹/₂in., 8.9cm.
Issued: 1922–1932
Price: $70 £45

TONY WELLER (Style two) M47
Designer: L. Harradine
Height: 4in., 10.1cm.
Issued: 1932–1982
Price: $60 £40

FIGURES

TOOTLES HN1680
Designer: L. Harradine
Height: 4³/₄in., 12cm.
Issued: 1935–1975
Price: $165 £110

TOP O' THE HILL HN1833
Designer: L. Harradine
Height: 7in., 17.8cm.
Issued: 1937–1971
Price: $250 £165

TOP O' THE HILL HN1834
Designer: L. Harradine
Height: 7in., 17.8cm.
Issued: 1937–
        Colour variation
Price: R.R.P.

TOP O' THE HILL HN1849
Designer: L. Harradine
Height: 7¹/₄in., 18.4cm.
Issued: 1938–1975
        Colour variation
Price: $250 £165

TOP O' THE HILL HN2126
Designer: P. Gee
Height: 4in., 10cm.
Issued: 1988
Price: $140 £95

TOP O' THE HILL HN3499
Designer: Leslie Harradine
Height: 4in., 10cm.
Issued: 1993
Price: R.R.P.

TOWN CRIER HN3261
Designer: P. Davies
Height: 4¹/₂in., 11.5cm.
Issued: 1989–1992
Price: $100 £65

TOWN CRIER HN2119
Designer: P. Davies
Height: 8¹/₂in., 21.6cm.
Issued: 1953–1976
Price: $290 £195

TOYMAKER HN2250
Designer: M. Nicoll
Height: 6in., 15.2cm.
Issued: 1959–1973
Price: $410 £275

TOYS HN1316
Designer: L. Harradine
Height: Unknown
Issued: 1929–1938
Price: $2250 £1500

TRACY HN2736
Designer: D. Tootle
Height: 7¹/₂in., 19cm.
Issued: 1983–
Price: R.R.P.

TRACY HN3291
Designer: D.V. Tootle
Height: 7¹/₂in., 19.1cm.
Issued: 1993
        Colour variation
        U.S.A. only
Price: R.R.P.

TILDY HN1576

TOM BROWN HN2941

TOM SAWYER HN2926

TRACY HN3291

TOP O' THE HILL HN1834

FIGURES

TRANQUILLITY HN2426
(Black)
Designer: P. Davies
Height: 12in., 30.5cm.
Issued: 1981–1986
Price: $150 £100

TRANQUILLITY HN2469
(White)
Designer: P. Davies
Height: 12in., 30.5cm.
Issued: 1981–1986
Price: $150 £100

TRAVELLERS' TALES
HN3185
Designer: E. J. Griffiths
Height: 9½in., 23.5cm.
Issued: 1988–1989
Price: $150 £100

TREASURE ISLAND HN2243
Designer: P. Davies
Height: 4¾in., 12cm.
Issued: 1962–1975
Price: $220 £145

TROTTY VECK M91
Designer: L. Harradine
Height: 4¼in., 10.8cm.
Issued: 1949–1982
Price: $60 £40

TULIPS HN466
Designer: Unknown
Height: 9½in., 24.1cm.
Issued: 1921–1938
Price: $1500 £1000

TULIPS HN488
Designer: Unknown
Height: 9½in., 24.1cm.
Issued: 1921–1938
       Colour variation
Price: $1500 £1000

TULIPS HN672
Designer: Unknown
Height: 9½in., 24.1cm.
Issued: 1924–1938
       Colour variation
Price: $1500 £1000

TULIPS HN747
Designer: Unknown
Height: 9½in., 24.1cm.
Issued: 1925–1938
       Colour variation
Price: $1500 £1000

TULIPS HN1334
Designer: Unknown
Height: 9½in., 24.1cm.
Issued: 1929–1938
       Colour variation
Price: $1050 £700

TUMBLER HN3181
Designer: D. Tootle
Height: 9in., 23cm.
Issued: 1989
Price: R.R.P.

TWILIGHT HN2256

TUMBLING HN3283

TZ'U HSI, THE EMPRESS
DOWAGER HN2391

TUMBLING HN3283
Designer: D. V. Tootle
Height: 9in., 23cm.
Issued: 1990
Price: R.R.P.

TUMBLING HN3289
Designer: D. V. Tootle
Height: 9in., 23cm.
Issued: 1991 in a limited
            edition of 2500
Price: $225 £150

TUPPENCE A BAG HN2320
Designer: M. Nicoll
Height: 5¹/₂in., 14cm.
Issued: 1968–
Price: R.R.P.

TWILIGHT HN2256
Designer: M. Nicoll
Height: 5in., 12.7cm.
Issued: 1971–1976
Price: $250 £165

TWO-A-PENNY HN1359
Designer: L. Harradine
Height: 8¹/₄in., 21cm.
Issued: 1929–1938
Price: $1500 £1000

**TZ'U HSI, THE EMPRESS
DOWAGER HN2391**
Designer: P. Davies
Height: 8in., 20cm.
Issued: 1983 in a limited
            edition of 750
Price: $900 £600

U

ULYSSES S. GRANT HN3403
Designer: Robert Tabbenor
Height: 11³/₄in., 30cm.
Issued: 1993 in a limited
            edition of 5000
Price: R.R.P

UNCLE NED HN2094
Designer: H. Fenton
Height: 6³/₄in., 17.2cm.
Issued: 1952–1965
Price: $340 £225

**UNDER THE GOOSEBERRY
BUSH HN49**
Designer: C. J. Noke
Height: 3¹/₂in., 8.9cm.
Issued: 1916–1938
Price: $900 £600

**"UPON HER CHEEKS SHE
WEPT" HN59**
Designer: L. Perugini
Height: 9in., 22.8cm.
Issued: 1916–1938
Price: $1800 £1200

**"UPON HER CHEEKS SHE
WEPT" HN511**
Designer: L. Perugini
Height: 9in., 22.8cm.
Issued: 1921–1938
            Colour variation
Price: $1800 £1200

TUPPENCE A BAG HN2320

UNCLE NED HN2094   ULYSSES S. GRANT HN3403

"UPON HER CHEEKS SHE WEPT" HN522
Designer: L. Perugini
Height: 9in., 22.8cm.
Issued: 1921–1938
Price: $1800 £1200

URIAH HEEP (Style one) HN545
Designer: L. Harradine
Height: 4in., 10.1cm.
Issued: 1922–1932
Price: $70 £45

URIAH HEEP (Style one) M45
Designer: L. Harradine
Height: 4in., 10.1cm.
Issued: 1932–1982
Price: $60 £40

URIAH HEEP (Style two) HN554
Designer: L. Harradine
Height: 7¼in., 18.4cm.
Issued: 1923–1939
Price: $300 £200

URIAH HEEP (Style two) HN1892
Designer: L. Harradine
Height: 7in., 17.8cm.
Issued: 1938–1952
Price: $300 £200

URIAH HEEP (Style three) HN2101
Designer: L. Harradine
Height: 7½in., 19.1cm.
Issued: 1952–1967
Price: $270 £180

V

VALERIE HN2107
Designer: P. Davies
Height: 4¾in., 12cm.
Issued: 1953–
Price: R.R.P.

VALERIE HN3620
Designer: P. Davies
Height: 4¾in., 12cm.
Issued: 1994
Colour variation
Price: R.R.P.

VANESSA HN1836
Designer: L. Harradine
Height: 7½in., 19.1cm.
Issued: 1938–1949
Price: $750 £500

VANESSA HN1838
Designer: L. Harradine
Height: 7½in., 19.1cm.
Issued: 1938–1949
Colour variation
Price: $750 £500

VANESSA HN3198
Designer: A. Hughes
Height: 8½in., 21.5cm.
Issued: 1989–1990
Price: $180 £120

VERENA HN1835

VENETA HN2722

VANITY HN2475

VANITY HN2475
Designer: P. Davies
Height: 5¼in., 13.3cm.
Issued: 1973–1992
Price: $110 £75

VENETA HN2722
Designer: W. K. Harper
Height: 8in., 20.3cm.
Issued: 1974–1980
Price: $220 £145

VERA HN1729
Designer: L. Harradine
Height: 4¼in., 10.8cm.
Issued: 1935–1938
Price: $600 £400

VERA HN1730
Designer: L. Harradine
Height: 4¼in., 10.8cm.
Issued: 1935–1938
Colour variation
Price: $600 £400

VERENA HN1835
Designer: L. Harradine
Height: 8¼in., 21cm.
Issued: 1938–1949
Price: $525 £350

VERENA HN1854
Designer: L. Harradine
Height: 8¼in., 21cm.
Issued: 1938–1949
Colour variation
Price: $900 £600

VERONICA (Style one) HN1517
Designer: L. Harradine
Height: 8in., 20.3cm.
Issued: 1932–1951
Price: $290 £195

VERONICA (Style one) HN1519
Designer: L. Harradine
Height: 8in., 20.3cm.
Issued: 1932–1938
Colour variation
Price: $410 £275

VERONICA (Style one) HN1650
Designer: L. Harradine
Height: 8in., 20.3cm.
Issued: 1934–1949
Colour variation
Price: $410 £275

VERONICA (Style one) HN1943
Designer: L. Harradine
Height: 8in., 20.3cm.
Issued: 1940–1949
Colour variation
Price: $410 £275

VERONICA (Style two) HN1915
Designer: L. Harradine
Height: 5¾in., 14.6cm.
Issued: 1939–1949
Price: $290 £195

VERONICA HN3205
Designer: A. Hughes
Height: 8in., 20.3cm.
Issued: 1989–1992
Price: $140 £95

VERONICA M64
Designer: L. Harradine
Height: 4¹/₂in., 10.8cm.
Issued: 1934–1949
Price: $300 £200

VERONICA M70
Designer: L. Harradine
Height: 4¹/₄in., 10.8cm.
Issued: 1936–1949
Colour variation
Price: $300 £200

VICTORIA HN2471
Designer: P. Davies
Height: 6¹/₂in., 16.5cm.
Issued: 1973–
Price: R.R.P.

VICTORIA HN3416
Designer: P. Davies
Height: 6¹/₂in., 16.5cm.
Issued: 1992 only
Price: $225 £150

VICTORIA & ALBERT
HN3256
Designer: D.V. Tootle
Height: 9¹/₄in., 23.5cm.
Issued: 1990 in a limited
edition of 2500
Price: R.R.P.

VICTORIAN LADY HN726
Designer: L. Harradine
Height: 7¹/₂in., 19.1cm.
Issued: 1925–1938
Price: $375 £250

VICTORIAN LADY HN727
Designer: L. Harradine
Height: 7¹/₂in., 19.1cm.
Issued: 1925–1938
Colour variation
Price: $292 £195

VICTORIAN LADY HN728
Designer: L. Harradine
Height: 7³/₄in., 19.7cm.
Issued: 1925–1952
Colour variation
Price: $247 £165

VICTORIAN LADY HN736
Designer: L. Harradine
Height: 7³/₄in., 19.7cm.
Issued: 1925–1938
Colour variation
Price: $375 £250

VICTORIAN LADY HN739
Designer: L. Harradine
Height: 7³/₄in., 19.7cm.
Issued: 1925–1938
Colour variation
Price: $410 £275

VICTORIAN LADY HN740
Designer: L. Harradine
Height: 7³/₄in., 19.7cm.
Issued: 1925–1938
Colour variation
Price: $340 £225

VICTORIA HN3416

VICTORIA HN2471

VICTORIA & ALBERT HN3256

VERONICA (Style one) HN1517

VICTORIAN LADY HN742
Designer: L. Harradine
Height: 7³/₄in., 19.7cm.
Issued: 1925–1938
Colour variation
Price: $490 £325

VICTORIAN LADY HN745
Designer: L. Harradine
Height: 7³/₄in., 19.7cm.
Issued: 1925–1938
Colour variation
Price: $410 £275

VICTORIAN LADY HN1208
Designer: L. Harradine
Height: 7³/₄in., 19.7cm.
Issued: 1926–1938
Colour variation
Price: $375 £250

VICTORIAN LADY HN1258
Designer: L. Harradine
Height: 7³/₄in., 19.7cm.
Issued: 1927–1938
Colour variation
Price: $375 £250

VICTORIAN LADY HN1276
Designer: L. Harradine
Height: 7¹/₂in., 19.1cm.
Issued: 1928–1938
Colour variation
Price: $410 £275

VICTORIAN LADY HN1277
Designer: L. Harradine
Height: 7³/₄in., 19.7cm.
Issued: 1928–1938
Colour variation
Price: $410 £275

VICTORIAN LADY HN1345
Designer: L. Harradine
Height: 7³/₄in., 19.7cm.
Issued: 1929–1949
Colour variation
Price: $340 £225

VICTORIAN LADY HN1452
Designer: L. Harradine
Height: 7³/₄in., 19.7cm.
Issued: 1931–1949
Colour variation
Price: $340 £225

VICTORIAN LADY HN1529
Designer: L. Harradine
Height: 7³/₄in., 19.7cm.
Issued: 1932–1938
Colour variation
Price: $375 £250

VICTORIAN LADY M1
Designer: L. Harradine
Height: 3³/₄in., 9.5cm.
Issued: 1932–1945
Price: $300 £200

VICTORIAN LADY M2
Designer: L. Harradine
Height: 3³/₄in., 9.5cm.
Issued: 1932–1945
Colour variation
Price: $300 £200

VIOLIN HN2432

VICTORIAN LADY HN728

VIVIENNE HN2073

VIKING HN2375

VICTORIAN LADY M25
Designer: L. Harradine
Height: 3³/₄in., 9.5cm.
Issued: 1932–1945
Colour variation
Price: $300 £200

VIKING HN2375
Designer: J. Bromley
Height: 8³/₄in., 22.2cm.
Issued: 1973–1976
Price: $290 £195

VIOLA D'AMORE HN2797
Designer: P. Davies
Height: 6in., 15.2cm.
Issued: 1976 in a limited
edition of 750
Price: $750 £500

VIOLIN HN2432
Designer: P. Davies
Height: 6¹/₄in., 15.9cm.
Issued: 1972 in a limited
edition of 750
Price: $750 £500

VIRGINALS HN2427
Designer: P. Davies
Height: 6¹/₄in., 15.9cm.
Issued: 1971 in a limited
edition of 750
Price: $750 £500

VIRGINIA HN1693
Designer: L. Harradine
Height: 7¹/₂in., 19.1cm.
Issued: 1935–1949
Price: $675 £450

VIRGINIA HN1694
Designer: L. Harradine
Height: 7¹/₂in., 19.1cm.
Issued: 1935–1949
Colour variation
Price: $675 £450

VIVIENNE HN2073
Designer: L. Harradine
Height: 7³/₄in., 19.7cm.
Issued: 1951–1967
Price: $340 £225

VOTES FOR WOMEN HN2816
Designer: W. K. Harper
Height: 9³/₄in., 24.7cm.
Issued: 1978–1981
Price: $290 £195

W

WAITING FOR A TRAIN HN3315
Designer: P. Gee
Height: 8¹/₂in., 21.6cm.
Issued: 1991 in a limited
edition 0f 500
Price: R.R.P.

VIRGINALS HN2427

VOTES FOR WOMEN HN2816

WAITING FOR A TRAIN
HN3315

VIOLA D'AMORE HN2797

267

WANDERING MINSTREL
HN1224
Designer: L. Harradine
Height: 7in., 17.8cm.
Issued: 1927–1938
Price: $1350 £900

WARDROBE MISTRESS
HN2145
Designer: P. Davies
Height: 5³/₄in., 14.6cm.
Issued: 1954–1967
Price: $370 £245

WATER MAIDEN HN3155
Designer: A. Hughes
Height: 12in., 30.5cm.
Issued: 1988–1991
Price: $150 £100

WAYFARER HN2362
Designer: M. Nicoll
Height: 5¹/₂in., 14cm.
Issued: 1970–1976
Price: $260 £175

WEDDING DAY HN2748
Designer: D. Tootle
Height: 12¹/₂in., 31.5cm.
Issued: 1987
Price: R.R.P.

WEDDING MORN HN1866
Designer: L. Harradine
Height: 10¹/₂in., 26.7cm.
Issued: 1938–1949
Price: $1275 £850

WEDDING MORN HN1867
Designer: L. Harradine
Height: 10¹/₂in., 26.7cm.
Issued: 1938–1949
Colour variation
Price: $1275 £850

WEDDING VOWS HN2750
Designer: D. Tootle
Height: 8in., 20cm.
Issued: 1988–1992
Price: $150 £100

WEE WILLIE WINKIE
HN2050
Designer: P. Davies
Height: 5¹/₄in., 13.3cm.
Issued: 1949–1953
Price: $270 £180

WEE WILLIE WINKIE
HN3031
Designer: A. Hughes
Height: 7³/₄in., 19.5cm.
Issued: 1984–1987
Price: $220 £145

WELCOME HOME HN3299
Designer: A. Hughes
Height: 8¹/₂in., 21.6cm.
Issued: 1992 in a limited edition of 9500
Price: R.R.P.

WELL DONE HN3362
Designer: V. Annand
Height: 4in., 10.1cm.
Issued: 1992
Price: R.R.P.

WARDROBE MISTRESS HN2145

WEE WILLIE WINKIE HN2050

WHAT FUN HN3364

WANDERING MINSTREL HN1224

WELCOME HOME HN3299

WELSH GIRL HN39
Designer: E. W. Light
Height: 12in., 30.5cm.
Issued: 1914–1938
Price: $2250 £1500

WELSH GIRL HN92
Designer: E. W. Light
Height: 12in., 30.5cm.
Issued: 1918–1938
Colour variation
Price: $2625 £1750

WELSH GIRL HN456
Designer: E. W. Light
Height: 12in., 30.5cm.
Issued: 1921–1938
Colour variation
Price: $2250 £1500

WELSH GIRL HN514
Designer: E. W. Light
Height: 12in., 30.5cm.
Issued: 1921–1938
Colour variation
Price: $3000 £2000

WELSH GIRL HN516
Designer: E. W. Light
Height: 12in., 30.5cm.
Issued: 1921–1938
Colour variation
Price: $3000 £2000

WELSH GIRL HN519
Designer: E. W. Light
Height: 12in., 30.5cm.
Issued: 1921–1938
Colour variation
Price: $3000 £2000

WELSH GIRL HN520
Designer: E. W. Light
Height: 12in., 30.5cm.
Issued: 1921–1938
Colour variation
Price: $3000 £2000

WELSH GIRL HN660
Designer: E. W. Light
Height: 12in., 30.5cm.
Issued: 1924–1938
Colour variation
Price: $1875 £1250

WELSH GIRL HN668
Designer: E. W. Light
Height: 12in., 30.5cm.
Issued: 1924–1938
Colour variation
Price: $2250 £1500

WELSH GIRL HN669
Designer: E. W. Light
Height: 12in., 30.5cm.
Issued: 1924–1938
Colour variation
Price: $1875 £1250

WELSH GIRL HN701
Designer: E. W. Light
Height: 12in., 30.5cm.
Issued: 1925–1938
Colour variation
Price: $1875 £1250

WELL DONE
HN3362

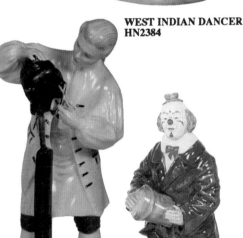

WEST INDIAN DANCER
HN2384

WIGMAKER OF
WILLIAMSBURG HN2239

WILL HE – WON'T HE?
HN3275

WELSH GIRL HN792
Designer: E. W. Light
Height: 12in., 30.5cm.
Issued: 1926–1938
Colour variation
Price: $1875 £1250

WENDY HN2109
Designer: L. Harradine
Height: 5in., 12.7cm.
Issued: 1953–
Price: R.R.P.

**WEST INDIAN DANCER
HN2384**
Designer: P. Davies
Height: 8³⁄₄in., 22.2cm.
Issued: 1981 in a limited
edition of 750
Price: $520 £325

WEST WIND HN1776
Designer: R. Garbe
Height: 14¹⁄₂in., 36.8cm.
Issued: 1933 in a limited
edition of 25
Price: $3750 £2500

WEST WIND HN1826
Designer: R. Garbe
Height: 14¹⁄₂in., 36.8cm.
Issued: 1937–1949
Price: $3750 £2500

WHAT FUN HN3364
Designer: V. Annand
Height: 4in., 10.1cm.
Issued: 1992
Price: R.R.P.

**WIGMAKER OF
WILLIAMSBURG HN2239**
Designer: P. Davies
Height: 7¹⁄₂in., 19.1cm.
Issued: 1960–1983
Price: $220 £145

**WILL HE – WON'T HE?
HN3275**
Designer: Robert Tabbenor
Height: 9in., 23cm.
Issued: 1990
Price: R.R.P.

WILLY-WON'T-HE HN1561
Designer: L. Harradine
Height: 6in., 15.2cm.
Issued: 1933–1949
Price: $410 £275

WILLY-WON'T-HE HN1584
Designer: L. Harradine
Height: 6in., 15.2cm.
Issued: 1933–1949
Colour variation
Price: $300 £200

WILLY-WON'T-HE HN2150
Designer: L. Harradine
Height: 5¹⁄₂in., 14cm.
Issued: 1955–1959
Colour variation
Price: $260 £175

FIGURES

WIMBLEDON HN3366
Designer: Valerie Annand
Height: 8in., 20cm.
Issued: 1995 in a limited
edition of 5000
Price: R.R.P.

WINDFLOWER (Style one)
HN1763
Designer: L. Harradine
Height: 7¼in., 18.4cm.
Issued: 1936–1949
Price: $410 £275

WINDFLOWER (Style one)
HN1764
Designer: L. Harradine
Height: 7¼in., 18.4cm.
Issued: 1936–1949
Colour variation
Price: $490 £325

WINDFLOWER (Style one)
HN2029
Designer: L. Harradine
Height: 7¾in., 19.6cm.
Issued: 1949–1952
Colour variation
Price: $410 £275

WINDFLOWER (Style two)
HN1920
Designer: L. Harradine
Height: 11in., 27.9cm.
Issued: 1939–1949
Price: $1050 £700

WINDFLOWER (Style two)
HN1939
Designer: L. Harradine
Height: 11in., 27.9cm.
Issued: 1940–1949
Colour variation
Price: $1050 £700

WINDFLOWER M78
Designer: L. Harradine
Height: 4in., 10.1cm.
Issued: 1939–1949
Price: $375 £250

WINDFLOWER M79
Designer: L. Harradine
Height: 4in., 10.1cm.
Issued: 1939–1949
Colour variation
Price: $375 £250

WINDFLOWER HN3077
Designer: A. Hughes
Height: 12¼in., 31cm.
Issued: 1987–1992
Price: $150 £100

WINDMILL LADY HN1400
Designer: L. Harradine
Height: 8½in., 21.6cm.
Issued: 1930–1938
Price: $1350 £900

WINDSWEPT HN3027
Designer: R. Jefferson
Height: 12in., 30.5cm.
Issued: 1985
Price: R.R.P.

WIMBLEDON HN3366

WINTERTIME HN3060

WINSTON S. CHURCHILL
HN3433

WINDFLOWER (Style one)
HN2029

270

FIGURES

WINNER HN1407
Designer: Unknown
Height: 6³/₄in., 17.2cm.
Issued: 1930–1938
Price: $3000 £2000

WINNING PUTT HN3279
Designer: Robert Tabbenor
Height: 8in., 20cm.
Issued: 1991
Price: R.R.P.

WINSOME HN2220
Designer: P. Davies
Height: 8in., 20.3cm.
Issued: 1960–1985
Price: $190 £125

**WINSTON S. CHURCHILL
HN3433**
Designer: Alan Maslankowski
Height: 12in., 30.5cm.
Issued: 1993 in a limited
        edition of 5000
Price: R.R.P.

WINTER (Style one) HN315
Designer: Unknown
Height: 7¹/₂in., 19.1cm.
Issued: 1918–1938
Price: $750 £500

WINTER (Style one) HN475
Designer: Unknown
Height: 7¹/₂in., 19.1cm.
Issued: 1921–1938
        Colour variation
Price: $975 £650

WINTER (Style two) HN2088
Designer: P. Davies
Height: 6¹/₄in., 15.9cm.
Issued: 1952–1959
Price: $410 £275

WINTER WELCOME HN3611
Designer: P. Davies
Height: 7¹/₂in., 19.1cm.
Issued: 1993
        Colourway red
Price: R.R.P.

WINTER'S WALK HN3052
Designer: A. Hughes
Height: 12¹/₄in., 31cm.
Issued: 1987
Price: R.R.P.

WINTERTIME HN3060
Designer: A. Hughes
Height: 8³/₄in., 22.2cm.
Issued: 1985
Price: $290 £195

WISTFUL HN2396
Designer: P. Davies
Height: 6¹/₂in., 16.5cm.
Issued: 1979–
Price: $165 £110

WINTER (Style two) HN2088

WINNING PUTT HN3279

WINTER WELCOME
HN3611

WISTFUL HN2472

WISTFUL HN2472
Designer: P. Davies
Height: 6¹/₂in., 16.5cm.
Issued: 1985–1986
Price: $220 £145

WITH LOVE HN3393
Designer: Alan Maslankowski
Height: 6in., 15cm.
Issued: 1992
Price: R.R.P.

WITH LOVE HN3492
Designer: A. Maslankowski
Height: 6in., 15cm.
Issued: 1994
Colour variation
Canada only
Price: R.R.P.

WIZARD HN2877
Designer: A. Maslankowski
Height: 9³/₄in., 24.8cm.
Issued: 1979–
Price: R.R.P.

WOMAN HOLDING CHILD HN462
Designer: Unknown
Height: 9¹/₄in., 23.5cm.
Issued: 1921–1938
Price: $2250 £1500

WOMAN HOLDING CHILD HN570
Designer: Unknown
Height: 9¹/₄in., 23.5cm.
Issued: 1923–1938
Colour variation
Price: $2250 £1500

WOMAN HOLDING CHILD HN703
Designer: Unknown
Height: 9¹/₄in., 23.5cm.
Issued: 1925–1938
Colour variation
Price: $2250 £1500

WOMAN HOLDING CHILD HN743
Designer: Unknown
Height: 9¹/₄in., 23.5cm.
Issued: 1925–1938
Colour variation
Price: $2250 £1500

WOMAN OF THE TIME OF HENRY VI HN43
Designer: E. W. Light
Height: 9¹/₄in., 23.4cm.
Issued: 1914–1938
Price: $3000 £2000

WOOD NYMPH HN2192
Designer: P. Davies
Height: 7¹/₄in., 18.4cm.
Issued: 1958–1962
Price: $260 £175

WOOD NYMPH HN2192   **WIZARD HN2877**

WRITING HN3049

FIGURES

WRITING HN3049
Designer: P. Parsons
Height: 7³/₄in., 19.5cm.
Issued: 1986 in a limited
edition of 750
Price: $750 £500

Y

YEARNING HN2920 (White)
Designer: P. Gee
Height: 11³/₄in., 29.8cm.
Issued: 1982–1986
Price: $150 £100

YEARNING HN2921 (Black)
Designer: P. Gee
Height: 11³/₄in., 29.8cm.
Issued: 1982–1986
Price: $150 £100

YEOMAN OF THE GUARD HN688
Designer: L. Harradine
Height: 5³/₄in., 14.6cm.
Issued: 1924–1938
Price: $800 £500

YEOMAN OF THE GUARD HN2122
Designer: L. Harradine
Height: 5³/₄in., 14.6cm.
Issued: 1954–1959
Price: $640 £400

YOUNG DREAMS HN3176
Designer: D. Tootle
Height: 6¹/₄in., 16cm.
Issued: 1988–1992
Price: $190 £125

YOUNG KNIGHT HN94
Designer: C. J. Noke
Height: 9¹/₂in., 24.1cm.
Issued: 1918–1936
Price: $3750 £2500

YOUNG LOVE HN2735
Designer: D. V. Tootle
Height: 10in., 25.4cm.
Issued: 1975–1990
Price: $450 £300

YOUNG MASTER HN2872
Designer: P. Davies
Height: 7in., 17.8cm.
Issued: 1980–1989
Price: $290 £195

WITH LOVE HN3393

YOUNG MASTER HN2872

YOUNG LOVE HN2735

273

YOUNG MISS NIGHTINGALE
HN2010
Designer: P. Davies
Height: 9¼in., 23.5cm.
Issued: 1948–1953
Price: $675 £450

YOUNG WIDOW HN1399
Designer: L. Harradine
Height: 8in., 20.3cm.
Issued: 1930–1938
Price: $1040 £650
Also called 'Little Mother'
(Style two)

YOURS FOREVER HN3354
Designer: Pauline Parsons
Height: 8in., 20cm.
Issued: 1992
Price: R.R.P.

YUM-YUM (Style one) HN1268
Designer: L. Harradine
Height: 5in., 12.7cm.
Issued: 1928–1938
Price: $384 £240

YUM-YUM (Style one) HN1287
Designer: L. Harradine
Height: 5in., 12.7cm.
Issued: 1928–1939
Colour variation
Price: $384 £240

YUM-YUM (Style two) HN2899
Designer: W. K. Harper
Height: 10¾in., 27.3cm.
Issued: 1980–1986
Price: $224 £140

YVONNE HN3038
Designer: A. Hughes
Height: 9in., 23cm.
Issued: 1987
Price: R.R.P.

YOURS FOREVER HN3354

YUM-YUM (Style two) HN2899

YOUNG MISS NIGHTINGALE
HN2010

YOUNG WIDOW HN1399

JUGS

Doulton Lambeth stoneware water jug with silver rim, 15cm high. $75 £50

A stoneware jug made for Style & Winch Ltd., 4¼in. high, circa 1910. $110 £75

Flowers Ales and Stout water jug by Doulton, 10½cm high. $225 £150

A water jug made for William Younger & Co., circa 1920. $75 £50

Pick-Kwik character jug, 4in. high, made in a limited edition of 2000, circa 1982. $100 £65

Greene King water jug by Doulton, 11cm high. $150 £100

King George IV Scotch Whisky by Doulton, 16cm high. $300 £200

Early 20th century 'Big Ben Scotch Whisky' jug. $144 £90

Doulton Kingsware jug, Peter Dawson's Scotch, 10½cm high. $300 £200

PUB JUGS

Greer's O.V.H Scotch
Whisky jug by Doulton,
13½cm high. $300 £200

Charrington's Toby Stout
water jug by Doulton, 11cm
high. $300 £200

Vat 69 Liquer Scotch
Whisky by Doulton, 14cm
high. $300 £200

Dirty Dicks Famous
Wines by Doulton, 23cm
high. $675 £450

Barnsley Brewery Co,
'Famous for mild and
bitter ales' by Doulton,
17cm high. $1125 £750

Melrose Highland Whisky
by Doulton, 20cm high.
                    $675 £450

Watsons Old Scotch
Whisky, manufactured by
Doulton, 14½cm high.
        $750 £500

R & H Jenner Southwark,
London, 1904 by Doulton,
16½cm high.
            $675 £450

Macnair Twinkle Scotch
Whisky by Doulton, 17cm
high. $560 £375

PUB JUGS

Thorne's Whisky jug by
Doulton, 15cm high.
$600 £400

Ushers Green Stripe Scotch
Whisky by Doulton, 15½cm
high. $450 £300

D.C.L. Gold Medal Scotch
Whisky, by Doulton, 15cm
high. $335 £225

Sporting Squire Kingsware
flask for Dewar's, circa 1909,
21cm high. $225 £150

Schweppes Green Ginger
Wine, 34cm high. $300 £200

Greenlee Brothers Claymore
Scotch Whisky by Royal
Doulton, 16.5cm high.
$675 £450

Sunderland Highland Whisky
by Grant Mackay & Co, by
Doulton, 17cm high.
$1200 £800

Johnnie Walker Whisky,
manufactured by Doulton,
15½cm high. $750 £500

Doulton Kingsware
Coronation flask for
George V and Queen Mary,
1911, 17cm high. $225 £150

PUB JUGS

Doulton Kingsware jug
for Peter Dawson's
Scotch, 9½cm high.
$300 £200

Truman's water jug by
Doulton,12cm high.
$300 £200

Simpson's Scotch Whisky
by Doulton, 15cm high.
$600 £400

R&H Jenner & Sons ' A
quart of ale is a dish for
a King'; 16.5cm high.
$600 £400

John Bull small size
flagon made for Jim Bean
Whiskey, 5in. high, 1984.
$100 £65

Sir Edward Lee's Scotch
Whisky, water jug by
Royal Doulton, 16½cm
high. $375 £250

Doulton Lambeth earthenware
jug, two tone brown, mask top
and plated lip, 7in. high.
(G. A. Key) £40 $67

Pick-Kwik character jug
inscribed 'Pick-Kwik, Derby,
Sells Jim Beam Whiskey', circa
1984. $100 £65

Royal Doulton slater patent jug,
designed in the 'Black Jack'
style and inscribed with
Landlords Caution, 7in. high
(G. A. Key) £35 $59

PUB JUGS

'Glen Garry Old Highland Whisky' jug with blue lettering, 7½in. high. $140 £95

Pick-Kwik small size flagon made for Jim Bean Whiskey, 5in. high. 1983. $100 £65

Doulton whisky jug made for Charles Wilkinson & Co., featuring Burns Cottage, Ayr. $130 £85

Charrington's Toby made by Royal Doulton, 23cm high. $700 £475

Uncle Sam small size flagon made for Jim Bean Whiskey, 5in. high, 1984. $100 £65

Bisquit's Brandy figure, water jug made by Doulton, 27cm high. $635 £425

R.H. Jenners & Sons Coronation 1911 by Royal Doulton, 16½cm high. $675 £450

Buzfuz small size character jug made for Pick-Kwik, Derby, 4in. high, 1984. $100 £65

Doulton Lambeth stoneware harvest water jug with applied slip scenes, 15½cm high. $60 £40

PUB JUGS

Usher's Scotch Whisky
water jug by Doulton,
10½cm high. $300 £200

'The McCallum', a large
Kingsware character jug made
for D. & J. McCallum Whisky
Distillers, circa 1930.
$1500 £1000

Blundell's Cabinet Whisky
by Doulton. $375 £250

Palmeira House, Brighton,
Great Glen Pure Malt
Whisky, by Doulton, 37cm
high. $600 £400

A Royal Doulton advertising
jug, William Grant, Specially
Commissioned for Wm. Grant
& Sons Ltd., limited edition of
500, 1986. $410 £275

' Wake up and get to
business', Watsons Scotch
Whisky, 23cm high.
$1125 £750

Very Old Duniva Highland
Whisky by Doulton, 16cm
high. $525 £350

King George IV Scotch
Whisky water jug by
Doulton. $225 £150

Greenlees Brothers,
Claymore Scotch Whisky
by Doulton. $675 £450

TOBY JUGS

ALBERT SAGGER THE POTTER
D6745
(Collectors' Club)
Designer: W. Harper
Height: Small 4in., 10cm.
Issued: 1986–1992
Price: $113 £75

CHARLIE CHAPLIN
Designer: Unknown
Height: Large 11in., 28cm.
Issued: c.1918
Price: $3000 £2000

CLIFF CORNELL
Designer: Unknown
Height: 9¼in., 23.5cm.
Issued: 1956 in a limited
edition of 500
Price: $375 £250 (Blue Suit)

CLIFF CORNELL
Designer: Unknown
Height: 9¼in., 23.5cm.
Issued: 1956 in a limited
edition of 500
Price: $375 £250 (Brown Suit)

CLIFF CORNELL
Designer: Unknown
Height: 9¼in., 23.5cm.
Issued: 1956 in a limited
edition of 350
Price: $375 £250 (Beige Suit)

THE CLOWN D6935
Designer: S. Taylor
Height: Medium 5½in., 14cm.
Issued: 1993
Price: R.R.P.

FALSTAFF D6062
Designer: C. Noke
Height: Large 8½in., 21.5cm.
Issued: 1939–1991
Price: $100 £65

FALSTAFF D6063
Designer: C. Noke
Height: Small 5¼in., 13.5cm.
Issued: 1939–1991
Price: $70 £45

FATHER CHRISTMAS D6940
Designer: W. K. Harper
Height: Medium 5½in., 14cm.
Issued: 1993
Price: R.R.P.

GEORGE ROBEY
Designer: Unknown
Height: Large 10½in., 26.5cm.
Issued: c.1925
Price: $3000 £2000

HAPPY JOHN D6031
Designer: H. Fenton
Height: Large 8¾in., 22cm.
Issued: 1939–1991
Price: $100 £65

HAPPY JOHN D6070
Designer: H. Fenton
Height: Small 5½in., 14cm.
Issued: 1939–1991
Price: $100 £65

ALBERT SAGGER THE POTTER
D6745

CHARLIE CHAPLIN

CLIFF CORNELL
(Brown Suit)

CLIFF CORNELL (Blue Suit)

CLIFF CORNELL (Beige Suit)

TOBY JUGS

HONEST MEASURE D6108
Designer: H. Fenton
Height: Small 4¹/₂in., 11.5cm.
Issued: 1939–1991
Price: $60 £40

HUNTSMAN D6320
Designer: H. Fenton
Height: Large 7¹/₂in., 19cm.
Issued: 1950–1991
Price: $100 £65

JOLLY TOBY D6109
Designer: H. Fenton
Height: Medium 6¹/₂in., 16.5cm.
Issued: 1939–1991
Price: $70 £45

LEPRECHAUN D6948
Designer: S. Taylor
Height: Medium 5¹/₄in., 13.5cm.
Issued: 1994 Limited edition 2500
Price: R.R.P.

OLD CHARLEY D6030
Designer: H. Fenton
Height: Large 8³/₄in., 22cm.
Issued: 1939–1960
Price: $220 £145

OLD CHARLEY D6069
Designer: H. Fenton
Height: Small 5¹/₂in., 14cm.
Issued: 1939–1960
Price: $165 £110

SHERLOCK HOLMES D6661
Designer: R. Tabbenor
Height: Large 8³/₄in., 22cm.
Issued: 1981–1991
Price: $100 £65

SIR FRANCIS DRAKE D6660
Designer: M. Abberley
Height: Large 9in., 23cm.
Issued: 1981–1991
Price: $100 £65

SQUIRE D6319
Designer: H. Fenton
Height: Medium 6in., 15cm.
Issued: 1950–1969
Price: $340 £225

THE BEST IS NOT TOO GOOD D6107
Designer: H. Fenton
Height: 4¹/₂in., 11.5cm.
Issued: 1939–1960
Price: $290 £195

TOBY XX D6088
Designer: H. Fenton
Height: 6¹/₂in., 16.5cm.
Issued: 1939–1969
Price: $220 £145

TOBY XX
Designer: Harry Simeon
Height: Large 7¹/₂in., 19cm.
Issued: 1922
Price: $240 £150

FALSTAFF D6063

HAPPY JOHN D6070

SIR FRANCIS DRAKE D6660

OLD CHARLEY D6030

TOBY JUGS

WINSTON CHURCHILL D6171
Designer: H. Fenton
Height: Large 9in., 23cm.
Issued: 1941–1991
Price: $110 £75

WINSTON CHURCHILL D6172
Designer: H. Fenton
Height: Medium 5½in., 14cm.
Issued: 1941–1991
Price: $70 £45

WINSTON CHURCHILL D6175
Designer: H. Fenton
Height: Small 4in., 10cm.
Issued: 1941–1991
Price: $50 £35

JOLLY TOBY D6109

GEORGE ROBEY

HUNTSMAN D6320

SHERLOCK HOLMES D6661

TOBY JUGS

JUGS

SQUIRE D6319

TOBY XX

TOBY XX D6088

MEASURE DRINK

WINSTON CHURCHILL
D6171

THE BEST IS NOT TOO GOOD D6107

WINSTON CHURCHILL
D6175

WINSTON CHURCHILL
D6172

DOULTONVILLE TOBIES

Designer: **W. Harper**
Size: **4in., 10cm.**

ALDERMAN MACE D6766
Issued: 1987–1991
Price: $50 £35

BETTY BITTERS D6716
Issued: 1984–1990
Price: $70 £45

CAPTAIN PROP D6812
Issued: 1988–1991
Price: $50 £35

CAPTAIN SALT D6721
Issued: 1985–1991
Price: $50 £35

CHARLIE CHEER D6768
Issued: 1987–1991
Price: $50 £35

DR. PULSE D6723
Issued: 1985–1991
Price: $50 £35

FLORA FUCHSIA D6767
Issued: 1987–1990
Price: $70 £45

FRED FEARLESS D6809
Issued: 1989–1991
Price: $50 £35

FRED FLY D6742
Issued: 1986–1991
Price: $50 £35

LEN LIFEBELT D6811
Issued: 1988–1991
Price: $50 £35

MADAME CRYSTAL D6714
Issued: 1984–1989
Price: $70 £45

MAJOR GREEN D6740
Issued: 1986–1991
Price: $50 £35

MIKE MINERAL D6741
Issued: 1986–1989
Price: $70 £45

MISS NOSTRUM D6700
Issued: 1983–1991
Price: $50 £35

MISS STUDIOUS D6722
Issued: 1985–1989
Price: $70 £45

MONSIEUR CHASSEUR D6769
Issued: 1987–1991
Price: $50 £35

MR BRISKET D6743
Issued: 1986–1991
Price: $50 £35

MR FURROW D6701
Issued: 1983–1989
Price: $70 £45

ALDERMAN MACE D6766

BETTY BITTERS D6716

CAPTAIN PROP D6812

CAPTAIN SALT D6721

CHARLIE CHEER D6768

DR. PULSE D6723

JUGS

DOULTONVILLE TOBIES

MR LITIGATE D6699
Issued: 1983–1991
Price: $50 £35

MRS LOAN D6715
Issued: 1984–1989
Price: $70 £45

MR TONSIL D6713
Issued: 1984–1991
Price: $50 £35

PAT PARCEL D6813
Issued: 1988–1992
Price: $70 £45

REV. CASSOCK D6702
Issued: 1983–1990
Price: $60 £40

SERGEANT PEELER D6720
Issued: 1985–1991
Price: $50 £35

FRED FEARLESS D6809

PAT PARCEL D6813

FRED FLY D6742

MADAME CRYSTAL
D6714

LEN LIFEBELT D6811

MAJOR GREEN D6740

MIKE MINERAL D6741

MISS NOSTRUM D6700

MISS STUDIOUS D6722

286

DOULTONVILLE TOBIES

MONSIEUR CHASSEUR
D6769

MR BRISKET D6743

MR FURROW D6701

MR TONSIL D6713

MR LITIGATE D6699

MRS LOAN D6715

FLORA FUCHSIA D6767

REV. CASSOCK D6702

SERGEANT PEELER
D6720

SMALL SEATED TOBIES

Designer: H. Fenton
Size: 4½in., 11.5cm.

MR PICKWICK D6261
Issued: 1948–1960
Price: $176 £120

MR MICAWBER D6262
Issued: 1948–1960
Price: $176 £120

SAIREY GAMP D6263
Issued: 1948–1960
Price: $184 £125

FAT BOY D6264
Issued: 1948–1960
Price: $176 £120

SAM WELLER D6265
Issued: 1948–1960
Price: $176 £120

CAP'N CUTTLE D6266
Issued: 1948–1960
Price: $176 £120

MR PICKWICK D6261

MR MICAWBER D6262

SAIREY GAMP D6263

SAM WELLER D6265

CAP'N CUTTLE D6266

FAT BOY D6264

KINGSWARE

Sailor's Story, a Royal Doulton Kingsware flask, circa 1910, 6^{1}/$_{2}$in. high. $450 £300

Pied Piper, a Royal Doulton Kingsware teapot, with silver mounts, circa 1905. $375 £250

Gillie and Fisherman, a Royal Doulton Kingsware flask made for Bulloch & Lade, circa 1919, 8^{1}/$_{2}$in. high. $525 £350

The Watchman, a Royal Doulton Kinsware flask made for Dewar's Whisky, 10^{1}/$_{2}$in. high, circa 1902. $208 £130

Royal Doulton Holbein Kingsware wall plaque decorated with a portrait of a gentleman in relief, 15^{3}/$_{4}$in. diam. $480 £320

George The Guard, a Kingsware pear shaped ewer made for Dewar's, 8^{1}/$_{4}$in. high, issued 1908. $192 £120

Beefeater, a Royal Doulton Kingsware flask made for Dewar's Whisky, by Noke, 7^{1}/$_{4}$in. high, circa 1908. $525 £350

Royal Doulton Kingsware tobacco jar decorated in relief with a gentleman smoking, 8^{1}/$_{4}$in. high. $120 £75

'Nelson', a Royal Doulton Kingsware flask, 7^{1}/$_{2}$in. high, circa 1909. $525 £350

The Macnab, a Kingsware flask, made for Dewar's, 9in. high, circa 1915. $208 £130

Weller, Senior, a miniature Royal Doulton Kingsware vase, with silver hallmarked rim, circa 1909, 2¹/₄in. high.
          $100 £65

Fagin, a Kingsware water jug, 8¹/₄in. high, circa 1908.
          $336 £210

'For Thy Sake Tobacco I Would Do Anything But Die', a Royal Doulton Kingsware water jug, hallmarked silver rim, 8³/₄in. high, circa 1908. $304 £190

The Leather Bottle, a Royal Doulton Kingsware flask, circa 1918, 6¹/₄in. high, 6in. long.
          $480 £300

Monks in the Cellar, a Royal Doulton Kingsware two-handled vase, 10¹/₄in. high, circa 1912.
          $272 £170

Mr. Pickwick and Sam Weller on the reverse, a Royal Doulton Kingsware flask, circa 1930, 9¹/₂in. high. $400 £250

Uncle Sam, a Kingsware flask made for Dewar's, yellow glaze, 7¹/₂in. high, circa 1908.
          $432 £270

The Connoisseur, a Kingsware pear shaped flask made for Dewar's, 8³/₄in. high.
          $432 £270

Stiggins, a Royal Doulton Kingsware whisky flask, issued 1936, 8in. high. $320 £200

Bardolph, a Royal Doulton Kingsware mustard pot with silver hallmarked rim, circa 1904, 3in. high. $110 £75

Artful Dodger and Oliver Twist, a Royal Doulton Kingsware whisky flask, circa 1912, 8in. high. $448 £280

A Hunting Scene (low relief) a Royal Doulton Kingsware water jug, circa 1909, 11in. high. $256 £160

A Royal Doulton Kingsware jardiniere decorated with seagulls, circa 1910, 5½in. high, 9in. wide. $224 £140

Pied Piper, a Royal Doulton Kingsware two-handled vase, signed Noke, circa 1910, 11¾in. high. $272 £170

George The Guard, a Royal Doulton Kingsware whisky flask, Dewar's Scotch Whisky, circa 1908, 8¼in. high. $224 £140

Sporting Squire, a Kingsware flask made for Dewar's, 6¾in. high, circa 1909. $208 £130

Tony Weller, a Royal Doulton Kingsware flask with the inscription, 'Tony Weller Bevare of the Vidders', 8in. high. $208 £130

Sporting Squire, a Royal Doulton Kingsware flask, made for Dewar's Whisky, Royal cypher on reverse, 6³/₄in. high, circa 1909. $240 £160

Peace flagon, a Kingsware flask with brown border, made for Dewar's, No. 181, 7¹/₂in. high, circa 1919. $400 £250

Micawber, a Royal Doulton Kingsware whisky flask made for Dewar's Scotch Whisky, 7in. high, issued 1909. $208 £130

Monks In the Cellar, a Royal Doulton Kingsware flask, Dewar's Scotch Whisky, circa 1905, 8¹/₂in. high. $208 £130

Dickens' Characters, a Royal Doulton Kingsware water jug, 7in. high. $410 £275

Bonnie Prince Charlie, a Royal Doulton Kingsware flask made for Dewar's Whisky, 7in. high, circa 1913. $208 £130

Crusader, a Royal Doulton Kingsware whisky flask, Greenlees Bros. Scotch whisky, circa 1913, 8in. high. $384 £240

Nightwatchman, a Kingsware water jug, by Noke, 5¹/₂in. high. $112 £70

Don Quixote, a Royal Doulton Kingsware flagon, 10¹/₂in. high, circa 1913. $300 £200

Mr. Pickwick Proposes The Toast, a Royal Doulton Kingsware flask, signed Noke, circa 1912, 8in. high. $352 £220

Mr. Pickwick, a miniature Royal Doulton Kingsware jug with silver hallmarked rim, circa 1907, 2¹/₂in. high. $112 £70

The Jovial Monk, a Kingsware flask made for Dewar's, 8in. high, circa 1908. $224 £140

Oyez, Oyez, ewer shaped Kingsware flask made for Dewar's Scotch Whisky, 10¹/₂in. high, issued 1909. $192 £120

Royal Doulton Kingsware mug with silver rim, 4in. high. $165 £110

Church-Warden, a Kingsware flask made for Dewar's Whisky, 9¹/₂in. high, circa 1907. $448 £280

George The Guard, a Royal Doulton Kingsware whisky flask, Dewar's Scotch Whisky, circa 1908, 10in. high. $208 £130

The Alchemist, a Royal Doulton Kingsware flask, by Noke, circa 1913, 8¹/₄in. high. $300 £200

Pied Piper, a Royal Doulton Kingsware milk jug with silver mounts, circa 1905. $110 £75

Bill Sykes, a miniature Royal
Doulton Kingsware loving cup
with silver hallmarked rim,
circa 1907, 2¹/₂in. high.
$128 £80

Witches, a small pair of Royal
Doulton Kingsware two-handled
vases, circa 1912, 4¹/₂in. high.
$176 £110

Sam Weller, a miniature Royal
Doulton Kingsware loving cup,
hallmarked silver rim, circa
1909, 1³/₄in. high. $128 £80

Royal Doulton Kingsware
single-handled jug depicting a
golfer and his caddie.
$448 £280

Nelson, a Royal Doulton Kingsware triangular flask, 8in. high,
6in. wide, 1914. $352 £220

Pirates, a Royal Doulton whisky
flask, by Noke, circa 1909, 6in.
high. $448 £280

Ben Jonson, a Kingsware flask
made for Dewar's Scotch
Whisky, issued 1909, 7in. high.
$192 £120

Sydney Harbour, a Royal
Doulton triangular Kingsware
flask, Dewar's Scotch Whisky,
6¹/₂in. high, circa 1914.
$512 £320

Double Foxes (one curled), a
Royal Doulton Kingsware
tobacco jug with silver hallmarked rim, circa 1912, 7¹/₂in.
high. $512 £320

Darby and Joan, a Royal
Doulton tea cup, circa 1912,
2³/₄in. high. $80 £50

Royal Doulton Kingsware sugar
bowl with silver mounts, circa
1905. $130 £85

Mr. Pickwick, a Royal Doulton
Kingsware tea cup in low relief,
circa 1912, 2¹/₂in. high.
                      $110 £75

He's A Jolly Good Fellow, Dr.
Johnson at The Cheshire
Cheese, a Royal Doulton Kingsware whisky flask, circa 1924,
8in. high. $525 £350

Royal Doulton Kingsware Duke
of York water jug, 7¹/₄in. high.
                      $288 £180

Admiral of the Fleet, a Royal
Doulton Kingsware flask,
Dewar's Scotch Whisky, circa
1916, 7¹/₂in. high. $464 £290

Don Quixote, a Royal Doulton
Kingsware mug, 4¹/₂in. high,
circa 1912. $112 £70

John Barleycorn, a Royal
Doulton Kingsware flask, circa
1931, 7in. high. $330 £220

Squire, a Kingsware Toby jug,
hallmarked silver rim, 6¹/₂in.
high. $480 £300

Peace flagon, a Kingsware flask with green border, made for Dewar's, No. 187, 7¹/₂in. high, circa 1919. $448 £280

Small fox, head down, a Royal Doulton Kingsware tobacco jar with hallmarked silver rim, circa 1912, 7³/₄in. high.
$525 £350

Watchman, a Kingsware globular shaped flask, 8in. high, with modelled head. $224 £140

Royal Doulton Kingsware single handled jug depicting golfers, 9in. high. $525 £350

Huntsman, a Royal Doulton Kingsware loving cup, issued 1932, 8in. high. $224 £140

Pied Piper, a Royal Doulton Kingsware two-handled vase, signed Noke, circa 1910, 11¹/₄in. high. $224 £140

Don Quixote, a Kingsware water jug, 10¹/₂in. high, circa 1913.
$216 £135

Memories, a Kingsware water jug depicting Dickens' characters. $225 £150

Pied Piper, a Royal Doulton Kingsware water jug with hallmarked silver rim and lid, 8¹/₂in. high. $240 £150

Bill Sykes, a Royal Doulton Kingsware pear-shaped whisky flask, circa 1905, 7³/₄in. high.
$352 £220

One of the Forty, a Royal Doulton Kingsware ashtray, designed by H. Tittensor, circa 1921, 3³/₄in. high, HN423.
$448 £280

The Crown, a Kingsware George VI commemorative flask, made for Dewar's Whisky, 1,000 issued 1937, 6in. high.
$544 £340

Bardolph, a Royal Doulton Kingsware water jug, 7¹/₄in. high, circa 1902. $144 £90

Pair of Royal Doulton Kingsware candlesticks, a Hunting Scene in low relief, circa 1912, 11in. high. $260 £175

The Alchemist, a Royal Doulton Kingsware clock, 7¹/₂in. high, circa 1913. $640 £400

Parson Jones, a Royal Doulton Kingsware water jug, 7¹/₂in. high, circa 1935. $224 £140

Tony Weller, a Royal Doulton Kingsware whisky flask, circa 1912, 9¹/₂in. high. $675 £450

Pied Piper, a Royal Doulton Kingsware coffee pot with silver mounts, circa 1905. $240 £150

Huntsman, a Royal Doulton Kingsware Toby jug, 7¹/₂in. high.　　$525　£350

Mr. Pecksniff, a miniature Royal Doulton Kingsware vase with hallmarked silver rim, circa 1909, 2in. high.
$112　£70

Ben Johnson, a Royal Doulton Kingsware flask made for Dewar's Scotch Whisky, 7in. high, issued in 1909.
$180　£120

Falstaff, green hat, a Royal Doulton Kingsware whisky flask, Dewar's Scotch Whisky, 7¹/₂in. high, circa 1907.
$208　£130

Nelson, a Kingsware flat-shaped flask made for Dewar's, circa 1914, 8¹/₂in. high.　$375　£250

Tavern Scenes, a Royal Doulton Kingsware two-handled vase, 6in. high, circa 1920.
$300　£200

Chadband (Bleak House), a Royal Doulton Kingsware whisky flask, 8in. high, circa 1912.　　$525　£350

Nightwatchman, a Royal Doulton Kingsware jug, by Noke, 7in. high.　$144　£90

Parson Brown, a Royal Doulton Kingsware water jug, 7¹/₂in. high, circa 1935.　$224　£140

Royal Doulton Kingsware whisky flask in the form of Tony Weller, 3¹/₂in. high. $525 £350

Memories, a Kingsware water jug depicting Dickens' characters. $300 £200

Jovial Monk, a Kingsware flask made for Dewar's Scotch Whisky, issued 1908, 7³/₄in. high. $330 £220

Fisherman, a Royal Doulton Kingsware flask, signed Noke, circa 1904, 7in. high. $352 £220

Royal Doulton jug in low relief by Charles Crombie, depicting a golfer, 9¹/₄in. high, circa 1910. $496 £310

A Hunting Scene, Kingsware water jug, 6¹/₂in. high. $160 £100

George V Coronation, a Kingsware jug with silver hallmarked rim, circa 1911, 6³/₄in. high. $352 £220

Mr. Pickwick and Sam Weller, a Royal Doulton Kingsware coffee pot with hallmarked silver rim, signed Noke, circa 1909, 6¹/₂in. high. $330 £220

Drink Wisely But Not Too Well, a Kingsware water jug of a pipe-smoking man, 8in. high. $208 £130

Wizard, a large Royal Doulton Kingsware ewer, circa 1905, 16¹/₂in. high. $560 £350

Royal Doulton Kingsware coffee pot, with silver mounts, circa 1905. $240 £150

Watchman, a Royal Doulton Kingsware flask, circa 1930, 10¹/₂in. high. $208 £130

A Kingsware two-handled vase 'Here's Health Unto His Majesty', 13in. high. $375 £250

Coachman, a Doulton Kingsware flagon, issued 1932, 10¹/₂in. high. $330 £220

Wizard, a Royal Doulton Kingsware flask decorated with a wizard standing over a cauldron, designed by Noke, 10in. high, issued 1904. $448 £280

LOVING CUPS & JUGS

ADMIRAL LORD NELSON LOVING CUP
Designed by C.J. Noke & H. Fenton, 10½in.
Issued 1935 in a limited edition of 600.

$750 £500

THE APOTHECARY LOVING CUP
Designed by C.J. Noke & H. Fenton, 6in. high,
Issued 1934 in a limited edition of 600.

$600 £400

CAPTAIN COOK LOVING CUP
Designed by C.J. Noke & H. Fenton, 9½in. high,
Issued 1933 in a limited edition of 350.

$3000 £2000

CAPTAIN PHILLIP JUG
Designed by C.J. Noke & H. Fenton, 9¼in. high,
Issued 1938 in a limited edition of 350.

$4800 £3000

CHARLES DICKENS JUG
Designed by C.J. Noke & H. Fenton, 10$\frac{1}{2}$in. high,
Issued 1936 in a limited edition of 1000.
$825 £550

DICKENS DREAM JUG
Designed by C.J. Noke, 10$\frac{1}{2}$in. high,
Issued 1933 in a limited edition of 1000.
$750 £500

GEORGE WASHINGTON BICENTENARY JUG
Designed by C.J. Noke & H. Fenton, 10$\frac{3}{4}$in. high, Issued 1932 in a limited edition of 1000, Colour variation on handle.
$7200 £4500

LOVING CUPS & JUGS

JACKDAW OF RHEIMS JUG
Designer - Unknown, 11in. high,
Issued - Trial Jug circa 1934. $4500 £3000

GEORGE WASHINGTON BICENTENARY JUG
Designed by C.J. Noke & H. Fenton, 10³/₄in. high,
Issued 1932 in a limited edition of 1000,
Variation on handle style.   **$5250 £3500**

JAN VAN RIEBECK LOVING CUP
Designed by C.J. Noke & H. Fenton, 10¹/₄in. high,
Issued circa 1935 in a limited edition of 300.
          $2400 £1500

GUY FAWKES JUG
Designed by H. Fenton, 7¹/₂in. high, Issued 1934 in a limited edition of 600.   **$675 £450**

JOHN PEEL LOVING CUP
Designer - Unknown, 9in. high,
Issued 1933 in a limited edition of 500.
$720 £450

**KING EDWARD VIII CORONATION LOVING
CUP (Small)**
Designed by C.J. Noke, 6½in. high,
Issued 1937 in a limited edition of 1000.
$320 £200

**KING EDWARD VIII CORONATION LOVING
CUP (Large)**
Designed by C.J. Noke & H. Fenton, 10in. high,
Issued 1937 in a limited edition of 2000.
$560 £350

**KING GEORGE V AND QUEEN MARY SILVER
JUBILEE LOVING CUP**
Designed by C.J. Noke & H. Fenton, 10in. high,
Issued 1935 in a limited edition of 1000.
$560 £350

**KING GEORGE VI AND QUEEN ELIZABETH
CORONATION LOVING CUP (Large)**
Designed by C.J. Noke & H. Fenton, 10$\frac{1}{2}$in. high,
Issued 1937 in a limited edition of 2000.
$560 £350

**KING GEORGE VI AND QUEEN ELIZABETH
CORONATION LOVING CUP (Small)**
Designed by C.J. Noke & H. Fenton, 6$\frac{1}{2}$in. high,
Issued 1937 in a limited edition of 2000.
$400 £250

MASTER OF FOXHOUNDS PRESENTATION JUG
Designed by C.J. Noke, 13in. high, Issued 1930 in a limited edition of 500. $675 £450

MAYFLOWER LOVING CUP
Designed by David Biggs, 10¼in. high,
Issued 1970 in a limited edition of 500.

$225 £150

PIED PIPER JUG
Designed by C.J. Noke & H. Fenton, 10in. high,
Issued 1934 in a limited edition of 600.

$825 £550

POTTERY IN THE PAST LOVING CUP
Designed by Graham Tongue, 6in. high, Issued 1983.

$220 £145

QUEEN ELIZABETH II CORONATION JUG
Designer - Unknown, 6¼in. high,
Issued 1953 unlimited.

$150 £100

QUEEN ELIZABETH II CORONATION LOVING CUP
Designed by C.J. Noke & H. Fenton, 10½in. high, Issued 1953 in a limited edition of 1000.

$450 £300

QUEEN ELIZABETH SILVER JUBILEE LOVING CUP
Designed by R. Johnson, 10½in. high,
Issued 1977 in a limited edition of 250.

$750 £500

REGENCY COACH JUG
Designed by C.J. Noke, 10in. high,
Issued 1931 in a limited edition of 500.

$640 £400

ROBIN HOOD LOVING CUP
Designed by C.J. Noke & H. Fenton, 8¹/₂in. high, Issued 1938 in a limited edition of 600.
$675 £450

SIR FRANCIS DRAKE JUG
Designed by C.J. Noke & H. Fenton, 10¹/₂in. high,
Issued 1933 in a limited edition of 500.
$675 £450

THE THREE MUSKETEERS LOVING CUP
Designed by C.J. Noke & H. Fenton, 10in. high,
Issued 1936 in a limited edition of 600.
$640 £400

TOWER OF LONDON JUG
Designed by C.J. Noke & H. Fenton, 9¹/₂in. high,
Issued 1933 in a limited edition of 500.
$675 £450

TREASURE ISLAND JUG
Designed by C.J. Noke & H. Fenton, 7¹/₂in. high,
Issued in 1934 in a limited edition of 600.
$560 £350

THE VILLAGE BLACKSMITH JUG
Designed by C.J. Noke, 7³/₄in. high, Issued 1936 in a limited edition of 600.   **$675 £450**

THE WANDERING MINSTREL LOVING CUP
Designed by C.J. Noke & H. Fenton, 5$^1/_2$in. high, Issued 1934 in a limited edition of 600.
$450 £300

WILLIAM SHAKESPEARE JUG
Designed by C.J. Noke, 10$^3/_4$in. high, Issued 1933 in a limited edition of 1000. $560 £350

WILLIAM WORDSWORTH LOVING CUP
Designed by C.J. Noke, 6$^1/_2$in. high, Issued 1933 unlimited. $1200 £750

MISCELLANEOUS WARE

ASH BOWLS

AULD MAC D6006
Size: 3in., 7.5cm.
Issued: 1939-1960
Price: $130 £85

FARMER JOHN D6007
Size: 3in., 7.5cm.
Issued: 1939-1960
Price: $130 £85

OLD CHARLEY D5925
Size: 3in., 7.5cm.
Issued: 1938-1960
Price: $130 £85

PADDY D5926
Size: 3in., 7.5cm.
Issued: 1938-1960
Price: $130 £85

PARSON BROWN D6008
Size: 3in., 7.5cm.
Issued: 1939-1960
Price: $130 £85

SAIREY GAMP D6009
Size: 3in., 7.5cm.
Issued: 1939-1960
Price: $130 £85

ASH TRAYS

DICK TURPIN D5601
Size: 2¾in., 7cm.
Issued: 1936-1960
Price: $110 £75

JOHN BARLEYCORN D5602
Size: 2¾in., 7cm.
Issued: 1936-1960
Price: $110 £75

OLD CHARLEY D5599
Size: 2¾in., 7cm.
Issued: 1936-1960
Price: $110 £75

PARSON BROWN D5600
Size: 2¾in., 7cm.
Issued: 1936-1960
Price: $110 £75

DICK TURPIN

JOHN BARLEYCORN

OLD CHARLEY

PARSON BROWN

311

BOOKENDS

MR MICAWBER HN1615
Size: 4in., 10cm.
Issued: 1934-c.1939
Price: $1125 £750

MR PICKWICK HN1623
Size: 4in., 10cm.
Issued: 1934-c.1939
Price: $1125 £750

SAIREY GAMP HN1625
Size: 4in., 10cm.
Issued: 1934-c.1939
Price: $1125 £750

TONY WELLER HN1616
Size: 4in., 10cm.
Issued: 1934-c.1939
Price: $1125 £750

BUSTS

HRH Princess Anne, designed by
E. J. Griffiths, introduced 1973,
11in. high, limited edition of 750,
to commemorate her marriage to
Captain Mark Phillips. $225 £150

HM Queen Elizabeth II and HRH
The Duke of Edinburgh, designed
by E. J. Griffiths, 10½in. and
11¼in. high, introduced 1972,
limited edition of 750. Royal Silver
Wedding Anniversary. $375 £250

Sir Winston Churchill, designed
by E. J. Griffiths, 11¼in. high,
introduced 1974, limited edition
of 750, to commemorate the
centenary of his birth. $375 £250

BUSTS

BUZ FUZ D6048
Issued: 1939-1960
Price: $100 £65

MR MICAWBER D6050
Issued: 1939-1960
Price: $100 £65

MR PICKWICK D6049
Issued: 1939-1960
Price: $100 £65

SAIREY GAMP D6047
Issued: 1939-1960
Price: $100 £65

SAM WELLER D6052
Issued: 1939-1960
Price: $100 £65

TONY WELLER D6051
Issued: 1939-1960
Price: $100 £65

BUZ FUZ

SAIREY GAMP

MR MICAWBER

SAM WELLER

MR PICKWICK

TONY WELLER

DICKENS TINIES

ARTFUL DODGER D6678
Designer: P. Gee
Issued: 1982
Price: $45 £30

BILL SYKES D6684
Designer: M. Abberley
Issued: 1982
Price: $45 £30

BETSY TROTWOOD D6684
Designer: M. Abberley
Issued: 1982
Price: $45 £30

CHARLES DICKENS D6688
Designer: E. Griffiths
Issued: 1982
Price: $70 £45

DAVID COPPERFIELD D6680
Designer: M. Abberley
Issued: 1982
Price: $45 £30

FAGIN D6679
Designer: R. Tabbenor
Issued: 1982
Price: $45 £30

LITTLE NELL D6681
Designer: M. Abberley
Issued: 1982
Price: $45 £30

MR BUMBLE D6686
Designer: R. Tabbenor
Issued: 1982
Price: $45 £30

MRS BARDELL D6687
Designer: R. Tabbenor
Issued: 1982
Price: $45 £30

OLIVER TWIST D6677
Designer: R. Tabbenor
Issued: 1982
Price: $45 £30

SCROOGE D6682
Designer: M. Abberley
Issued: 1982
Price: $45 £30

URIAH HEEP D6682
Designer: R. Tabbenor
Issued: 1982
Price: $45 £30

MUSICAL JUGS

AULD MAC D5889
Issued: 1938-c.1939
Price: $525 £350

OLD CHARLEY D5858
Issued: 1937-c.1939
Price: $525 £350

OLD KING COLE D6014
Issued: 1939
Price: $1275 £850

OLD KING COLE (Yellow Crown) D6014
Issued: 1939
Price: $2480 £1550

PADDY D5887
Issued: 1938-1939
Price: $525 £350

TONY WELLER D5888
Issued: 1938-1939
Price: $525 £350

OLD KING COLE

NAPKIN RINGS

FAT BOY M59
Issued: 1935-1939
Price: $375 £250

MR MICAWBER M58
Issued: 1935-1939
Price: $375 £250

MR PICKWICK M57
Issued: 1935-1939
Price: $375 £250

SAIREY GAMP M62
Issued: 1935-1939
Price: $375 £250

SAM WELLER M61
Issued: 1935-1939
Price: $375 £250

TONY WELLER M60
Issued: 1935-1939
Price: $375 £250

FAT BOY   MR MICAWBER   MR PICKWICK

SAIREY GAMP   SAM WELLER   TONY WELLER

SUGAR BOWLS

OLD CHARLEY D6012
Size: 2½in., 6.5cm.
Issued: 1939
Price: $450 £300

SAIREY GAMP D6011
Size: 2½in., 6.5cm.
Issued: 1939
Price: $450 £300

TONY WELLER D6013
Size: 2½in., 6.5cm.
Issued: 1939
Price: $450 £300

OLD CHARLEY   SAIREY GAMP   TONY WELLER

TABLE LIGHTERS

BACCHUS D6505
Size: 3½in., 9cm.
Issued: 1964-1974
Price: $165 £110

BEEFEATER D6233
Size: 3½in., 9cm.
Issued: 1958-1973
Price: $165 £110

BUZ FUZ D5838
Size: 3½in., 9cm.
Issued: 1958
Price: $190 £125

BACCHUS   BEEFEATER   BUZ FUZ

CAPTAIN AHAB D6506
Size: 3½in., 9cm.
Issued: 1964-1974
Price: $250 £165

CAP'N CUTTLE D5842
Size: 3½in., 9cm.
Issued: 1958
Price: $190 £125

FALSTAFF D6385
Size: 3½in., 9cm.
Issued: 1958-1973
Price: $180 £120

CAPTAIN AHAB   CAP'N CUTTLE   FALSTAFF

LAWYER D6504
Size: 3½in., 9cm.
Issued: 1962-1974
Price: $190 £125

LONG JOHN SILVER D6386
Size: 3½in., 9cm.
Issued: 1958-1973
Price: $165 £110

MR MICAWBER D5843
Size: 3½in., 9cm.
Issued: 1958
Price: $195 £130

MR PICKWICK D5839
Size: 3½in., 9cm.
Issued: 1958-1961
Price: $220 £145

LAWYER   LONG JOHN SILVER   MR MICAWBER

OLD CHARLEY D5527
Size: 3½in., 9cm.
Issued: 1959-1973
Price: $190 £125

POACHER D6464
Size: 3½in., 9cm.
Issued: 1958-1973
Price: $190 £125

PORTHOS D6453
Size: 3½in., 9cm.
Issued: 1958
Price: $450 £300

RIP VAN WINKLE D6463
Size: 3½in., 9cm.
Issued: 1958
Price: $450 £300

MR PICKWICK   POACHER   RIP VAN WINKLE

315

TEAPOTS

FALSTAFF D6854
Designer: W.K. Harper
Size: 6¹/₂in., 16.5cm.
Issued: 1989-1992
Price: $110 £75

LONG JOHN SILVER D6853
Designer: W.K. Harper
Size: 6¹/₂in., 16.5cm.
Issued: 1989-1992
Price: $110 £75

OLD BALLOON SELLER D6855
Designer: W.K. Harper
Size: 6¹/₂in., 16.5cm.
Issued: 1990-1992
Price: $130 £85

OLD CHARLEY D6017
Size: 7in., 18cm.
Issued: 1939
Price: $1125 £750

OLD SALT D6818
(Collectors' Club)
Designer: W.K. Harper
Size: 6¹/₂in., 16.5cm.
Issued: 1988
Price: $165 £110

SAIREY GAMP D6015
Size: 7in., 18cm.
Issued: 1939
Price: $1125 £750

TONY WELLER D6016
Size: 7in., 18cm.
Issued: 1939
Price: $1275 £850

OLD SALT

SAIREY GAMP

OLD CHARLEY

TOBACCO JARS

OLD CHARLEY D5844
Size: 5½in., 14cm.
Issued: 1938-1941
Price: $1125 £750

PADDY D5854
Size: 5½in., 14cm.
Issued: 1938-1941
Price: $1125 £750

OLD CHARLEY   PADDY

TOOTHPICK HOLDERS

OLD CHARLEY D6152
Size: 2¼in., 5.5cm.
Issued: 1940-1941
Price: $525 £350

PADDY D6151
Size: 2¼in., 5.5cm.
Issued: 1940-1941
Price: $750 £500

SAIREY GAMP D6150
Size: 2¼in., 5.5cm.
Issued: 1940-1941
Price: $375 £250

OLD CHARLEY   PADDY   SAIREY GAMP

WALL VASES

JESTER D6111
Size: 7¼in., 18cm.
Issued: 1940-1941
Price: $1425 £950

OLD CHARLEY D6110
Size: 7¼in., 18cm.
Issued: 1940-1941
Price: $1425 £950

WALL MASKS

A Royal Doulton miniature face mask, 'Jester', possibly HN1611, 7.7cm. long, c.m. $525 £350

A Royal Doulton face mask, 'Jester', probably HN1630, 28.5cm. long, c.m.l. & c., date code for 1937.   £450 £300

A Royal Doulton miniature face mask, 'Jester', possibly HN1609, 7.5cm. long, c.m. $490 £325

A Royal Doulton 'Grey Friar' wall mask, 7¼in. high, circa 1940-41. $975 £650

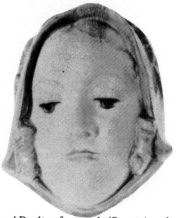

A Royal Doulton face mask, 'Sweet Anne', HN1590, design attributed to L. Harradine, 20.2cm. long, c.m.l. & c., impressed date 4.7.33. $450 £300

A Royal Doulton miniature face mask, possibly by L. Harradine, HN1614, 7cm. high, c.m. $480 £300

PANELS

In the early 20th century the Doulton works began producing decorative pottery tiles in large numbers for the embellishment of both interiors and exteriors of shops, bars and other establishments.

Making pictures and decorations from tiles was however far from being a new idea for as far back as the Egyptian Pharaohs the device had been used and some very beautiful tiles can still be seen in mosques of Iran and other Moslem countries. The Persian tile with its intricate foliage decoration and brilliant colours was an artistic masterpiece.

Doulton's idea of making whole pictures from tiles however was a new departure and their creations were used in the decoration of hospital wards, especially children's wards, where the artists let their fancies run free. The results were wonderful creations of nursery rhymes and fantasy children's scenes which must have diverted the minds of many small patients.

Tiled walls were not only decorative but they also had the advantage of being easily washed down and cleaned for it was a time when medical authorities were beginning to realise the importance of hygiene in hospitals.

By the 1950's however, modernisation programmes meant that tiled walls were either torn out or covered over with boarding. Those that have survived are now being preserved as works of art. Prices range from a few hundred pounds for a pictorial set of six to as much as ten thousand pounds for a large pictorial wall panel.

HERE WE GO GATHERING NUTS IN MAY

SIMPLE SIMON MET A PIEMAN

HANSEL AND GRETEL

THE GOOSE GIRL

SLEEPING BEAUTY

OLD MOTHER HUBBARD

CINDERELLA

PUSS IN BOOTS

LITTLE MISS MUFFET

SLEEPING PRINCESS   **THERE WAS AN OLD WOMAN WHO LIVED IN A SHOE**

LADY QUEEN ANNE

LITTLE BOY BLUE

THE QUEEN OF HEARTS

HIGGLEDY, PIGGLEDY, MY BLACK HEN

LITTLE BO-PEEP

PUSS IN BOOTS

OLD KING COLE WAS A MERRY OLD SOUL

LITTLE JACK HORNER

DING, DONG, BELL, PUSSY'S IN THE WELL

LITTLE RED RIDING HOOD

SEE-SAW, MARGERY DAW

SERIES WARE

Gaffers Series sugar bowl, 3in. high, circa 1915, depicting a gaffer outside a cottage.
$70 £45

Coaching Days, a Series ware jardiniere, 6½in. high.
$260 £175

Monks in the Cellar Series sugar bowl, 3½in. high, circa 1909, depicting a monk drinking.
$100 £65

Willow Pattern Series jar and cover, 6½in. high, circa 1912.
$120 £75

English Cottages Series, two-handled cup, 4in. high, circa 1924, depicting an old English cottage.
$70 £45

Silhouette Series biscuit barrel, silver plated rim and lid, 5½in. high, depicting Country Scenes.
$140 £95

Oliver Twist tankard in low relief, designed by C.J. Noke, issued 1949-1960. $220 £145

The Gleaners, Series ware sandwich tray.
$70 £45

Nightwatchman Series tobacco jar, 5½in. high circa 1909, by Noke, depicting a watchman carrying a pike.
$140 £95

A Royal Doulton Cecil Aldin Series ware jardiniere, the decoration from the 'Old English Scenes', 18cm. high. $375 £250

A sampler pattern Series ware tankard, 7in. high. $100 £65

Shakespeare Series art pot, 7¹/₂in. high, 10in. diam., circa 1922. $240 £160

'Country Garden', Series ware tray 'Old Man with Scythe', 1929. $90 £60

Dickens' ware 'Friar' shape jug depicting 'Poor Joe', 4³/₄in. high. $100 £65

Rural England Series candlesticks, 7in. high, circa 1925. $140 £95

Hunting Series spirit barrel and stand, 7in. high, circa 1924. $450 £300

Sunday Smocks Series, two-handled bowl, 3in. high, circa 1936, depicting an old man holding a basket. $100 £65

Nightwatchman Series sugar bowl and cover, 3½in. high, circa 1909. $100 £65

Under The Greenwood Tree Series sugar bowl and cover, 4in. high, circa 1914, depicting life in Sherwood Forest.
                                $100 £65

'Hastings Castle', Churches and Castle Series vase, 8in. high, circa 1901. $100 £65

'Country Garden' Series dish depicting the 'Maid at the Well', circa 1929. $75 £50

Royal Doulton Series ware coffee pot, 7½in. tall, D5506, 1934. $140 £95

Robert Burns portrait plaque with his cottage in the background, 10¼in. diam.
                                $60 £40

A Royal Doulton jug and basin set depicting Sydney Carton.
                                $525 £350

Gallant Fishers large Series art pot, by Izaak Walton, 12in. high, circa 1908. $448 £280

JUGS

'Little Nell', Dickens' Series jug, 7in. high, circa 1908.
$100 £65

Countryside Series water jug, 7in. high, circa 1936. $100 £65

Country Garden Series jug and cover, 7¹/₂in. high, circa 1929.
$110 £75

Rural England Series jug, 7in. high, circa 1933, depicting lambs in a field. $70 £45

Gleaners and Gypsies Series water jug, 7in. high, circa 1909, depicting a gypsy with bundle of corn. $110 £75

Egyptian Series jug, 7in. high, circa 1902. $100 £65

Rural England (Welsh) Series water jug, 12¹/₂in. high, circa 1907, depicting a woman in traditional dress. $140 £95

Oliver Twist jug designed by C.J. Noke, depicting 'Fagin and Bumble', D5617. $220 £145

The Bayeux Tapestry Series jug, 6¹/₂in. high, circa 1907, depicting Harold on horseback.
$130 £85

JUGS

'Mr Pickwick', Dickens' Series jug, 7in. high, circa 1912. $110 £75

Desert Scenes Series water jug, 6in. high, circa 1909, depicting a woman on a camel. $90 £60

Gondoliers Series jug, 7in. high, circa 1909, depicting a Venice scene. $130 £85

Gallant Fishers Series jug, by Izaak Walton, 7in. high, circa 1906, depicting a fisherman on the bank. $140 £95

A Jacobean jug 'Ye Old Belle' depicting a serving wench and two cavaliers, 6½in. high. $130 £85

Sunday Smocks Series jug and cover, 8in. high, circa 1936, depicting a man under a tree. $110 £75

'Sam Weller', Dickens' Series jug, 7¼in. high, circa 1912. $110 £75

Under The Greenwood Tree Series jug, 8in. high, circa 1937, depicting Friar Tuck and Robin Hood. $130 £85

Nightwatchman Series water jug, by C.J. Noke, 6¾in. high, circa 1907. $100 £65

Silhouette Series jug, 4in. high, depicting Country Scenes. $70 £45

Old Moreton Hall Series water jug, 4¹/₂in. high, circa 1915, depicting gentlemen in a mid 16th century scene. $100 £65

Sir Roger de Coverley Series cream jug, 3¹/₂in. high, circa 1911, depicting Sir Roger on horseback. $75 £50

Canterbury Pilgrims Series jug, 7¹/₂in. high, circa 1909, depicting Pilgrims on Horseback. $100 £65

'Nightwatchman', a Series ware jug by C.J. Noke, 8¹/₂in. high, D1198, 1903. $140 £95

Shakespeare Series jug, 12in. high, circa 1912, depicting 'Wolsey'. $110 £75

Huntsman Series water jug, 11in. high, circa 1906, depicting two huntsmen at the inn. $150 £100

Rural England Series Country Gardens jug, 7in. high, circa 1929, depicting a cottage by a pond. $90 £60

Under The Greenwood Tree Series water jug, 8¹/₂in. high, circa 1937. $130 £85

JUGS

Water jug in low relief depicting 'Tony Weller', D6397.
$140 £95

'Old London' jug in low relief designed by C.J. Noke, issued 1949-1960, D6291. $260 £175

Famous Sailing Ships Series jug, 4½in. high, circa 1938.
$80 £55

Monks in the Cellar Series water jug, 8in. high, circa 1909.
$90 £60

Under The Greenwood Tree Series, jug, 7in. high, circa 1937, depicting Friar Tuck and Robin Hood. $130 £85

New Cavaliers Series water jug, 12in. high, circa 1907, depicting two cavaliers toasting.
$110 £75

'Sir Toby Belch', Shakespeare Series jug, 8½in. high, circa 1904, quotation 'Maria, I Say a Stoop of Wine'. $130 £85

'Fagin', Dickens' Series jug, 6½in. high, circa 1912.
$130 £85

Wedlock Series water jug, 11in. high, circa 1905, depicting a gentleman and a lady with a fan.
$140 £95

PLATES

'Sairey Gamp' rack plate,
Dickens' Series, 10¼in. diam.,
circa 1912. $100 £65

'The Fleur-De-Lys, St. Albans'
rack plate, Old English Inns
Series, 10¼in. diam., circa 1939.
                $70 £45

'Painted Feelings' rack plate,
Behind the Painted Masque
Limited Edition Series, 9in.
diam., 1982. $140 £95

'Thunder in the Air' rack plate,
Aged in Wood Limited Edition
Series, 10½in. diam. $70 £45

'Gibson Girl' rack plate
designed by Charles Dana
Gibson, circa 1901. $140 £95

'Marshlands' rack plate,
Collectors Limited Edition
Series, 10½in. diam., 1981.
                $50 £35

Early Motoring Series titled
'Deaf', 10½in. diam., circa 1906.
                $260 £175

Series ware rack plate 'Mother
Kangaroo and Toby', 10½in.
diam. $40 £25

'Noble Heritage' rack plate,
Collectors Series, Limited
Edition, 8¼in. diam., 1981.
                $40 £25

PLATES

'Arabian Nights' rack plate, 'The Arrival of the Unknown Princess', 10¼in. diam. $80 £55

'Kathleen and Child' plate, Collectors Limited Edition Series, 8¼in. diam., 1981. $70 £45

Old English Inns Series ware rack plate depicting 'The Bear's Head', 10in. diam. $70 £45

'At the Cheshire Cheese', Dr. Johnson Series rack plate, 13in. diam., circa 1909. $90 £60

'Gibson Girl' rack plate, by Charles Dana Gibson, circa 1901. $140 £95

'Winning Colours' rack plate, Collectors Limited Edition Series, 10½in. diam. $50 £35

'Weathering the Storm' rack plate, Aged in Wood Limited Edition Series, 10¼in. diam., $70 £45

'Short Headed Salmon', a Royal Doulton rack plate, signed by J. Birbeck, 9½in. diam., circa 1913. $192 £120

'Edinburgh Castle', rack plate, 10½in. diam. $50 £35

PLATES

'The Old Balloon Seller' rack plate in low relief, 10¹/₂in. diam. $110 £75

'Make Me Laugh' rack plate, Behind the Painted Masque Limited Edition Series, 9in. diam., 1982. $130 £85

'Aero', a Royal Doulton commemorative rack plate, 1909. $300 £200

Rack plate 'Autumn' from 'The Seasons'. $45 £30

Charles Dickens portrait plate with a border of Dickens' characters, 10¹/₄in. diam. $60 £40

Series ware rack plate 'The Seasons', 'Winter' $45 £30

Royal Doulton rack plate 'Short Headed Salmon', signed J. Birbeck, 9¹/₂in. diam., circa 1909. $192 £120

'Valentine's Day' Series ware rack plate, 1985, 6¹/₄in. diam. $40 £25

'Gibson Girl' rack plate designed by Charles Dana Gibson, circa 1901. $140 £95

TEAPOTS

'Gallant Fishers' teapot, by
Izaak Walton, 6in. high, circa
1906. $225 £150

Under The Greenwood Tree
teapot, 4¹/₂in. high, circa 1937,
depicting Robin Hood and Friar
Tuck. $225 $150

Gondoliers Series teapot, 5¹/₂in.
high, circa 1909. $225 £150

Silhouette Series teapot, 5in.
high, depicting Country Scenes.
                    $150 £100

A Series ware teapot, 5¹/₂in.
high, circa 1930, depicting the
Old Woman Who Lived in the
Shoe. $240 £160

Old Moreton Hall Series teapot,
4¹/₂in. high, circa 1915,
depicting Queen Elizabeth I
outside. $220 £145

'Fagin', Dickens' Series teapot,
5¹/₂in. high, circa 1930.
                    $260 £175

Jackdaw of Rheims Series
teapot, 6¹/₂in. high, circa 1908,
depicting The Cardinal.
                    $225 £150

Sir Roger de Coverley Series
teapot, 5in. high, circa 1911,
depicting Sir Roger in the
garden. $220 £145

Arabian Nights Series teapot,
5in. high, circa 1909, depicting
the attendants. $220 £145

'Old Moreton Hall' Series ware
teapot, 5¹/₂in. high. $67 £42

Monks in the Cellar Series
teapot, 4¹/₂in. high, circa 1909,
depicting a monk inspecting the
food. $180 £120

VASES

Rural England (Welsh) Series, two-handled vase, 12¹/₂in. high, circa 1907, depicting a woman in traditional dress. $165 £110

Rural England Series vase, 4¹/₂in. high, circa 1916, depicting a girl gathering bluebells. $100 £65

'Orlando', Shakespeare Series vase, 8in. high, circa 1912. $142 £95

Old Moreton Hall Series vase, depicting the hall at Moreton, 9in. high, circa 1915. $110 £75

Gleaners and Gypsies Series vase, 7¹/₂in. high, circa 1909, depicting a Gypsy and Child. $110 £75

Feminine Society Series vase, 7¹/₂in. high, circa 1934, depicting a family taking tea. $110 £75

Under The Greenwood Tree Series vase, 7³/₄in. high, circa 1937, depicting 'Robin Hood and Friar Tuck'. $110 £75

Royal Doulton two-handled vase, designed by Charles Crombie, depicting two golfers and a caddie, 8in. high. $525 £350

'Old Houses, All-Saints St. Hastings', Rural England Series vase, 8in. high, circa 1930. $110 £75

STONEWARE

A salt cellar with incised blue leaves and bead work, c.m 1877, 2¼in. high. $130 £85

An hexagonal salt cellar, the interior glazed blue, o.u.m., circa 1872, 3in. diameter. $150 £100

A teaset by Edith Kemp comprising tea-pot, cream jug and sugar bowl, c.m., 1880, height of tea-pot 4¼in. $300 £200

A vase painted with yellow fruit and dark brown foliage on a brown field, c.m.l & c., circa 1912, 9in. high. $112 £70

A pair of candlesticks with incised geometric patterns in blue and brown on a buff ground, o.u.m., circa 1872, 11in. high. $375 £250

A mounted jug, the mottled brown ground with applied geometric and leaf patterns, c.m., 1878, 9½in. high. $165 £110

A tapered jug, with applied blue and green stylised flower heads, c.m., 1880, 9½in. high. $165 £110

A Punch and Judy clockcase, the buff stoneware with a bright blue glaze, c.m.l. & c., circa 1905, 11½in. high. $1875 £1250

A jug, the light buff body with incised diamonds and applied blue slip flowers, impressed Doulton Lambeth, circa 1868, 9½in. high. $144 £90

341

STONEWARE

A pepper pot by Alice Budden
with incised leaves and bead
work, c.m., 1880, 2½in. high.
$150 £100

A massive pair of candlesticks
by Alice E. Budden, incised
overall, r.m., 1881, 11¾in.
high. $375 £250

A jug by Jane S. Hurst with
applied green and white
geometric patterns in high
relief, r.m., 1881, 9½in. high.
$160 £100

A vase by Elizabeth Atkins, the
buff ground with an incised
scale pattern and four panels,
r.m., 1883, 7in. high.
$176 £110

A pair of vases by Margaret
Aitken, the white ground with
incised flowering foliage
painted in green and white pâte-
sur-pâte, r.m., 1881, 8in. high.
$270 £180

A vase by Harry Barnard, the
cream ground with incised
bands of chevrons on which are
painted tadpoles, r.m., 1882,
10¼in. high. $224 £140

A vase by Alberta L. Green with
incised green leaves growing
from a central ochre band,
r.m., circa 1882, 8¾in. high.
$128 £80

A pair of vases by Bertha Evans,
the mottled blue ground with
incised brown scrolls, r.m.,
1883, 7in. high. $400 £250

A vase by Ellen Gathercole, the
incised brown ground with
green plants having white
flowers, r.m., 1882, 8¼in. high.
$240 £150

342

A vase possibly by Emily Welch, the grey-green ground with applied blue flowering branches, r.m., circa 1885, 11¾in. high. $165 £110

A pair of vases by Mary Capes painted with green flowers outlined in gilt, r.m., 1884, 7¾in. high. $272 £170

A white stoneware jug with an incised diamond pattern, glazed alternately blue and brown with applied flower heads, o.u.m., the silver cover hallmarked 1872, 7in. high. $375 £250

A jug by Ellen Gathercole decorated in the traditional manner with applied vignettes of sporting scenes, r.m., 1882, 8¾in. high. $525 £350

A pair of candlesticks by Nellie Garbott with incised brown and blue leaves, c.m., 1879, 6¾in. high. $300 £200

A large vase by Harry Barnard, the buff ground with incised foliage, r.m., 1881, 14¼in. high. $975 £650

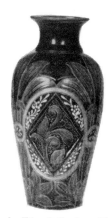

A vase by Annie Gentle, with painted white lattice-work and incised green and yellow foliage, c.m., 1879, 9¾in. high. $225 £150

A pair of vases by Margaret Aitken, with incised and carved brown and blue leaves, r.m., 1882, 7½in. $330 £220

A vase by Eliza S. Banks, with carved panels of blue foliage surrounded by painted white flowers, r.m., 1882, 8½in. high. $240 £150

STONEWARE

An unattributed jug moulded as a uniformed man with peaked hat, r.m., circa 1888, 9¼in. high. $300 £200

A small circular clockcase in buff stoneware with applied rough cast chips, circa 1890, 7¼in. high. $272 £170

An unattributed pair of vases, each with incised pale green and yellow foliage, r.m., circa 1885, 11½in. high. $375 £250

An unattributed beaker, the buff ground with painted white foliage and coloured lines, c.m.l. & c., circa 1902, 5½in. high. $96 £60

A late vase with stylised blue flowers and green leaves edged in white, c.m. & l., circa 1922, 7½in. high. $135 £90

A vase painted with formal purple flowers and green leaves against a white ground, c.m.l. & c., circa 1912, 7¾in. high. $135 £90

An unattributed salt cellar, the bowl with incised brown leaves, c.m., circa 1880, 3½in. high. $240 £150

A monumental clockcase glazed in shades of blue and brown with carved and incised details .and applied bead work, c.m., 1879, 15½in. high. $2000 £1250

An unattributed vase with upright blue handles, c.m., 1879, 7½in. high. $152 £95

A vase, the mottled blue ground with incised lines, modelled in high relief with a dragon biting the neck, r.m., 1886, 10in. high. $300 £200

An early architectural clockcase glazed ochre and blue, with incised blue, green, and purple leaves, o.m., 1875, 14½in. high. $1440 £900

An unattributed jug, the combed buff ground with incised green fish and plants, DLE, circa 1895, 13¼in. high. $450 £300

A vase with black and purple designs on a white ground, c.m.l. & c., circa 1920, 8¼in. high. $135 £90

An architectural clockcase glazed in dark brown, blue and green, r.m., 1884, 10¼in. high. $975 £650

A cylindrical vase with blue, green and black geometric designs on a lovat ground, c.m.l. & c., circa 1920, 7¾in. high. $130 £85

An unattributed jug, the buff ground with white bead work and incised blue and brown leaves, c.m., 1879, 7¾in. high. $225 £150

An unattributed hexagonal open-work basket pierced with brown lattice, r.m., 1880, 5¼in. high. $192 £120

An unattributed horn cup moulded with a blue and ochre sphinx, c.m., 1876, 9in. high. $450 £300

A tapered jug with mottled
brown glaze and applied blue
flower heads, o.m., 1875,
10½in. high. $112 £70

A bulbous jug with applied
geometric and floral patterns in
purple and green, c.m., 1879,
7¼in. high. $304 £190

A jug by Harriet E. Hibbut, the
blue ground with an applied
carpet of large flowers predominantly blue, c.m., 1880, 9¼in.
high. $165 £110

A vase by Bessie Youatt, the
white ground with an incised
spiral green leafy branch, c.m.,
1879, 8in. high. $208 £130

A pair of vases by Emily A.
London with a blue hatched
ground, r.m., 1883, 4½in. high.
                     $195 £130

A vase by Bessie Youatt, the
white neck finely combed and
the body painted with brown
leaves, c.m., 1880, 9½in. high.
                     $256 £160

A pâte-sur-pâte jug, the buff
ground with finely incised and
applied green leaves and bead
work, r.m., circa 1882, 8½in.
high. $165 £110

A shaped jug with applied blue
geometric patterns in high
relief, c.m., 1877, 8½in. high.
                     $192 £120

A jug with an overall incised
diamond pattern, glazed
alternately in brown and blue,
r.m., circa 1882, 8¾in. high.
                     $135 £90

A jug, with applied dark green and white shell motifs within various applied borders, c.m., 1880, 9½in. high. $165 £110

A modelled owl with detachable head, the feathers formed by applied motifs in shades of blue, ochre and brown, r.m., circa 1880, 8in. high. $520 £325

A vase, the light buff body stencilled overall with impressed concentric circles, r.m., circa 1882, 12¼in. high. $128 £80

A jug by Bessie Youatt, incised and applied with a ring of blue flower heads, c.m., 1879, 8½in. high. $224 £140

A pair of vases by Bessie Youatt, each with four incised shaped panels, r.m., 1883, 10¾in. high. $576 £360

A baluster-shaped jug with incised blue shield-shaped panels on a brown ground, r.m., 1882, 9½in. high. $144 £90

A jug by Emma Shute with applied pale blue and white motifs, c.m., 1880, 9¼in. high. $165 £110

A mug by Constance E. Redford, the buff ground with white dots and incised blue scrolls, r.m., 1882, 5in. high. $180 £120

A jug by Harriett E. Hibbut, the mottled brown body with applied grey and blue leaves, and flower heads, c.m., 1976, 9in. high. $150 £100

A cylindrical jug with a dark brown glaze and applied flower heads, blue triangles and white beads, c.m., 1878, 6¾in. high.
$180 £120

A vase by Mary Aitken of baluster shape, with overall applied bands of graduated beads, r.m., 1880, 14½in. high.
$240 £150

A small bowl by Emily Welch with impressed gilt concentric circles, r.m., circa 1888, 4in. high.
$300 £200

A brown glazed jug with incised acorns, flowers, and leaves, filled with blue slip, o.u.m., circa 1871, 8in. high.
$210 £140

A cruet set by Charlotte Lamb, both bottles with incised flowering plants, c.m., 1879, 4¼in. high.
$288 £180

A blue stoneware jug with carved stylised leaves and a band of applied flower heads, the base incised F.M. and impressed with the letter B, o.u.m., circa 1871, 7¼in. high.
$180 £120

An incised jug, the light buff body with cattle and a goat below leaf bands filled with brown slip, o.u.m., circa 1871, 7in. high.
$525 £350

A small bowl by Sarah Fisher, the cover pierced with green and blue scrolls, c.m., 1879, 4in. high.
$208 £130

A baluster-shaped jug with a mottled blue glaze, applied blue leaf motifs, and brown bead work, r.m., 1883, 8¼in. high.
$176 £110

A mounted jug with applied geometric patterns and a frieze of multi-coloured applied circles, r.m., 1880, 9½in. high.
$165 £110

An egg cup stand by Mary Davies, the ochre stand with incised green foliate scrolls, r.m., 1884, 6in. diameter.
$300 £200

A jug, the cream body with incised and applied blue lily of the valley, o.u.m., circa 1871, 7¼in. high. $210 £140

An inscribed vase by Alice Groom, the buff body with incised green and brown leaves and blue flowers, r.m., 1886, 6½in. high. $208 £130

A large vase attributed to Cund, with two modelled monkeys clinging to the sides, r.m., 1881, 18in. high. $1360 £850

A jug by Jane S. Hurst with overall applied green and grey motifs, c.m., 1879, 9¼in. high.
$165 £110

A pair of vases by Nellie Garbott with incised pale blue flowers on a dark blue ground, r.m., 1881, 6in. high. $256 £160

A jug covered with a pale brown glaze, with applied clusters of green shells. o.m., 1875, 6½in. high. $144 £90

A slip-cast vase by William Rowe with green leaves and a black and white checkered design, s.c.m., circa 1920, 9in. high. $150 £100

Nelson's Centenary, a moulded statuette of the admiral glazed green, c.m.l. & c., circa 1905, 8¼in. high. **$600 £400**

A vase modelled with shaped panels in relief, on each an applied moulded portrait glazed dark green, r.m., 1888, 9¾in. high. **$336 £210**

An unattributed jug with an incised green and brown scale pattern, r.m., 1884, 7in. high. **$165 £110**

An unattributed vase, the pale blue ground with carved green flowering plants, r.m., 1880, 14¼in. high. **$272 £170**

A pair of unattributed cylindrical vases, each with applied medallions of fish and a lobster, r.m., circa 1885, 10¼in. high. **$352 £220**

An unattributed vase decorated with natural coloured foliage, r.m., circa 1885, 11½in. high. **$416 £260**

A vase painted with plums against buff, purple and pink bands, c.m.l. & c., circa 1912, 7½in. high. **$150 £100**

A ribbed vase moulded with a cellular pattern and glazed olive-green, s.c.m., circa 1920, 6½in. high. **$96 £60**

A vase painted with stylised yellow chrysanthemums against a mottled pink ground, c.m.l. & c., circa 1912, 9in. high. **$150 £100**

CLARA BARKER

A vase by Clara Barker, with incised green scrolls on a hatched blue ground, r.m., 1884, 6in. high. $176 £110

A small tazza by Clara Barker, the stem moulded with eight blue dolphins, c.m., 1878, 3¾in. high. $240 £160

A vase by Clara Barker, the white ground with an incised continuous green foliate band, r.m., 1882, 6½in. high.
$176 £110

ARTHUR BARLOW

A jug with incised green, blue and brown leaves on a white background, o.m., 1875, 10in. high. $272 £170

A pair of vases decorated with incised blue and green stylised leaf designs on a buff ground, o.m., circa 1873, 8³/₄in. high.
$480 £300

A ewer with deeply incised foliage and geometric patterns, and applied flower heads, o.m., 1874, 10½in. high. $280 £175

A jug with incised green and brown scrolling foliage on a white ground, o.m., 1873, 8¾in. high. $225 £150

A candlestick with lightly incised leaves glazed brown and blue, and applied borders, o.m., 1874, 9½in. high.
$150 £100

A jug with incised blue foliate scrolls on a white ground, o.m., the silver mount hallmarked 1872, 8in. high. $300 £200

ARTHUR BARLOW

A jug with incised pink and blue foliage on a pale green ground, o.m., 1874, 10¼in. high.
$264 £165

A flask with incised brown foliage on a ground impressed with stars, o.m., 1875, 8¼in. high. $300 £200

A pierced vase, the outer wall with foliage glazed dark brown on a buff ground, o.u.m., circa 1872, 7¼in. high. $224 £140

A pepper pot by Arthur Barlow, o.u.m., the silver cover hallmarked 1872, 3¼in. high.
$112 £70

A jug with carved scrolling foliage and applied flower heads and beads in brown, green and blue, o.m., 1874, 6¼in. high.
$300 £200

A large jug with incised brown foliage, applied bead decoration and blue flower heads, o.m., 1876, 12¼in. high. $512 £320

A ewer, the body with unusual leaf motifs incised in blue, white and green, assistants monogram: Mary A. Thomson, o.m., 1875, 10in. high.
$320 £200

A jug with incised mottled brown leaves on a pale buff ground, o.u.m., circa 1871, 7¼in. high. $270 £180

A vase with incised brown foliate scrolls and applied white flowers on a buff ground, o.m., 1874, 9½in. high. $256 £160

ARTHUR BARLOW

A vase with incised leaves glazed bright blue on a hatched ground, glazed brown, o.u.m., circa 1872, 9in. high. $400 £250

A mug by Arthur Barlow, the light buff body with an incised blue leaf band and applied shell motifs, o.u.m., the silver rim hallmarked, 1871, 4½in. high. $225 £150

A ewer with incised foliate scrolls in blue and green on a buff ground, o.m., 1873, 9¾in. high. $330 £220

A large jug with incised blue and green foliage below various incised and applied borders, o.m., 1874, 14¾in. high. $720 £450

A dish with incised concave flower heads surrounded by bands of leaves and basketwork in green, brown and blue, o.m., 1874, 10½in. diam. $240 £150

A ewer, the light buff body with incised stiff leaves glazed mottled brown, signed A. B. Barlow, o.u.m., circa 1872, 11in. high. $400 £250

A jug with incised dark brown foliage on a mottled pink ground, o.m., 1874, 10in. high. $272 £170

A beaker with applied bead decoration and blue flowerheads, c.m., 1876, 5¼in. high. $165 £110

A vase with finely incised blue and pale green foliage on a brown ground, o.m., 1874, 10in. high. $330 £220

353

FLORENCE BARLOW

A turkey vase painted in bright green and brown pâte-sur-pâte with a frieze of turkeys, r.m. & e., circa 1895, 14in. high.
$750 £500

A biscuit barrel with plate cover and mounts, the sides painted in pâte-sur-pâte with four cockatoos, r.m., 1886, 5½in. high. $410 £275

A doubled-handled vase with various incised leaf and scroll designs, c.m., 1878, 11¼in. high.
$825 £550

A vase by Florence Barlow, with three panels of young birds amongst coloured grasses, DSL, 1885, 10½in. high. $600 £400

A pair of vases, the alternating panels with incised and cut out stylised flowers and foliage in various shades of blue, c.m., 1878, 10¾in. high. $450 £300

A pair of vases incised on the buff ground with finches amongst grasses, c.m., 1878, 11in. high. $825 £550

A vase with incised brown foliate scrolls on a buff ground, the base with incised green and blue leaves, c.m., 1878, 10in. high. $450 £300

An oil lamp, the stoneware stand modelled on both sides with fox-gloves and a field mouse in high relief, r.m., 1882, 15¼in. high. $900 £600

A vase decorated in pâte-sur-pâte, the four oval panels each with a garden bird, r.m., 1883, 8in. high. $675 £450

FLORENCE BARLOW

A jug, the stippled buff ground painted in pâte-sur-pâte with two green and white crested birds, r.m., circa 1885, 5½in. high. $450 £300

A tall vase, decorated with five pâte-sur-pâte tit-mice perched on a branch, r.m. & e., circa 1895, 16in. high. $975 £650

A jug with incised scrolling brown foliage and applied white bead work, c.m., 1876, 6¾in. high. $360 £240

A jug painted in pâte-sur-pâte with a hen and her chicks in a shaped panel, r.m., circa 1885, 9in. high, with a beaker en suite, 5½in. high. $450 £300

A pair of ewers, each with two shaped panels painted in pâte-sur-pâte with a parrot on a branch, r.m. & e., circa 1895, 10¼in. high. $975 £650

A tapering jug painted in white, with ducks amongst rushes on a buff ground, c.m., 1879, 9½in. high, with two beakers en suite, 5¼in. high. $450 £300

A jug with incised horses in blue and brown slip on a buff ground, c.m., 1877, 6¾in. high. $450 £300

A massive vase painted in green and white pâte-sur-pâte with garden birds amongst branches and numerous ducks amongst rushes, circa 1880, 26½in. high. $1500 £1000

A jug decorated with a shaped panel containing two pâte-sur-pâte black swans reserved on a buff ground, r.m., 1884, 7¾in. high. $525 £350

FLORENCE BARLOW

A vase decorated with brown leaves and blue birds on a buff lace ground, impressed date for 1880 and Doulton Lambeth, 10in. high. $525 £350

A jug with incised squirrels on a buff ground, the base with incised stiff green and blue leaves, c.m., 1877, 7¾in. high, with a beaker en suite, 4½in. high. $600 £400

An early jug, incised in a white ground with herons standing in water, o.m., 1874, 7½in. high. $525 £350

A pair of vases, each with incised horses and sheep in shaped panels with garden birds in pâte-sur-pâte, the animals by Hannah Barlow; the birds by Florence Barlow, r.m. & e., circa 1895, 16½in. high. $1500 £1000

Australiana, a tall vase painted in green and brown pâte-sur-pâte with cassowaries, r.m. & e., circa 1895, 28¼in. high. $1350 £900

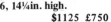

A pair of vases, each painted in green and white pâte-sur-pâte with storks standing amongst grasses, c.m.l. & c., date letter for 1906, 14¼in. high. $1125 £750

A doubled-handled vase painted in pâte-sur-pâte with a green and white titmouse perched on a branch, DLE, circa 1895, 9½in. high. $525 £350

A pair of covered vases with upright handles, c.m., 1878, 7¾in. high. $1050 £700

A vase painted on either side with a swallow-tailed butterfly, c.m.l. & c., circa 1906, 11¾in. high. $600 £400

FLORENCE BARLOW

A large vase painted with herons fighting over a fish, the reverse side with herons and a bat against the moon, r.m. & e., circa 1895, 19¾in. high. $1050 £700

A large pair of vases, each with three shaped panels painted with garden birds amongst foliage, r.m. & e., circa 1895, 14½in. high. $1500 £1000

A vase, modelled in high relief, with two budgerigars perched on green leafy branches, r.m., 1886, 12¼in. high. $675 £450

A pair of vases, each with three panels decorated in relief with garden birds perched amongst blossom, c.m.l. & c., date letter for 1903, 11½in. high. $1125 £750

A lavishly decorated vase commemorating the 1897 Jubilee, the central panel with painted white VR monograms and applied moulded portraits of the Queen, signed in full: F. E. Barlow, r.m. & e., circa 1897, 24¼in. high. $1875 £1250

A small pair of vases painted in green and white pâte-sur-pâte with a frieze of ducks, r.m. & e., circa 1895, 6¾in. high. $600 £400

A large vase with three stippled buff panels painted with garden birds, r.m., circa 1885, 25½in. high. $1200 £800

A pair of vases with a frieze of ducks and grass, r.m. & e., circa 1895, 9¾in. high. $1050 £700

A vase painted in pâte-sur-pâte, with a green bunting perched on a branch, r.m. & e., circa 1895, 13¼in. high. $675 £450

HANNAH BARLOW

A pepper pot by Hannah
Barlow, o.u.m., the silver cover
hallmarked 1872, 3in. high.
$144 £90

A mug with an incised frieze of
running deer on a buff ground,
c.m., 1878, 3½in. high.
$300 £200

A cream jug with incised
puppies and blue and brown
leaves on a buff ground, o.m.,
1874, 4¾in. high. $420 £280

An early jug with incised stiff
leaves filled with blue and
brown slip on a buff ground,
o.m., silver mount hallmarked,
1872, 6¾in. high. $264 £165

A large pair of vases, each with
two quatrefoil panels, one of
cats and the other of dogs, the
birds by Florence Barlow, the
background by Eliza
Simmance, r.m. & e., circa
1895, 18in. high. $2250 £1500

A cup and saucer with incised
sheep and lambs on a buff
ground, r.m., 1884, the cup 2in.
high. $200 £125

A vase with three shaped panels,
each painted with a cat in pâte-
sur-pâte, r.m., 1884. 9in. high.
$525 £350

A jug with an incised white dog
wearing a ruff, DLE, circa
1895, 6½in. high. $375 £250

A vase with finely incised ponies
and goats in a landscape, c.m.,
1878, 8in. high. $525 £350

HANNAH BARLOW

A small jug with incised goats in pasture on a dark buff ground, o.m., 1874, 5¾in. high.
$375 £250

A tobacco jar and cover, the body with incised brown glazed cows frolicking amongst incised green foliage, r.m. & e., circa 1895, 6½in. high. $420 £280

A small jug with an incised bird on a branch and flowering plants, o.m., circa 1872, 6in. high.
$420 £280

A tall jug with incised deer in a wreath of foliage below incised scrolls, o.m., 1873, 10¾in. high.
$480 £320

A large pair of vases with a boldly incised frieze of goats, borders by Frank Butler, r.m. & e., circa 1895, 21½in. high.
$3000 £2000

A jug with an incised pride of lions on a buff ground, DLE, circa 1895, 8½in. high.
$600 £400

A jug, the buff body incised with a dog and plants, titled 'Lost', o.u.m., circa 1871, possibly the work of Hannah Barlow, 6³/₄in. high.
$450 £300

A tyg with three incised groups of rabbits in a landscape, the handles with incised flowers, o.m., 1873, 5¾in. high.
$525 £350

A jug with incised lions in a landscape, filled with a dark blue slip on a light buff ground, o.m., circa 1872, 8in. high.
$525 £35ſ

HANNAH BARLOW

A small jug with an incised fox stalking a rabbit, filled with a blue slip on a buff ground, o.m., 1875, 6½in. high. $420 £280

A loving cup in buff glazed stoneware, with two boldly incised lions, o.m., silver rim hallmarked 1872, 6½in. high. $450 £300

A jug with incised cat and rabbits between incised stiff leaves, o.m., circa 1872, 8in. high. $450 £300

A jug with incised stiff leaves, scrolls, and a frieze of rabbits, o.m., circa 1872, 7½in. high. $480 £320

A terracotta picture, titled 'So near and yet so far', the animals modelled in high-relief in buff terracotta, 1890, 10 x 7in. $900 £600

A large vase with an incised frieze of frightened deer being pursued by wolves, o.m., circa 1872, 15¾in. high. $1425 £950

A waisted beaker with an incised frieze of running dogs, o.m., 1873, 6¼in. high. $360 £240

A large tankard with incised water rats stealing eggs from an enraged swan, o.m., circa 1872, 6¾in. high. $420 £280

A tall tankard with an incised heron and ears of corn, filled with a bright blue slip, o.m., circa 1872, 10in. high. $480 £320

HANNAH BARLOW

A waisted beaker with incised sheep and lambs above stiff leaves, o.m., 1873, 6in. high. $360 £240

A salt cellar by Hannah Barlow of hexagonal trencher type, o.u.m., circa 1872, 3in. diameter. $225 £150

A vase with incised herons flying amongst reeds, glazed blue on a white ground, c.m., 1876, 8¼in. high. $570 £380

A tapering jug with incised sheep by a fence, filled with blue slip on a white ground, c.m., 1877, 9¼in. high. $450 £300

A massive vase, the white ground impressed with blue flower heads and with incised lions in two shaped buff panels, further decorated by Frank Butler, r.m., 1886, 33in. high. $4500 £3000

A jug with an incised band of pheasants above blue and brown leaves, o.m., 1873, 6in. high. $360 £240

A two-handled vase with incised horses between borders of stiff blue leaves on a buff ground, o.m., circa 1872, 10in. high. $690 £460

A vase, the sides modelled in high relief with wolves chasing deer, o.m., circa 1872, 11¼in. high. $2100 £1400

A jug with incised leaves and flowers glazed dark blue on a pale blue ground, r.m., 1880, 7in. high. $330 £220

361

HANNAH BARLOW

A vase with incised horses grazing in a field, filled with blue slip on a buff ground, r.m., circa 1882, 13½in. high.
$1125 £750

A double-handled jardinière with an incised frieze of horses, r.m., 1880. 6¾in. high.
$825 £550

A vase with two modelled brown glazed dogs, the body with incised blue, green and brown leaves, r.m., 1889, 14in. high.
$1200 £800

A jug with an incised frieze of cows in pasture on a white ground, c.m., 1878, 9in. high.
$600 £400

A pair of vases, one with incised children playing with puppies, the companion with a girl watching dogs chase a rabbit, r.m., 1885, 10¾in. high.
$1350 £900

An amusing jug with an incised dog growling at a bristling cat defending its kittens playing on a tree, r.m., 1883, 9¼in. high.
$750 £500

A jug with incised gun dogs sniffing a scent and a fox hiding behind the handle in long grass, c.m., 1880, 9½in. high.
$600 £400

A tankard with incised farm horses in a landscape, one ploughing, o.m., silver rim hallmarked 1872, 6¾in. high.
$480 £320

A jug with incised herons amongst reeds, in a bright blue slip on a buff ground, c.m., 1877, 9in. high. $525 £350

HANNAH BARLOW

A two-handled vase with an incised frieze of kangaroos, filled with blue slip on a white ground, r.m., 1886, 14¼in. high. $1275 £850

A jardinière with an incised frieze of deer in a landscape on a light buff ground, c.m., 1877. 6½in. high. $825 £550

An unusual vase, with an incised frieze of sheep in pasture, c.m.l. & c., circa 1905, 7¾in. high. $360 £240

A mounted jug with incised horses in a landscape on a white ground, c.m., 1878, 9¼in. high. $570 £380

A large pair of vases, each with an incised frieze of wolves and their cubs amongst foliage, r.m., 1885, 16½in. high. $1800 £1200

A large vase painted in green and white pate-sur-pâte with a frieze of cattle, r.m. & e., circa 1895, 18½in. high. $1350 £900

A jug with the incised figure of a young girl behind a tree watching pigs, r.m., 1883, 8¾in. high. $570 £380

A jardinière with a frieze of incised lions, and borders with incised foliage, r.m., 1882, 9¾in. high. $975 £650

A vase with an incised frieze of horses, and foliate borders in green, blue and brown, r.m., 1883, 9in. high. $600 £400

HANNAH BARLOW

A vase decorated with incised goats grazing, with blue and brown slip designs on a brown ground, r.m., 13³/₄in. high.
$825 £550

A ewer decorated with incised goats grazing, leaves and bead designs on a stippled brown ground, DLE, 12in. high.
$675 £450

A vase decorated with incised goats, beads and foliage designs on a blue brown ground, r.m., impressed date for 1881, 9³/₄in. high.
$600 £400

A tea-set, comprising a teapot, cream jug and sugar bowl, each piece with an incised frieze of goats on a buff ground, o.m., 1875, the teapot 4¹/₄in. high.
$975 £650

A vase decorated with incised lions, stiff leaves and beads on a blue ground, r.m. & e., 1891-1902, 10¹/₂in. high. $720 £480

A tea-set, comprising a teapot, cream jug and sugar bowl, each with an incised frieze of rabbits above green and blue leaves, c.m., 1880, 1886, 4¹/₂in. high.
$975 £650

A vase decorated with an incised frieze of goats and donkeys with slip design scroll borders on a brown and green ground, r.m. & e., 12in. high. $675 £450

A large pair of vases with an incised frieze of white deer in a mountainous landscape, borders by Florence Barlow, DLE, circa 1895, 17¹/₄in. high.
$1600 £1000

A jug with an incised farm worker and a donkey pulling a cart loaded with tree branches, r.m., 1887, 9¹/₄in. high.
$570 £380

HANNAH BARLOW

A vase with three incised donkeys in a landscape on a buff ground, r.m. & e., circa 1892, 9in. high. $675 £450

A pair of ewers, each with incised lions in a landscape on a white ground, r.m., 1883, 11¾in. high. $1200 £800

A vase with incised horses in a landscape, borders by Bessie Youatt, c.m., 1879, 10¼in. high. $720 £480

A tea-set, comprising a teapot, cream jug and sugar bowl, each piece with incised kangaroos and emus, c.m., 1878, the teapot 4½in. high. $975 £650

A vase decorated with incised moorland ponies, a band of stiff leaves and flowers on a blue green ground, impressed date 1880 and Doulton Lambeth, 9½in. high. $675 £450

A tea-set, comprising a teapot, cream jug and sugar bowl, each piece with an incised frieze of rabbits, borders by Lucy Barlow, r.m., 1883, the teapot 4½in. high. $975 £650

A jug with an incised frieze of goats in a rocky landscape, c.m., 1879, 10½in. high. $570 £380

A vase with a quatrefoil panel incised with two kittens, r.m. & e., circa 1895, 10in. high. $675 £450

A tapering jug with incised stags and does in a landscape, c.m., 1878, 9½in. high. $570 £380

JOHN BROAD

"The Boer War Soldier", a buff glazed figure of an infantry man, r.m. & e., circa 1900, 12½in. high. $975 £650

A modelled group, on a circular base with a buff glazed donkey, c.m., 1879 6½in. high. $975 £650

A terracotta statuette of King Edward VII standing against a column, the base inscribed ERI, c.m.l. & c., circa 1901, 16¾in. high. $1120 £700

A slip-cast figure of "The Bather", the white glazed nude seated on a purple sphere, s.c.m., circa 1912, 13in. high. $1360 £850

Queen Victoria, a buff salt-glaze figure commemorating her life, incised Doulton Co. Ltd. Lambeth, circa 1901, 11³/₄in. high. $1500 £1000

Pitt's Centenary, a grey terracotta portrait-bust of the statesman, the shaped based inscribed "William Pitt 1759-1806", Sc., c.m.l. & c., circa 1906, 13³/₄in. high. $832 £520

ROSINA BROWN

A large vase with running green glaze by Rosina Brown, c.m.l. & c., 14½in. high. $136 £85

A jug by Rosina Brown, the shaded green ground with incised scrolls, r.m. & e., circa 1892, 7¼in. high. $232 £145

A pierced vase by Rosina Brown cut with geometric patterns, r.m., circa 1885, 7in. high. $256 £160

FRANK BUTLER

A small early jug, the buff body with deeply incised foliate scrolls, o.u.m., silver mount hallmarked 1873, 5in. high.
$300 £200

A candlestick with incised geometric and leaf designs, o.m., 1874, 5in. high. $260 £175

A flask of flattened circular shape incised in green, brown and purple, c.m., 1878, 8in. high. $330 £220

A jug with incised stiff leaves and scrolls in green, blue and brown, o.m., 1873, 7in. high.
$256 £160

A jardinière decorated with a frieze of applied moulded bust-portraits representing Queen Victoria, Victor Emmanuel of Italy, Napoleon III, Empress Eugenie and Kaiser Wilhelm of Germany, o.m., 1874, 8¼in. high. $1350 £900

A jug with incised blue leaves on a brown ground, o.m., 1874, 5¼in. high. $270 £180

A jug with deeply incised brown and blue foliage, o.m., 1873, 9 in. high. $272 £170

A vase with shaped projections, incised leaves in blue and brown, o.m., 1874, 9½in. high.
$288 £180

A vase with incised blue leaves, applied white beads on a sepia ground, c.m., 1876, 7½in. high.
$240 £150

FRANK BUTLER

A vase modelled in relief with a stylised plant, r.m., circa 1890, 12in. high. $512 £320

A shaped bowl richly decorated on the inside and outside with incised leaves and foliate scrolls, c.m., 1880, 10¼in. diameter. $640 £400

An egg cup by Frank Butler with incised blue leaves on a buff ground, circa 1872, 3½in. high. $176 £110

A jug with carved and incised blue leaf patterns on a stippled buff ground, r.m., 1881, 13½in. high. $450 £300

A large pair of vases, the three panels with incised foliate scrolls in lovat, blue and ochre, r.m., 1882, 17½in. high. $900 £600

A portrait jug, the dark blue ground with impressed flower motifs, c.m., 1877, 10½in. high. $448 £280

A vase with incised green and blue foliage and brown cross-hatched panels, r.m., 1884, 7¾in. high. $288 £180

An inscribed bowl with incised blue flowers and scrolls on an olive-green ground, 1894, 8¼in. diameter. $352 £220

A large vase, the central panel with carved brown scrolls on a hatched blue ground between incised leaf and scroll borders, r.m., 1884, 14¼in. high. $1072 £670

FRANK BUTLER

A goblet-shaped vase, with applied stylised blue flowers on a brown panel, c.m.l. & c., circa 1905, 8½in. high.
$232 £145

A shallow dish with incised scrolls and the name K. B. Smallfield, 1897, on a green ground, r.m., 6½in. diameter.
$264 £165

A tall vase with incised dark green plants on a brown ground, c.m.l. & c., date letter for 1909, 17½in. high.
$450 £300

A large jug, ornately decorated with incised, applied and impressed work. o.m., 1874, 17in. high. $784 £490

A pair of vases, each with incised scrolls and leaves, c.m., 1876, 14¼in. high. $825 £550

A jug with a profusion of incised leaves in blue, green, pink and brown, o.m., 1875, 14½in. high. $496 £310

A jug with incised green and purple leaves on a brown ground, c.m., 1878, 10in. high.
$352 £220

A shell-shaped bowl painted with white flowers on a green panel, r.m. & e., circa 1895, 4¾in. high. $512 £320

A jug, modelled in relief with depressed fan-shaped motifs, c.m., 1879, 8¼in. high.
$576 £360

FRANK BUTLER

A vase with flowering plants against a brown background, r.m. & e., circa 1895, 13in. high. $672 £420

A pair of vases, modelled with stylised plants having green bulbs, brown stems and leaves, and blue flowers, DLE, circa 1895, 9¾in. high. $608 £380

A vase with stylised flowering plants in blue and brown, r.m. & e., circa 1895, 13¼in. high. $752 £470

A covered sprinkler, the squashed body with incised blue and green flowers, FAB., 1894, 10¼in. high. $336 £210

A pair of vases, modelled with projecting brown forms growing from a green ground, c.m.l. & c., date letter for 1906, 7in. high. $448 £280

An Art Nouveau vase with dark blue flowers and seed pods on a pale blue ground, DLE, circa 1900, 13in. high. $416 £260

A shaped flask, each side decorated with pierced and carved green foliate scrolls, r.m. & e., circa 1895, 9½in. high. $480 £300

A pair of vases, the mottled green ground modelled with projections divided by graduated brown and blue circles, r.m. & e., circa 1895, 9¾in. high. $432 £270

A vase modelled with projecting flowers, with green leaves and brown stems, c.m.l. & c., date letter for 1909, 14¾in. high. $450 £300

LOUISA DAVIS

A mounted jug, the incised buff ground with impressed flowers, c.m., 1880, 9½in. high.
$272 £170

A jug, the brown ground with impressed flower motifs, c.m., 1876, 6in. high. $300 £200

A vase, the white ground with an incised spiral band of foliage with blue flowers, c.m., 1877, 11¾in. high. $280 £175

A vase, the buff ground with incised long lovat leaves, brown foliage, and blue flowers, c.m., 1877, 9¾in. high. $225 £150

A bowl, the brown ground with incised blue flowers and scrolling, c.m., 1878, 7½in. high. $360 £240

A vase decorated with incised blue leaves and flowers with bands of applied beads and florets, on a blue ground, impressed dated for 1878 and Doulton Lambeth, 9¼in. high. $256 £160

W. EDWARD DUNN

A small vase by W. Edward Dunn, painted in green and white pâte-sur-pâte with a dog's head, r.m., 1883, 5¼in. high. $225 £150

A pilgrim bottle by W. Edward Dunn, one side with incised sheep in a landscape glazed green, the other with women gleaning, r.m., 1883, 9in. high. $496 £310

A vase by W. Edward Dunn, each side with an incised blue bird on a buff panel, r.m., 1882, 12in. high. $512 £320

EMILY EDWARDS

A jug by Emily J. Edwards with a mottled brown glaze and applied flower heads within incised borders, o.u.m., circa 1872, 7in. high. $224 £140

A flower-shaped dish, the brown ground with incised lines and green and purple leaves, impressed Doulton Lambeth, 1876, 10½in. diameter.
$165 £110

A jug with incised green scrolls and blue leaves on a scored brown ground, o.m., 1873, 7¼in. high. $224 £140

LOUISA EDWARDS

A jug with incised dark brown leaf scrolls on a buff ground, c.m., 1878, 10¾in. high.
$225 £150

A jug with incised green and yellow plants with blue flowers, c.m., 1878, 7¼in. high.
$224 £140

A vase, the pale blue ground with finely incised foliage, r.m., 1881, 10in. high. $270 £180

A jug, the buff ground with fine incised lines and impressed flower heads, c.m., 1879, 9½in. high. $180 £120

A vase with incised blue flowering foliage on a pale blue ground, c.m., 1879, 11in. high.
$225 £150

A jug, the body with incised bands of stylised leaves in green and purple, c.m., 1879, 9½in. high. $165 £110

HERBERT ELLIS

A cream coloured terracotta figure of a partly draped woman holding a plaque, impressed Doulton & Co., Lambeth, incised H. Ellis Sc., circa 1910, 13½in. high. $525 £350

An unglazed cream coloured terracotta figure of a nude woman kneeling on a net, incised H. Ellis Sc., circa 1910, 9½in. high. $525 £350

An unglazed moulded terracotta figure, the partly draped woman holding a branch of foliage. Impressed Doulton & Co., Lambeth, circa 1910, 11in. high. $525 £350

ELIZABETH FISHER

A jug, the brown ground with incised panels in green, purple and brown, c.m., 1876, 9in. high. $288 £180

A pair of vases with incised foliate scrolls in two shades of blue, r.m., 1883, 11in. high. $525 £350

A jug, the blue ground with incised leaves, buff panels with impressed flower heads, c.m., 1878, 8½in. high. $256 £160

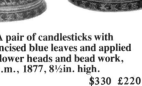

A beaker, the brown ground with impressed flower heads, c.m., 1876, 5¼in. high. $144 £90

A pair of candlesticks with incised blue leaves and applied flower heads and bead work, c.m., 1877, 8½in. high. $330 £220

A jug, incised in blue and brown on a buff ground, r.m., 1881, 9¼in. high. $208 £130

373

LESLIE HARRADINE

A brown salt-glaze spirit flask modelled as John Burns, the Labour leader, DLE, circa 1912, 7¼in. high. $360 £225

A cast figure of Sairey Gamp, the light buff glaze, s.c.m., circa 1913, 8in. high. $450 £300

A brown salt-glaze spirit flask modelled as David Lloyd George, DLE, circa 1912, 7¾in. high. $360 £225

A vase by Leslie Harradine cast into a square section and moulded with laburnum, s.c.m., circa 1912, 8¾in. high. $144 £90

A brown terracotta bust of George V, the reverse stamped Doulton Lambeth, L. Harradine Sc., circa 1910, 7½in. high. $448 £280

A vase after a design by Leslie Harradine with moulded yellow flowers, s.c.m., circa 1910, 9¾in. high. $192 £120

A slip-cast figure of Mr. Pickwick in a light buff glaze, s.c.m., circa 1913, 8½in. high. $560 £350

A white glazed figure of a peasant woman wearing a blue checkered dress, RDE, circa 1905, 8½in. high. $330 £220

A moulded figure of a farm labourer holding a scythe, wearing a blue shirt, circa 1905, 7½in. high. $450 £300

LESLIE HARRADINE

A brown salt-glaze spirit flask modelled as President Roosevelt, DLE, circa 1912, 7½in. high.
$360 £225

"Motherhood", a white glazed figure of a mother cradling her baby, the dress with blue flowers, RDE, circa 1912, 6in. high.
$560 £350

A brown salt-glaze spirit flask modelled in the traditional style with Austen Chamberlain, DLE, circa 1912, 7¾in. high.
$360 £225

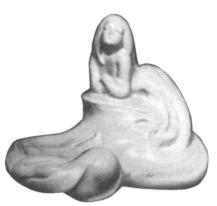

A brown salt-glaze figure of Mr. Pecksniff, s.c.m., circa 1913, 9¼in. high
$560 £350

A white slip-cast group modelled with two mermaids, s.c.m., circa 1910, length 7in.
$400 £250

Dickens, a moulded white glazed stoneware figure of Mr. Squeers, s.c.m., circa 1913, 9¼in. high.
$560 £350

VERA HUGGINS

A large vase with incised green flowering foliage on a mottled blue ground, c.m. & l., circa 1925, 12¾in. high. $330 £220

A bowl painted with pink and blue flowers against a brown field, c.m. & l., 1926, 5in. high.
$180 £120

A vase glazed in green, blue and brown with incised and raised borders, c.m. & l., circa 1925, 11¼in. high. $200 £125

FRANCES LEE

A vase, the buff ground with impressed concentric circles, heightened with gold, c.m., 1886, 10in. high. $320 £200

A pair of vases, the panels with incised green leaves and bordered by purple leaves, c.m., 1877, 9¾in. high.
$375 £250

A vase, the royal blue ground with four stippled buff panels painted with dolphins, c.m., 1883, 9¾in. high. $288 £180

A jug with four oval panels with incised green foliage, c.m., 1878, 5¼in. high. $176 £110

A shallow bowl with incised green and blue panels supported by three columns, c.m., 1884, 8¼in. high.
$512 £320

A jug, the neck with incised blue flowers on a brown ground, c.m., 1879, 6¾in. high.
$180 £120

A jug, the incised brown leaves with applied bead work and flower heads, c.m., 1877, 9¼in. high. $264 £165

A pair of vases, with finely incised foliage, painted overall in pâte-sur-pâte with blossom, c.m., 1882, 9in. high.
$448 £280

A jug carved with green flower heads on a blue ground, c.m., 1881, 9½in. high. $224 £140

EDITH LUPTON

A jug with incised green, blue and brown leaves, o.m., 1875, 6½in. high. $160 £100

A large pierced vase with three shaped panels painted in pâte-sur-pâte with wild flowers, r.m., 1882, 14in. high.
$576 £360

A jug with incised stiff blue leaves and carved seed pods, c.m., 1876, 8¼in. high.
$208 £130

A small jug with incised green foliage on a brown ground, c.m., 1876, 7½in. high.
$240 £150

A pair of salt cellars with incised leaves, o.m., 1875, 3¼in. high.
$560 £350

A candlestick modelled with three buff cranes between incised green and blue columns, c.m., 1875, 8in. high. $224 £140

A mounted jug with incised blue and green leaves, o.m., 1875, 6¾in. high. $208 £130

A vase by Edith Lupton with chocolate panels painted with blue flowers, DSL, 1884, 9½in. high. $300 £200

A large vase by Edith Lupton, pierced overall with flowering plants and foliage, DSL, 1884, 15¼in. high. $512 £320

EDITH LUPTON

A large vase with incised
mottled foliage and seed pods,
r.m., 1886, 14in. high.
$480 £300

A vase with incised green leaves
and painted blossom and
berries, r.m., 1886, 6¾in. high.
$165 £110

A jug with incised blue and
white leaves on a brown ground,
c.m., 1876, 7½in. high.
$240 £160

An ecclesiastical vase modelled
in the form of a tower, and on
each corner the letters IHS in
brown shields, r.m., 1881,
13¾in. high $512 £320

A small pair of church vases, the
quatrefoil necks with incised
blue scrolls, r.m. & e., circa
1892, 6in. high. $416 £260

A jug with incised dark brown
scrolls on a royal blue ground,
c.m., 1880, 9in. high.
$280 £175

A tapering jug with incised green,
brown and blue scrolls, 9½in.
high, with two beakers en suite,
5½in. high, c.m., 1879. $375 £250

A globular vase, the stippled
buff ground with incised
fruiting vine, r.m., 1886, 10in.
high. $560 £350

A mounted jug with incised
foliate scrolls in shades of blue
and green, r.m., 1880, 9½in.
high. $264 £165

MARK V. MARSHALL

A large vase, one side modelled with a profile female portrait, the other with a bird amongst flowers, r.m. & e., circa 1895, 15in. high. $1040 £650

A paperweight modelled as a smiling creature glazed brown, RDE, circa 1902, 2½in. high. $448 £280

A vase after a design by Mark V. Marshall with purple foliage and sepia fruit, c.m. & l., circa 1922, 8¼in. high. $256 £160

A vase with pink swirling panels painted with blue flowers and green leaves, c.m.l. & c., date letter for 1905, 12in. high. $375 £250

A pair of vases pressed from the inside with pink fruits against green foliage on a pale pink ground, c.m.l. & c., date letter for 1903, 10¾in. high. $600 £400

A vase painted with pink flowers and brown veined white leaves, c.m.l. & c., date letter for 1906, 11½in. high. $416 £260

A buff coloured vase with two modelled monkeys grasping the neck of the vase, r.m. & e., circa 1895, 6¾in. high. $736 £460

An unusual bowl of flattened disc shape painted with purple foliage in shaped sepia panels, c.m., circa 1890, 4in. height, 14½in. diameter. $300 £200

An elaborate jug with incised lip and blue neck, the base of the handle modelled with the head of a dark-skinned Arab wearing a kefiya, r.m. & e., circa 1895, 11¼in. high. $1125 £750

MARK V. MARSHALL

A tankard, the grey-green ground indented with purple foliate scrolls and a grotesque mask, DLE, circa 1895, 6½in. high. $208 £130

A jug modelled as a fabulous fish with legs and cloven feet, c.m., circa 1885, 9in. high.
$900 £600

A vase pressed from the inside with russet and lovat foliate scrolls, r.m. & e., circa 1895, 10¾in. high. $300 £200

A paperweight modelled as a duck with mottled blue and green glaze, c.m.l & c., circa 1902, 2³/₄in. high. $368 £230

An inkwell modelled as a stylised bird glazed blue and green, RDE, circa 1902, 2¼in. high. $368 £230

A paperweight modelled as a green glazed cat with grinning features, RDE, circa 1902, 3¼in. long. $368 £230

A dark blue glazed vase, the body modelled in high relief with a sinuous dragon rising from blue waves, c.m., 1880, 10in. high. $1125 £750

An Art Nouveau jug, the base of the handle modelled with a hare's head, c.m.l & c., date letter for 1909, 10³/₄in. high.
$525 £350

A standing bowl attributed to Mark V. Marshall, supported by three moulded and modelled heraldic beasts, c.m.l. & c., circa 1902, 9in. high. $816 £510

MARK V. MARSHALL

A gourd-shaped vase, incised and modelled in relief with fruiting foliage in brown and white, c.m.l. & c., date letter for 1904, 10½in. high.
$450 £300

An early grotesque bowl modelled as a fish, 8½in. high.
$525 £350

A vase, the glaze shading from white through purple to blue at the base, around which climbs a fabulous buff scaly creature, c.m.l. & c., date letter for 1904, 10½in. high.
$900 £600

A salt cellar modelled as a frog glazed brown, DLE, circa 1900, 1¾in. high.
$336 £210

A 'Borogove' vase modelled as a hedgehog-like creature, r.m., circa 1890, 8in. high. $525 £350

An unattributed model of a rabbit glazed light brown, c.m. & l., circa 1922, 2¾in. long.
$210 £140

A vase painted on either side with a stylised plant in shades of green, r.m. & e., circa 1895, 8¼in. high.
$352 £220

An inkwell modelled with two fabulous beasts glazed ochre, blue and brown, r.m., 1884, 5¼in. high.
$1125 £750

A jug modelled in low relief with brown leaves against a royal blue ground, DLE, circa 1895, 8½in. high.
$448 £280

MARK V. MARSHALL

A vase modelled in low relief, with purple and pink sea-weed on a claret ground, r.m. & e., circa 1895, 9in. high. $352 £220

A trumpet-shaped vase, incised overall and glazed blue, circa 1879, 10¼in. high. $450 £300

A paperweight modelled as a bird glazed brown, c.m.l. & c., circa 1902, 3in. high. $352 £220

A tall jug, decorated with rambling blue and pink roses on which perch garden birds, c.m., circa 1880, 19¼in. high. $675 £450

A pair of vases, each decorated with four ribbed panels in brown and pale green, c.m.l. & c., date letter for 1903, 12½in. high. $720 £480

A large covered vase, each side modelled in relief, one with a music conductor with human head and the body of a bird, the other with a lizard and flowering plants, c.m., circa 1885, 26¾in. high. $3375 £2250

A slender vase painted in outline with three long-tailed birds perched amongst foliage, c.m.l. & c., circa 1902, 10in. high. $416 £260

A pot-pourri bowl with pierced blue cover overlaid with green foliate scrolls in high relief, r.m. & e., circa 1895, 5½in. high. $240 £150

A shaped vase, the mottled blue ground with incised green markings and white neck, c.m., circa 1890, 8½in. high. $352 £220

ISABELLA MILLER

A vase by Isabella Miller, the mottled purple ground with incised green and blue scrolls, c.m., 1880, 7¼in. high.
$240 £150

A vase by Isabella Miller, the green and ochre ground with incised dark green scrolls and plants, r.m., 1884, 10¼in. high.
$288 £180

A ewer by Isabella Miller with incised green and blue leaves and flowers, c.m., 1880, 6½in. high. $180 £120

MARY MITCHELL

A vase by Mary Mitchell, with the incised figures of two girls playing with a ball, r.m., 1881, 10¾in. high. $360 £240

A jug by Mary Mitchell, with two oval panels, with incised children in a landscape, c.m., 1879, 9¼in. high $416 £260

A vase by Mary Mitchell, the white ground with incised green foliage and purple flowers, c.m., 1879, 7in. high.
$200 £125

WILLIAM PARKER

A massive jug carved in high relief with green and brown flowers, c.m., 1879, 15¼in. high. $525 £350

A vase with incised flowers on a pale buff ground, r.m., 1883, 7½in. high. $272 £170

An inscribed jug with carved and incised pale green leaves, the neck with incised patterns and blue borders, c.m., 1881, 13¼in. high. $525 £350

WILLIAM PARKER

A vase with incised foliate
scrolls in shades of blue, c.m.,
1879, 11¾in. high. $270 £180

A vase incised through the
celadon ground with blue and
white flowering plants, r.m.,
1883, 7in. high. $270 £180

A vase with finely incised
flowering plants in mottled blue
and green, r.m., 1884, 8¼in.
high. $240 £150

A vase with finely incised blue
convolvulous, sweet-peas, and
clover, r.m., 1883, 9½in. high.
$256 £160

A pair of vases, with an incised
continuous blue branch bearing
yellow fruits, r.m., 1884, 9½in.
high. $512 £320

A vase carved with a frieze of
green foliage scrolls within blue
and green incised borders,
c.m., 1881, 13¼in. high.
$450 £300

FRANCIS POPE

A bottle with applied handle,
and incised blue and green
foliage, c.m.l. & c., silver rim
hallmarked 1913, 8¼in. high.
$192 £120

A slip-cast vase of gourd-shape
with projecting ribs and a
mottled blue glaze, circa 1920,
5¾in. high. $128 £80

A vase painted with green
flowers growing from black
stems, c.m.l. & c., circa 1905,
10in. high. $208 £130

FRANCIS POPE

An unusual vase, modelled in relief with a mermaid riding on a fish amongst underwater plants, c.m.l. & c., circa 1905, 11¾in. high. $352 £220

A pair of tall vases, each with incised mottled blue, pink and green leaves, c.m.l. & c., date letter for 1904, 15¼in. high. $525 £350

A handled bottle or spirit decanter with incised green leaves, c.m.l. & c., silver hall-marked 1913, 7½in. high. $195 £130

A slip-cast vase, the mottled blue body with brown ribs and pale blue scrolls in relief, s.c.m., circa 1920, 6¼in. high. $176 £110

A slip-cast vase moulded with arched panels covered in a mottled ochre and pale blue glaze, s.c.m., circa 1920, 6¼in. high. $120 £75

A vase with deeply incised black and brown scrolls on a green ground, c.m.l. & c., 5½in. high. $136 £85

A vase modelled in relief with a white bird amongst white foliage, c.m.l. & c., circa 1905, 9¾in. high. $240 £150

A pair of slip-cast vases of hexagonal section with a mottled green glaze, s.c., circa 1910, 11in. high. $420 £280

A slip-cast vase of square section, moulded on each side with a blue bird, s.c.m., circa 1920, 8¾in. high. $224 £140

FLORENCE ROBERTS

A mug by Florence C. Roberts, the combed buff ground with impressed flowers, r.m., 1884, 5¼in. high. $130 £85

A pair of vases by Florence C. Roberts, the buff ground modelled in relief with green, blue and brown stylised flowers and leaves, r.m., 1884, 10¼in. high. $450 £300

A vase, the buff ground stippled and modelled in relief with blue flowers and mottled green foliage, r.m., 1885, 12in. high. $400 £250

EDITH ROGERS

A vase with incised blue flowers heightened with white, r.m., 1883, 7¾in. high. $272 £170

A jug, the silicon body painted in rust and blue, DSL, 1884, 7¼in. high. $224 £140

A vase, with finely incised blue flowering plants, the ground over-glazed in brown, r.m., 1883, 8in. high. $256 £160

A vase painted in green and white pâte-sur-pâte with foliate scrolls on an orange ground, r.m., 1881, 10½in. high. $225 £150

A pair of vases with overall incised white and buff scrolls, one with three plaques inscribed 'Burns, Scott and Keats', r.m., 1882, 11½in. high. $510 £340

A vase, the white ground with a thick dark olive-green glaze, r.m., 1882, 10¼in. high. $352 £220

MARTHA ROGERS

A vase, the buff ground with finely incised foliage, r.m., 1881, 7¾in. high. $240 £150

A vase, the buff ground with painted white foliage, r.m., 1881, 12¾in. high. $375 £250

A vase, the dark blue ground with incised pale blue foliage edged with gilt piping, r.m., 1884, 11in. high. $352 £220

A vase, the pale ground with incised brown foliate scrolls bordered by incised blue leaves, r.m., 1883, 12¼in. high.
$300 £200

A pair of vases, the orange ground with painted white motifs, r.m., 1882, 8¾in. high.
$480 £300

A vase by Martha M. Rogers, the stippled frieze glazed blue, with pale blue scrolls, DSL, 1883, 10½in. high. $240 £150

ELIZA SAYERS

A flask of flattened shape, each side with incised green berried foliage, c.m., 1880, 8½in. high.
$288 £180

A jug with incised dark brown and blue stylised foliage enriched with white bead work, c.m., 1877, 9in. high.
$352 £220

A jug with incised green foliage and applied beads on a brown ground, c.m., 1877, 7in. high.
$240 £150

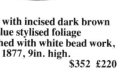

HARRY SIMEON

A vase painted with ears of corn in brown, green and purple against a mottled blue ground, c.m. & l., circa 1922, 9in. high. $240 £160

A vase painted with a parrot amongst green tropical foliage, c.m. & l., circa 1922, 10½in. high. $240 £150

A vase painted in polychrome colours with a cockerel and a blue pheasant, c.m. & l., circa 1922, 9¾in. high. $224 £140

ELIZA SIMMANCE

A jug painted with vine leaves and purple grapes against a pink ground, c.m.l. & c., date letter for 1910, 8½in. high. $240 £150

A ewer with incised brown foliage and impressed clusters of fruit, r.m. & e., circa 1895, 12in. high. $330 £220

A jug with incised yellow leaves and impressed brown berries against a mottled blue ground, c.m.l. & c., date letter for 1909, 9in. high. $272 £170

A vase with incised pale blue flowers and brown foliage edged in white, DLE, circa 1895, 14in. high. $420 £280

A waisted jar and cover painted with rings of white flowers, c.m.l. & c., date letter for 1907, 6½in. high. $270 £180

A large ribbed vase painted with blue leaves and pale blue flowers, c.m.l. & c., date letter for 1906, 15in. high. $560 £350

ELIZA SIMMANCE

A vase modelled with orange
trees against a blue sky with
birds, c.m.l. & c., date letter for
1905, 13in. high. $390 £260

A pair of vases with incised and
painted pale blue cornflowers,
r.m. & e., circa 1895, 11¼in.
high. $525 £350

A vase painted with purple and
green flowering plants, c.m.l. &
c., date letter for 1915, 12¾in.
high. $270 £180

A vase painted with purple
berried trees against a pale blue
background, c.m.l. & c., date
letter for 1907, 13¾in. high.
$420 £280

A pair of ribbed vases with
incised green leaves, c.m.l. &
c., date letter for 1910, 10in.
high. $360 £240

A vase with a frieze of green
trees edged in white, c.m.l. &
c., circa 1907, 13½in. high.
$448 £280

A vase painted with pink roses,
the stems brown against a pale
pink ground, c.m.l. & c., date
letter for 1910, 11in. high.
$256 £160

A pair of vases after Charles
Rennie Mackintosh, with incised
green roses, c.m.l. & c., date
letter for 1910, 9in. high.
$390 £260

A tall vase painted with pink
pomegranates growing against
a green ground, c.m.l. & c.,
date letter for 1910, 19¼in.
high. $480 £320

ELIZA SIMMANCE

A vase with incised blue flowers against a buff panel of white scrolls, r.m. & e., circa 1895, 14in. high. $375 £250

A pair of vases by Eliza Simmance, the smooth cream ground with incised and painted flowering plants, r.m., circa 1890, 7¾in. high. $368 £230

A vase painted with green and white pâte-sur-pâte blossom on a stippled buff ground, r.m. & e., circa 1892, 8¼in. high.
$256 £160

A vase painted with pale green foliate scrolls on a darker green ground, r.m., 1884, 8¼in. high.
$180 £120

A stoneware bracket clockcase by Eliza Simmance, inspired by 18th century models, r.m. & e., circa 1895, 14½in. high.
$1125 £750

A vase with shaped panels painted in pâte-sur-pâte natural colours with blackberries, r.m., 1881, 10¾in. high. $432 £270

A vase with shaped panels of incised stylised flowers in blue and green, r.m., 1884, 11in. high. $330 £220

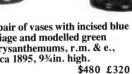

A pair of vases with incised blue foliage and modelled green chrysanthemums, r.m. & e., circa 1895, 9¾in. high.
$480 £320

A vase painted with pale green and blue leaf sprays, r.m., 1883, 9¼in. high. $320 £200

ELIZA SIMMANCE

A vase painted with blue dolphins and green sea-weed on a pale pink ground, c.m.l. & c., date letter for 1910, 10½in. high. $352 £220

A bowl painted with alternate floral panels in pale green and blue on a dark green ground, r.m., 1883, 7in. high.
$360 £240

A vase with incised green and brown sea-weed on an undulating green ground, c.m.l. & c., circa 1905, 9in. high. $288 £180

A jug with incised green and blue leaves on a buff ground, silver mount hallmarked 1875, 8in. high. $304 £190

A pair of vases by Eliza Simmance, the light grey ground with incised and painted brown plants, DSL, 1884, 7¼in. high. $512 £320

A pepper pot attributed to Eliza Simmance with pottery sprinkler and pierced base, r.m., 1884, 3¼in. high.
$120 £75

A vase by Eliza Simmance, the brown ground with three shaped panels, DSL, 1884, 8in. high. $180 £120

An octagonal plate painted with white pâte-sur-pâte flowers on a brown ground, c.m., 1878, 10in. diameter. $150 £100

An Art Union vase and cover painted with green and white pâte-sur-pâte blossom on a buff stippled ground, r.m. & e., circa 1895, 11½in. high.
$675 £450

ELIZA SIMMANCE

A cachepot with a broad pâte-sur-pâte band of Renaissance scrollwork and grotesques on an olive-green ground, dated 1882, 20cm. high. $640 £400

A vase by Eliza Simmance, the glazed buff ground with incised scrolls, r.m., 1881, 3¾in. high. $104 £65

A vase modelled with yellow apples growing from green branches, r.m., 1887, 9½in. high. $360 £240

A vase with incised royal blue flowers and leaves, r.m., circa 1887, 10in. high. $400 £250

A pair of cylindrical vases incised through the pale blue glaze onto the white body, c.m., 1879, 6¾in. high. $320 £200

One of a pair of vases with incised and modelled blue flowers, c.m.l. & c., date letter for 1909, 9³⁄₄in. high. $510 £340

A vase painted with green and white pâte-sur-pâte blossom on a Doulton and Slater buff lace ground, r.m., circa 1889, 6½in. high. $208 £130

A tazza, the surface with an incised blue and brown leaf pattern, c.m., 1877, 6½in. high. $384 £240

A vase with an incised foliate design in pale green and dark blue, c.m., 1876, 7¼in. high. $240 £150

ELIZA SIMMANCE

A small vase by Eliza Simmance, the brown ground painted with white blossom and dark brown leaves, DSL, 1884, 4in. high. $165 £110

A vase with incised blue and white flowers and green foliage on a dark green ground, r.m. & e., circa 1895, 14in. high. $432 £270

A three-handled loving cup with green and white pâte-sur-pâte flowering scrolls, r.m., 1881, 6in. high. $330 £220

A pair of vases painted with long-tailed blue birds, c.m.l. & c., date letter for 1916?, 15¾in. high. $600 £400

A mustard pot by Eliza Simmance, the handle and body with incised blue leaves, o.m., 1875, 2¼in. high. $120 £75

A pair of vases by Eliza Simmance, with incised and painted brown garden birds and white daisies, DSL, 1885, 10¼in. high. $592 £370

ELIZABETH SMALL

A vase, the mottled blue ground with incised bright blue flowering foliage, r.m., 1884, 12½in. high. $360 £240

A pair of vases with incised blue and brown berried foliage on a mottled pale blue ground, r.m., 1884, 10¼in. high. $420 £280

A beaker, the buff ground with incised blue foliage, the entwined panels painted with white flowers, r.m., 1882, 4¾in. high. $152 £95

EMILY STORMER

A pair of vases, each with incised brown foliage above stiff green leaves, c.m., 1877, 10¾in. high $450 £300

A pair of flasks, with white bead work and an incised green, blue, and brown flower, c.m., 1878, 8¼in. high. $608 £380

A vase, the handles modelled as brown peacocks, the body with incised blue and yellow foliate scrolls, r.m. & e., circa 1892, 12½in. high. $525 £350

A candlestick, the base with carved green stylised leaves, r.m., 1886, 7in. high,
$210 £140

A mounted jug with incised green flowers on a blue ground with incised brown scrolls, r.m., 1884, 6¾in. high.
$240 £150

A jug, the buff body with impressed white circles and incised blue foliage and leaves, c.m., 1879, 9¼in. high.
$272 £170

GEORGE H. TABOR

A vase by G. H. Tabor with carved blue oak branches and acorns, r.m., 1883, 9¼in. high.
$195 £130

A pair of vases by G. H. Tabor, the green ground with overall incised blue masks, r.m., 1884, 9½in. high. $510 £340

A vase by G. H. Tabor, the buff stippled ground with incised brown masks, urns and foliate scrolls, r.m., 1881, 10¾in. high. $300 £200

GEORGE TINWORTH

A baluster vase, the mottled brown ground with incised blue foliate scrolls, r.m. & e., circa 1892, 12½in. high. $600 £400

A frog and mouse group with frogs riding mice over a water jump, o.m., circa 1875, 4½in. high. $1875 £1250

A large jug, the hatched pale green ground with incised green and brown scrolls, o.m., 1874, 11¼in. high. $608 £380

A brightly glazed jug, the green ground with an incised shaped blue panel, c.m., 1876, 9¾in. high. $480 £300

A terracotta picture tile moulded and carved in low relief with Christ in the Garden of Gethsemane, DLE., circa 1880, 8½in.×8½in. $975 £650

A mounted jug, with an incised green foliate meander, c.m., 1877, 9½in. high $480 £300

An early pair of candlesticks glazed blue, with incised leaves each supported by two buff winged putti, o.m., 1875, 7in. high. $1425 £950

A monkey group inscribed A United Family, sitting on a bench and sheltering under an ochre umbrella, r.m. & e., circa 1892, 5in. high. $1875 £1250

An early vase, the burnt sienna ground with incised blue and pale green scrolls, o.u.m., circa 1871, 9¾in. high. $480 £300

395

GEORGE TINWORTH

A carpenter's bag attributed to George Tinworth, glazed in shades of brown, c.m., circa 1880, length 5in. $675 £450

The young carpenter, a brown salt-glaze model of a young boy planing at a bench, DLE, circa 1892, 5¼in. high. $975 £650

A salt cellar, the bowl and stand glazed blue and brown, the moulded drummer boy glazed buff, r.m., circa 1885, 3½in. high. $672 £420

A jug, the lovat ground with an incised blue and buff fence decorated with pale blue bead work, c.m., 1879, 9½in. high.
$480 £300

A blue glazed frog playing cricket with a brown bat, r.m., circa 1880, 4¾in. high.
$1875 £1250

A tapering jug, the dark brown ground with an incised spiral band, c.m., 1878, 9¾in. high.
$480 £300

A jug, the light buff ground with incised scrolling blue foliage, o.u.m., circa 1872, 10½in. high.
$480 £300

A blue glazed group of two frogs riding on the backs of two mice, o.m., circa 1875, 3¾in. high.
$1500 £1000

One of a pair of vases, the buff ground with a painted white cellular pattern, c.m.l. & c., date letter for 1903, 10¾in. high.
$832 £520

GEORGE TINWORTH

A candlestick with incised blue leaves on a brown ground, c.m., 1876, 8¼in. high. $675 £450

A quatrefoil inkwell with cover and liner, the body with incised blue leaves, c.m., 1879, 4in. high. $1152 £720

Mr Pickwick, the modelled figure glazed green and standing on a brown chair inscribed Pickwick Bachelor, DLE, circa 1895, 5in. high. $825 £550

A vase with a mottled blue ground with incised dark brown scrolls and applied flower heads, o.u.m., circa 1872, 9½in. high. $480 £300

A model of a green frog riding a yellow and brown penny farthing, r.m., circa 1880, 4½in. high. $1875 £1250

A vase, the brilliant royal blue ground with incised mottled brown scroll-work, r.m. & e., circa 1892, 8in. high.
                                 $448 £280

A standing salt cellar, supported by moulded blue and brown dolphins, incised Doulton & Co., Lambeth, with the monogram GT, 4in. high. $525 £350

A double vase, the moulded buff putti with a blue garland standing on a brown sphere, r.m., circa 1885, 5¼in. high.
                                 $975 £650

The eagle and the fox, a fable group with a brown trumpet-shaped vase, incised Doulton & Co., Lambeth, circa 1882, 7in. high. $1875 £1250

GEORGE TINWORTH

A letter rack, the stoneware compartments with incised leaves and flowers in brown, blue and green, r.m., circa 1885, length 14in.

$975 £650

The drunken husband, a modelled fable group with an old man wearing a blue night-gown, sitting on the detachable lid of a coffin, r.m., 1881, length 7¾in. $2250 £1500

A brown salt-glazed group modelled with a frog painting and a country mouse holding an upturned basket of fruit, circa 1885, length 7in. $2250 £1500

A pair of mantle ornaments, each moulded with a kneeling figure of a young Egyptian boy, r.m., circa 1885, 9in. high.
$1040 £650

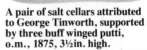

An umbrella stand modelled naturalistically with a brown glazed kangaroo holding a dark brown ring, incised Doulton Lambeth, circa 1885, 38¾in. high. $3750 £2500

A pair of salt cellars attributed to George Tinworth, supported by three buff winged putti, o.m., 1875, 3½in. high.
$1500 £1000

A brown glazed stoneware mirror frame carved in low relief with a head and shoulders portrait of a young girl, c.m., circa 1880, 18in. high.
$880 £550

The Fables Clock, the stone-ware case modelled with the interior of a house and numerous figures and animals, the base inscribed: H. Doulton & Co., Lambeth, and G. Tinworth, circa 1882, 11¼in. high. $7500 £5000

The vain jackdaw, a fable group with the peacock's display forming a fan-shaped vase, incised H. Doulton, Lambeth, circa 1882, 6in. high.
$1875 £1250

A boy kicking a tambourine, DLE, incised Doulton Lambeth, circa 1895, 5in. high.
$750 £500

A kneeling boy playing a harp, RDE, circa 1902, 3³/₄in. high. $750 £500

A moulded and modelled figure of a seated boy with a cittern, DLE, circa 1895, 4³/₄in. high.
$750 £500

A cello played by a seated boy, DLE, circa 1895, 4¹/₂in. high. $75 £50

A boy with a white face playing a cello, RDE, circa 1902, 4³/₄in. high.
$750 £500

An upright piano played by a boy seated on a stool, printed circle mark: Doulton Lambeth England, circa 1895, 4in. high. $975 £650

A brown glazed figure of a boy playing a rebec, DLE, circa 1895, 5¹/₄in. high. $750 £500

A seated boy playing a harp, DLE, circa 1895, 4in. high.
$750 £500

A cornet played by a seated cross-legged boy, RDE, circa 1902, 4¹/₂in. high. $750 £500

A boy leaning against a cylinder playing a concertina, DLE, circa 1895, 4¹/₂in. high.
$750 £500

A boy playing a fiddle supported on his foot, DLE, circa 1895, 4¹/₄in. high. $750 £500

A seated figure with a light buff face playing a French horn, RDE, circa 1902, 4³/₄in. high.
$750 £500

GEORGE TINWORTH, MOUSE FIGURES

A mouse group with a white mouse playing a tuba and a little mouse playing the cornet, o.m., circa 1875, 3³/₄in. high.
$1360 £850

A knight from a chess set glazed white, r.m., 1884, 3¼in. high.
$520 £325

Play Goers, the group glazed pale brown with a blue and brown shaped base, r.m., 1886, 5¹/₄in. high. $2000 £1250

A mouse group with a green vase and pale green mice playing ochre double-basses, r.m., circa 1885, 5¼in. high.
$1360 £850

A tea party with pale green mice seated on brown chairs, the hollow oval base inscribed Tea-Time Scandal, r.m., circa 1885, 3½in. high. $1875 £1250

A green vase on an oval base modelled with a pale green mouse playing a brown harp, and a little mouse playing a cornet, r.m., circa 1885, 5¼in. high. $1360 £850

A blue spill vase, with a mouse sleeping on the ground with a broom, r.m., circa 1885, 4in. high. $675 £450

A menu holder with a white mouse playing a harp and a little mouse playing a double bass, r.m., 1885, 3¾in. high.
$1360 £850

A bishop from a chess set, glazed white with a blue mitre, r.m., 1884, 3in. high. $520 £325

GEORGE TINWORTH, MOUSE FIGURES

A menu holder with two white mice playing a double-base and a cornet, inscribed Doulton Lambeth, circa 1880, 3¾in. high. $1360 £850

A brown glazed mouse-pawn holding an axe, r.m., 1884, 2½in. high. $520 £325

A tobacco jar, the lid with a green mouse sitting on a blue cushion smoking a brown pipe, r.m., circa 1885, 7in. high. $560 £350

A musical group with a blue vase and pale green mice, one playing an organ and the other a triangle, r.m., circa 1885, 5½in. high. $1360 £850

A mouse group moulded with three minstrels on a green mound, r.m., circa 1885, 3¾in. high. $1440 £900

A mouse-pawn glazed white, inscribed Pawn, r.m., 1884, 2¹/₂in. high. $520 £325

A model of a blue mouse eating a currant taken from the brown bun on which he sits, circa 1880, 2¾in. high. $480 £300

A blue spill vase modelled with a pale green mouse sitting comfortably in a brown chair, r.m. & e., circa 1895, 4½in. high. $675 £450

A menu holder with a little mouse about to steal an apple from a stall, r.m., circa 1885, 3¾in. high. $1360 £850

GEORGE TINWORTH,
PLAQUES

A Guard's Chapel maquette glazed green, blue and brown, and modelled with the parable of the lost piece of silver, inscribed H. Doulton & Co., Lambeth, G. Tinworth, circa 1877, 12in. x 9in. $1275 £850

A cream coloured terracotta self-portrait plaque inscribed G. Tinworth, circa 1913, 5³/₄in. x 4³/₄in. $675 £450

Tinworth's boyhood, a terracotta plaque modelled in high relief with George Tinworth as a young boy carving a small wooden bust in his father's wheelwright's workshop while his mother looks on, and a small boy watches for the possible arrival of his father, circa 1877, 8in. x 8in. $1125 £750

A terracotta tile picture moulded and carved in low relief with Samson, DLE, circa 1880, 8¹/₂in. x 8¹/₂in. $675 £450

A terracotta tile picture moulded and carved in low relief with the Saviour and woman at the well, DLE, circa 1880, 8¹/₂in. x 8¹/₂in.
          $675 £450

A stoneware maquette with blue and brown glaze of David and Goliath, inscribed: H. Doulton & Co., Lambeth, G. Tinworth, with impressed oval stamps Doulton & Co., Lambeth London, circa 1877, 12in. x 9in. $1275 £850

**GEORGE TINWORTH,
PLAQUES**

A Station of the Cross, a terracotta plaque modelled in high relief with some free-standing figures, incised: H. Doulton & Co., Lambeth, G. Tinworth, circa 1878, 6in. x 13in. $1500 £1000

The Four Seasons, a set of four plaques in salt-glaze stoneware carved in high relief and glazed in shades of brown and blue, circa 1875, 8½in.×4in. $2560 £1600

Zacchaeus, a terracotta plaque modelled in high relief and inscribed Make Haste and Come Down for Today I Must Abide at Thy House and He Made Haste and Come Down, and Received Him Joyfully, in ebonised frame, circa 1878, 6in.×13in.
$1500 £1000

GEORGE TINWORTH,
PLAQUES

A religious plaque glazed in brown and blue and carved in high relief with the
Resurrection, circa 1880, 12¼in.×4½in. $1500 £1000

A religious terracotta plaque modelled in high relief and inscribed When She Had
Heard of Jesus Came in the Press Behind and Touched His Garment, inscribed: H.
Doulton & Co., Lambeth, G. Tinworth, circa 1878, 6in.×13in. $1500 £1000

John the Baptist, a terracotta plaque modelled in high relief with Salome demanding
the head of John the Baptist, circa 1878, 6in×13in. $1500 £1000

GEORGE TINWORTH,
PLAQUES

The Nativity, a terracotta plaque modelled in high relief and inscribed And They
Came with Haste and Found Mary, and Joseph, and the Babe Lying in a Manger, the
Poor of this World Rich in Faith, circa 1878, 5½in. x 12in. $1500 £1000

A small plaque, the stoneware glazed blue and brown on a white ground and carved in
high relief, circa 1875, 8½in. × 4in. $1500 £1000

A Parable, a terracotta plaque modelled in high relief and incised And Jesus Called
a Little Child Unto Him and Set Him in the Midst of Them, Humble Yourselves
Therefore Under the Mighty Hand of God, circa 1878, 5½in. x 12in. $1500 £1000

BIBELOTS

A match striker advertising Dewar's Whisky, c.m.l. & c., 2½in. high.   **$110 £75**

A tray glazed green and brown, with a central blue horse's head, c.m.l. & c., circa 1910, 4¼in. diameter.   **$180 £120**

A match striker with Art Nouveau designs, DLE, 4in. high.   **$90 £60**

A moulded tray centred by a brown mouse and a tree stump, s.c.m., circa 1925, 4in. high.   **$285 £190**

The Suffragette Movement, an inkwell modelled as a baby with hinged head, R.D.E., circa 1905, 3¼in. high.   **$375 £250**

A circular ring tray, slip-cast with a glazed brown rabbit, s.c.m., circa 1925, 3¼in. high.   **$330 £220**

An inkwell moulded with a grumpy old lady, the green apron inscribed 'Votes for Women', c.m.l. & c., circa 1905, 3½in. high.   **$375 £250**

A book-end glazed dark brown and modelled with a monkey clutching its young, DLE, circa 1900, 6½in. high.   **$330 £220**

A moulded ring tray edged with green leaves on which sits a bird, DLE, Made in England, circa 1925, 4in. high **$300 £200**

BIBELOTS

A group of two white ducklings squatting on a blue rockwork base, c.m.l. & c., circa 1920, 4¼in. high.　　$300 £200

An ashtray match holder, 'Queen Anne's Mansion', DLE.　　$150 £100

A ring tray attributed to Vera Huggins with a brown and buff owl. s.c.m., circa 1925, 4in. high.　　$270 £180

A trump indicator attributed to Leslie Harradine, RDE, circa 1910, 4in. high.　　$525 £350

A slip-cast ring tray modelled with a nymph seated on a ring of flowers, s.c.m., circa 1925, 4¼in. high.　　$360 £240

A match striker attributed to Harry Simeon, modelled with an old soldier seated next to a hollow drum, DLE, 4¾in. high.　　$570 £380

A shaped blue and brown ring tray on which perches a large billed bird, s.c.m., circa 1925, 4¼in. high.　　$270 £180

A match striker attributed to Harry Simeon with a toper wearing a blue coat, s.c.m., circa 1925, 3¾in. high.　　$420 £280

A whist booby attributed to Leslie Harradine, moulded with a skeleton, RDE, circa 1910, 4¼in. high.　　$390 £260

COMMEMORATIVE WARE

A jug with white relief lettering 'Christopher Columbus sighted America Oct 12 1491', flanking a buff portrait of the explorer, r.m. & e., 6¹/₄in. high.
$180 £120

A shallow bowl, with applied moulded celadon portraits of the young Queen Victoria, r.m., circa 1885, 6in. diameter.
$300 £200

A jug commemorating Benjamin Disraeli, the buff portrait in high relief flanked by a quotation, r.m., 6¹/₂in. high
$210 £140

A tankard designed by John Broad commemorating the 1897 Jubilee, DLE, circa 1897, 6¹/₂in. high.
$144 £90

A bellarmine jug commemorating Queen Victoria's Golden Jubilee, r.m., 9in. high.
$240 £150

A coronation jug commemorating the accession of Edward VII and Queen Alexandra, DLE, circa 1902, 7¹/₂in. high.
$210 £140

A jug with a portrait of H. M. Stanley below the inscription 'Emin Pasha Relief Expedition 1887-1889', r.m. & e., 7¹/₂in. high.
$210 £140

A vase with a grey Doulton & Slater lace ground with an applied white bust of the Prince of Wales, r.m. & DSP., circa 1885, 6¹/₄in. high.
$208 £130

General Gordon, a jug commemorating his death at Khartoum in 1884, the buff ground with applied motifs and inscriptions, r.m., dated 1884, 7¹/₂in. high.
$210 £140

COMMEMORATIVE WARE

A three-handled mug commemorating the coronation of King George V in 1911, moulded with relief portraits in pale green and blue, c.m.l. & c., 6¼in. high.
$210 £140

A jug commemorating the Golden Jubilee of Queen Victoria, with green glazed portraits of the Young and Old Queen on a blue ground, DLE, 9in. high. $210 £140

A three-handled mug commemorating the hoisting of the flag at Pretoria, DLE, 6½in. high.
$330 £220

A jug commemorating the hoisting of the flag at Pretoria, DLE, circa 1900, 8¼in. high.
$300 £200

A double-handled tankard commemorating War in the Sudan, r.m., 1883, 6in. high.
$270 £180

An oviform vase made to commemorate the Coronation of Edward VII and Queen Alexandra in 1902, c.m.l. & c., 27.5cm. high. $240 £150

William Ewart Gladstone, the jug printed with quotations below the title, 'England's Great Commoner', DLE, 7½in. high.
$210 £140

A small jug designed by John Broad commemorating the 1887 Jubilee, DL, 4½in. high.
$165 £110

A Nelson jug, moulded with a portrait of the famous admiral flanked by naval battle scenes, c.m.l. & c., 8in. high.
$360 £240

DOULTON & SLATER'S PATENT

A jug, overlaid with a grey and brown lace pattern on which mistletoe is applied, r.m. & DSP, circa 1888, 7¾in. high. $144 £90

A pair of ewers with rough brown lace ground decorated with floral sprays, Slater's Patent 'Chine', DLE, 8in. high. $176 £110

A dated vase with brown lion's head handles and applied green foliage on a brilliant blue ground, r.m. & DSP, 1886, 11in. high. $375 £250

A jug, the dark green elaborate lace ground overlaid with two celadon classical portraits, r.m. & DSP, circa 1888, 7½in. high. $144 £90

A jug, the blue lace ground with the impressions of large ferns and overlaid with bouquets of ochre flowers, r.m. & DSP, circa 1890, 7in. high. $128 £80

A jug, with a grey lace panel overlaid with moulded white and brown foliage enclosing six oval medallions, r.m. & DSP, circa 1888, 6in. high. $195 £130

A vase decorated with bands of applied stiff leaves on a blue ground, Slater's Patent 'Chine', DLE, 11¾in. high. $136 £85

A pair of vases, each with three panels of white flowering foliage, r.m. & e. & DSP, circa 1895, 10in. high. $330 £220

One of a pair of vases with rough brown lace ground decorated with floral sprays, Slater's Patent 'Chine', c.m.l. & c., 14¼in. high. $208 £130

STONEWARE

DOULTON & SLATER'S PATENT

A vase with four moulded blue-glazed cupids and numerous stars superimposed on a plain dark green lace ground, r.m. & DSP, circa 1888, 10¼in. high.
$210 £140

A pair of vases moulded with celadon fish and dragon medallions, r.m. & DSP, 1885, 9¼in. high. $208 £130

A vase with rough brown lace ground decorated with floral sprays, Slater's Patent 'Chine', r.m. & e., 10¾in. high.
$180 £120

A jug with applied pale blossom in high relief and two moulded medallions, one of a snake and a mouse, r.m. & DSP, circa 1888, 7½in. high. $270 £180

A teapot with rough brown lace ground decorated with floral sprays, Slater's Patent 'Chine', r.m., 4¾in. high. $104 £65

A jug, with two impressed lace patterns and decorated round the centre with three white medallions, r.m. & DSP, circa 1888, 6¾in. high. $195 £130

A vase with blue handles and neck, the rough brown lace ground with incised brown and blue foliage, r.m. & e. & DSP, circa 1895, 12in. high.
$256 £160

A pair of oriental vases, applied flower head and brown dragons supporting beige lace impressed medallions, r.m. & DSP, circa 1888, 8in. high. $480 £300

A small vase with a blue lace frieze in which are the impressions of dark green ferns, r.m. & DSP, circa 1890, 5½in. high. $128 £80

411

MINIATURES

Miniature Doulton Lambeth stoneware mug with silver hallmarked rim and decorated with applied toping scenes.
$75 £50

A narrow vase with incised blue leaves and bead work, c.m., 1877, 5in. high. $140 £95

Miniature Doulton Lambeth stoneware jug with applied toping scenes. $70 £45

A bowl by Alberta Green, the buff ground with white bead work, r.m., 1887, 3¼in. high.
$104 £65

A double-handled vase with incised blue and green flowers, r.m. & e., circa 1892, 5in. high.
$120 £75

Doulton Lambeth miniature stoneware mustard pot with 'Colman's' in relief and applied moulding. $60 £40

A handled bottle with overall applied pink, brown, and white fan-shaped patterns, r.m., 1882, 3¼in. high. $88 £55

A miniature Doulton Lambeth stoneware caster with plated lid and applied moulding.
$75 £50

A jug by Edith Lupton with green panels painted in pâte-sur-pâte, c.m., 1878, 4¾in. high. $104 £65

412

STONEWARE

NATURAL FOLIAGE WARE

A 'natural foliage-ware' vase with the impression of veined leaves glazed olive-green, c.m.l. & c., circa 1905, 8¾in. high.
$176 £110

A pair of 'natural foliage-ware' vases with the impression of veined leaves, r.m. & e., 16¼in. high. $390 £260

A 'natural foliage-ware' vase, the rough ochre ground impressed with two types of reddish-brown leaves, DLE, circa 1895, 12½in. high
$240 £150

SIMULATED WARE

Cast iron, a covered box in silicon ware, simulating an iron 14 lb. weight, DSL & e., the silver handle hallmarked 1898. 5in. high. $110 £75

A silicon jug, the dark brown body simulating leather with stitched joints, 9¾in. high, with two beakers en suite, hallmarked 1899, 4¼in. high, DSL & e. $210 £140

A jug, the silicon body with copper coloured glaze and imitation joints, 7in. high, DSL & e., 1900. $112 £70

A Doulton & Slater's patent mug, simulating brown leather with stitched panels, r.m. & e. & DSL, the silver rim hall-marked 1893, 6¼in high.
$144 £90

A Doulton Lambeth silicon stoneware match holder with silver rim, simulating a leather cricket ball, 3in. diam.
$390 £260

A stoneware jug simulating a black jack, the dark brown leather with stitched joints, DLE, the silver rim hallmarked 1897, 9in. high. $144 £90

413

SILICON WARE

A small vase of hexagonal section inscribed on either side 'The Waning of the Honey-Moon', supported on an oval base with two hares sitting defiantly at either end, r.m., 1880, 4³/₄in. high. $900 £600

A pair of ewers decorated with applied slip flower, leaf and bead designs, DSL, circa 1891, 7¹/₄in. high. $150 £100

A jug with impressed flower and leaf motifs, and applied blue flower heads, DSL, 1884, 5½in. high. $140 £95

A jardiniere decorated with applied and incised flower and leaf designs on a blue ground, DSL, 7¹/₂in. high. $165 £110

A modelled owl with brown wings and feet, the detachable head and the body decorated with applied blue, green and white motifs, DSL, circa 1880, 7½in. high. $525 £350

A jardiniere decorated with blue floret and incised designs on a buff ground, DLE, impressed date for 1884, 6³/₄in. high. $136 £85

A water filter with incised, carved and applied decoration on a buff ground, DSL, 14¹/₂in. high. $525 £350

A tobacco jar decorated with applied blue and white beads, r.m., impressed date for 1888, 4¹/₄in. high. $75 £50

A tapering jug with overall incised diamond patterns, DSL, circa 1880, 8in. high. $96 £60

414

SPORTING SUBJECTS

A cricketing jug printed in dark brown, with portraits of George Griffin, W.G. Grace and K.S. Ranjitsinhji on the buff ground, DLE, 7in. high $525 £350

A silver mounted cycling jug and two beakers, DLE, circa 1900, the jug 8in. high, the beakers 4³/₄in. high.
$600 £400

A sporting jug commemorating the untimely death of F.J. Archer, the champion jockey in 1886, r.m., 6¹/₂in. high.
$390 £260

A golfing jug, sprigged in white, with the panels of the 'Last Ball', 'Putting' and 'Driving', impressed Lambeth mark, circa 1880, 20cm. high. $675 £450

A waisted mug applied with moulded white figures of a bowler, wicket keeper, and a batsman, DLE, circa 1900, 6in. high. $525 £350

A cricketing jug, the moulded relief figures against the buff salt glaze ground within stylised floral borders outlined in white slip and coloured in blue and green, DLE, circa 1900, 9¹/₄in. high. $675 £450

A silver mounted sporting tyg, DLE, circa 1900, 6in. high, the silver rim maker's mark H.W., Sheffield. $560 £375

A cricketer's mug applied with moulded white figures of a bowler, wicket keeper and a batsman, circa 1880, 15.5cm. high. $450 £300

A cricketing tyg, impressed Registration mark, r.m., and dated 1884, 6¹/₄in. high.
$675 £450

SPORTING SUBJECTS

A mug with applied moulded golfing vignettes of 'the drive', and 'the lost ball', DLE, circa 1900, 5in. high. $464 £290

A beaker with relief white figures of a shot putter, a runner, and a long-jumper, DLE, the silver rim hallmarked 1900, 5in. high. $300 £200

A cycling mug with three applied white figures inscribed Military, Road, and Path, DLE, circa 1900, 4¾in. high.
$420 £280

A cycling jug with three white vignettes, inscribed Military, Road and Path, DLE, circa 1900, 7¼in. high. $192 £120

A sporting jug with three moulded white vignettes, a man running, men playing football, and a man putting the shot, DLE, circa 1900, 8in. high.
$525 £350

A cricket jug with applied vignettes of a bowler, wicket keeper and a batsman, DLE, circa 1900, 7in. high. $675 £450

A rugby football jug with vignettes of two men kicking a ball, a scrummage and two of the men running with a ball, r.m., 1883, 7½in. high. $450 £300

A cricket mug with three applied figures of batsmen in high relief, registration mark of 1880, r.m., 1882, 5¼in. high.
$600 £400

A golfing jug with three applied white vignettes of 'the lost ball', 'putting', and 'driving', DLE, circa 1900, 7¾in. high.
$825 £550

ARTISTS & ASSISTANTS

Adelaide	AARON	aO
Christine	ABBOT	CA
Elizabeth J.	ADAMS	LA
Ella H.	ADAMS	aa A
Matilda S.	ADAMS	MsA
Margaret	AITKEN	AM
Mary	AITKEN	MA
Emily	ALLEN	EEA
Fannie J.	ALLEN	Æ
E.	ARCHER	1
Helen A.	ARDING	A
Mary M.	ARDING	M.M.A
Margaret M.	ARMSTRONG	
A.	ASKEW	⠒ a
Elizabeth	ATKINS	EA
N.	ATKINS	¢
Lizzie	AXFORD	a⠒
Louisa	AYLING	a
Agnes E. M.	BAIGENT	ÆB
Clara	BAKER	bbb
Emily	BAKER	b⠒b
Edith H.	BALL	B̄ bq
E.	BANFIELD	bd
Eliza S.	BANKS	EfB
Alice M. E.	BARKER	b⠒ B AMB
Clara S.	BARKER	CSB
G.	BARKER	-//-
Arthur B.	BARLOW	AB
Florence E.	BARLOW	FEB
Hannah B.	BARLOW	HB
Lucy A.	BARLOW	AL
Harry	BARNARD	B
V.	BARNES	V
W.	BARON	W3
Mary A.	BARRETT	bbO MAB
Ethel	BEARD	EB
George W.	BEARNE	B
Acidalia E. C.	BECK	AB
N.	BEEDEN	7
Arthur	BEERE	AB
G.	BENSON	℅
A.	BENTLEY	ر
Augusta M.	BIRNIE	b̄ AB
Florence M.	BIRT	qb
Ernest R.	BISHOP	B
Eborah	BISSMIRE	bOO
F.	BLACKSTAFFE	)-(
H.	BLAKE	b
O.	BOUCHER	br
Maud	BOWDEN	MB
Florence	BOWDITCH	⬛b⬛
Jessie	BOWDITCH	JB
Eliza	BOWEN	bb⬛
L. F.	BOWEN	LfB
Winnie	BOWSTEAD	W.B
Jessie	BOYCE	J.B

417

N.	BRAKE	⋀
Daisy	BRIANT	D.B
John	BROAD	ℬ
D.	BROND	F
F.	BROOKE	F
Rosina	BROWN	R B
Alice E.	BUDDEN	A&B. b
Mary	BUDDEN	obo
C.	BUNN	tᴜ
Alice L.	BURLTON	ALB. B
Georgina	BURR	b+ G.D.B
Eleanor	BURRELL	ⓑ
Emma A.	BURROWS	o b
Frank A.	BUTLER	℔
Mary	BUTTER	bb M.B
Mary	BUTTERTON	℔
Alice	CAFFIN	A
Alice	CAMPBELL	A.C.
Bertha M.	CAPES	ℬ
Mary	CAPES	M
Annie M.	CASTLE	A6.
Kate J.	CASTLE	c
M.	CAUTY	cᶜc m.b.
Margaret M.	CHALLIS	MM
Emily M.	CHANDLER	ℒ ℑ
J.	CHANDLER	ℭ
Clara	CHURCHER	▰c▰
Emily	CLARK	E.C.
Fanny	CLARK	FC
L.	CLARK	C
E.	CLARKE	⌇
Frances	CLEMENTS	⊊
Miss	COCKS	co
Edith M.	COLEMAN	ℰℰ
F.M.	COLLINS	CM
Rose	COLLINS	RC
Miss	CONGDON	c▰▰
Alice	COOKE	ccO
D.	CORDERO	ℊ
Joan	COWPER	Joan Cowper
Minna L.	CRAWLEY	ℳ ℳ
D.	CROFTS	≢
Ellen	CROSBY	ℰ
Emily	CROSBY	cOO
James R.	CRUICKSHANK	₵
Annie	CUPIT	cc
Lilian	CURTIS	L.C. c c▰
Lizzie M.	DAINTREE	dO
Olive	DALE	d▰
A.	DANIELS	ƚ
Kate M.	DAVIS	KD.
Louisa J.	DAVIS	⊕
Mary A.	DAVIS	ℳ d+
W.	DAVISON	ⅅ
Elizabeth	DAYTON	ⓓ
Mary	DENLEY	Ⓜ
Ada	DENNIS	A.D A) d▰
Florence	DENNIS	≢. dd▰
Miss	DOUTHWAITE	ddd
Amelia A.	DRAKE	A.D.
M.	DRIVER	⊕
A.	DUNCAN	⅃
Edward	DUNN	ℰ ℰ
W. Edward	DUNN	wℰ

Name	Mark
M. DUNTON	
Beatrice M. DURTNALL	D
Josephine A. DURTNALL	J.D
L. Imogen DURTNALL	ID dd
Alice K. EARL	
Florence EARL	e
Alice ECKENSTEIN	e A.E.
Lottie ECKENSTEIN	eeO
M. EDERMANIGER	
Emily J. EDWARDS	
Louisa E. EDWARDS	
Edward E. EGGLETON	
Fanny ELLIOTT	
Herbert ELLIS	HE
Sarah ELLIS	SE
C. EMERTON	E
Bertha EVANS	E e
Kate EVERETT	ee
John EYRE	J̵ Eyre
Miss FELTON	f
Ada E. FIMISTER	AF
Elizabeth FISHER	
Sarah FISHER	SF f
Emily A. FORSEY	fO E.A.F.
Minnie FORSTER	ff
E. FORSYTH	
Constance FOSTER	ff
M. FOX	M.F.
D. FRAMPTON	
Catherine FRANCIS	F
L. FRANCIS	f
May FREAKES	fr
Lizzie FRENCH	ff
A. E. FRENCH	AF
M. FRICKER	f
Elizabeth A. GADSDON	gg
Jessie GANDY	JG gO
Walter GANDY	W G
Nellie GARBETT	g EG
Ellen GATHERCOLE	NG g g
Sarah P. GATHERCOLE	g
Annie GENTLE	AG.
Kate R. GIBLIN	G gO
Elizabeth M. GILLMAN	g
Emily J. GILLMAN	
L. GOLDSACK	LG
Mary A. GOODE	gg
Laura GOODERHAM	ggO
M. GOODING	g
E. GRAVER	M
M. GRAY	
Alberta L. GREEN	AG
Edith GREEN	G
Laura GREEN	g
Lydia GREIG	OgO
A. GRIGGS	g
Alice E. GROOM	AG .G.
Jessie GUEST	gOO
Alice HALL	A
Elizabeth HAMILTON	E.H.
J. B. HARDING	BH
B. HARMAN	h
A. Leslie HARRADINE	LH
Edith HARRINGTON	hOO

419

Name	Monogram	Name	Monogram
Rosina HARRIS	*RH*	Florence L. HUNT	*J.H.*
Emma C. HARRISON	H	Jane S. HURST	H
Nellie HARRISON	hn	John HUSKINSON	H
W. HASTINGS	W	Ernest JARRETT	(symbol)
Lizzie HAUGHTON	HH	E. JESSETT	(symbol)
Ethel HAWKINS	h k	Doris JOHNSON	DJ
Emily M. HAWKSBY	hh■ *E.M.H.*	Florrie JONES	FJ
Emily HAYNES	hh	Gladys JOYCE	J
A. HAYS	AH	Ivy JOYCE	j
E. Violet HAYWARD	hd	Rosa KEEN	RK
L. HAYWARD	(symbol)	Edith KELSEY	J
Rosetta HAZELDINE	■h■	Edith L. KEMP	K EK
O. HEATH	hOh	Harriette E. E. KNIGHT	k
Alice G. HELLIS	h̄	Alice LACY	ll O
E. HENDERSON	(·)	Charlotte LAMB	CL
Alice M. HERAPATH	H h■ *A.M.H*	Ulrique LARCHER	UL
Edith HERAPATH	hh	J. LASHAM	(ll)
F. HEWITT	hhh	Marion LAYZELL	ll
K. HEYWOOD	(symbol)	Francis E. LEE	FEL
E. HIBBERD	(symbol)	Harriette E. LEE	L ll
Harriett E. HIBBUT	HEH	Nellie LEGGE	+1
Jessie HINCHLIFF	(h)	Esther LEWIS	£
Marion HOLBROOK	*MH*	Florence E. LEWIS	£
Eliza J. HOLLIS	hhO *E.H.*	Isabel LEWIS	L
Joan HONEY	JH	Ada C. LILLEY	ll:
Agnes S. HORNE	ho H̄	Mary M. S. LILLEY	l:
Annie HORTON	ho■	Frances M. LINNELL	(symbol)
Agnete HOY	AH	Ada LONDON	l
Eliza L. HUBERT	ELH	Emily A. LONDON	L EA
Vera HUGGINS	v·H H YH	Alice LONGHURST	l::
Kate HUGHES	h:: K.H	Jessie LORD	ld
Annie M. HULFORD	H.x.	Edith D. LUPTON	EDL

Name	Mark	Name	Mark
Annie LYONS	⅄ A.L.	Annie NEAL	n
W. W. MACKAY	⋏	Minnie NEAL	Z
B. MACNAE	⟨X	William J. NEATBY	WJN
Matilda MARLYN	m∎m	Bessie NEWBERY	BN
Emma MARRIOTT	⊟⊟	Josephine E. NEWNHAM	N
L. MARRIOTT	÷	Mary NEWSON	mn
Alice MARSHALL	A.M.	E. NOBLE	•n•
Mark V. MARSHALL	M·V·M	Lilla NOTTINGHAM	N
Susan MARSHALL	m	E. NORRIS	×⟩
Eliza MARTIN	m m	F. NORRISH	⌒ᴗ
Emma MARTIN	ℰM.	W. J. W. NUNN	𝕎
M. MARTIN	m∎m	Gertrude NYE	X
Matilda MARTYN	m m m	A. ORCHIN	Ⓐ
F. MASKELL	米	Lizzie PADBURY P	LP
Louisa MATTERSON	mO	D. PAINTER	𝒫
Ada MAYCOCK	m∎	Ellen PALMER	Op
Emily MAYES	m	L. PARKER	⬦
Emily W. MAYNE	EM.	William PARKER	ωp
John H. McLENNAN	J.H.Mᶜ	Emily J. PARTINGTON	EP
L. MEAR	HC	Lily PARTINGTON	LP
Miss MEDLICOTT	mt	Annie PARTRIDGE	P∎
Miss MIDDLEMISS	mi	Arthur E. PEARCE AℰP P
Alice MILBORROW	∎∎m	Georgina PEARSON	P∎P
Isabella MILLER M ℳ	S. PEARSON	P.
A. MILLS	⟨	Helena M. PENNETT	PP
Annie MILNE	ⓜ	F. PERRIN	⤳X
Mary MITCHELL	MM	E. PHEBY	∎P∎
Ada MORGAN	mOO	E. PICKERSGILL	Pᴘ
Joseph H. MOTT	JHM	F. POMEROY	FP
Iza M. MUNDAY	EM	Francis C. POPE P.	F·C·P
E. NAISH	⤵	A. POTTERTON	⤵Z
H. NAISH	ⓝ	R. PRITCHARD	R

Name	Mark	Name	Mark
M. PRYCE	⚥	Agnes D. SANDES	A.S.
Jane RABBIT	rrO	F. SAWYER	2
Emily RANDALL	E.R.	A. SAYERS	sO AS.
L. RAWLINGS	rg	Elizabeth A. SAYERS	EAS
Frank W. READER	R FR	Fanny SAYERS	sOO
Constance E. REDFORD	Æ r:	Rosalie SCOTT	ssO
George W. RHEAD	GWR	G. SHARPE	X
S. RICKARDS	r:	G. SHEARS	sr
Alice M. RITCHIN	AR	Elizabeth SHELLEY	E.S
Emma ROBERTS	ER	Annie SHELTON	ss:
Florence C. ROBERTS	FER	Lizzie SHETTLEWORTH	SL
Emily L. ROBINSON	R	F. SHIPMAN	Υ
Alice ROBJENT	(r)	A. SHUTE	ss:
Edith ROGERS	EER	Emma SHUTE	ES.
Isabel ROGERS	JR	Harry SIMEON	HS
Kate ROGERS	R	Eliza SIMMANCE	S ES
L. ROGERS	(II)	Alice M. M. SKIDMORE	OsO
Martha M. ROGERS	MMR	Mary SLATTER	M.S.
A. ROHSS	F	Elizabeth M. SMALL	EMS
Letitia ROSEVEAR	r	Katherine B. SMALLFIELD	KBS &c
William ROWE	WR	Mildred B. SMALLFIELD	MBS
M. RUCKSTUHL	mr	Alice G. SMITH	A.S.
E. RUDDOCK	E.R	Ellen B. SMITH	E.B.S S. ss
Agnes M. RUFF	AMR	E. SMITH	⌒
Ellen RUMBOL	ER RO	Frances SMITH	F.S.
Jane RUMBOL	rOO	Georgie SMITH	GS
Alice RUSSELL	:r:	Gertrude SMITH	S G
F. RUSSELL	⚡	Catherine A. SPARKES	CAS
Kate E. RUSSELL	rɹ	E. SPONG	(S)
Louisa RUSSELL	�7ᴸ R LR	A. SPURRELL	↓
Clara RYMER	rO	Fanny STABLE	F.S.
Susanna M. SANDERSON	S.S	Mary STAREY	SMS s:

Name	Mark	Name	Mark
Eliza STOCK	s	Bessie M. VARNEY	v
Emily E. STORMER	*EES*	C. VIGOR	C.V.
N. STRAKER	[symbol]	Emily M. VINER	E.Y.
Emilie M. STRATFORD	s•s	E. WAKELY	w•
E. STRATTON	st	Louisa WAKELY	w LW
Katherine STURGEON	[symbol]	K. WALKER	[symbol]
George Hugo TABOR	GTH	Helen WALTERS	X
Winifred TALBOT	tl	L. WATERS	L.W.
N. TAYLOR	[symbol]	Linnie WATT	Watt
Florence TEGETMEIER	to	Minnie WEBB	MW
A. Euphemia THATCHER	[symbol]	Jenny F. WEEKES	wO
Elsie S. THOMAS	tt	Emily M. R. WELCH	EW
Margaret E. THOMPSON	TM [symbol]	M. WELSBY	[symbol]
Marie E. THOMPSON	tx	Georgina WHITE	G.W.
Minnie G. THOMPSON	MGT	Onslow E. WHITING	O.W.
Mary Ann THOMSON	[symbol]	K. WHITTON	[symbol]
Walter THORNEMAN	[symbol]	H. WILKINSON	[symbol]
M. THORNTON	%	Arthur WILLCOCK	[symbol]
George TINWORTH	[symbol]	A. WILSON	[symbol]
H. TOLAND	[symbol]	Edgar W. WILSON	[symbol]
Louisa E. TOMKINS	[symbol]	Louie WILSON	[symbol]
F. TOMLYN	[11]	R. WILSON	[symbol]
Ada TOSEN	AT	Ada M. WOOD	wOO
A. TOSEN	[symbol]	Christina WOOD	C.W
Eleanor TOSEN	ttt	Emily WOOD	ww
Ellen C. TOWNSEND	t••	Edith H. WOODINGTON	W
A. TRANTER	[symbol]	Rosetta S. WOODS	RW
Ethel TRANTER	tOO	Ada L. WORTHEY	A.W.
A. TURNER	[symbol]	C. M. WRAY	[symbol]
M. UNWIN	U•	Bessie J. YOUATT	[symbol]
C. VARGAS	[symbol]	L. YOUNG	y
R. VARGAS	[symbol]	A. ZURCHER	Z

MARKS

DOULTON & WATTS — Impressed or incised mark used on stoneware, 1827–1858.

 Circular mark impressed with date, used on Doulton Ware and Lambeth Faience, 1876–1880.

DOULTON & WATTS
LAMBETH POTTERY
LONDON — Impressed or incised mark used on stoneware, 1827–1858.

 Impressed or printed mark used on stoneware, with England added after 1891, 1879–1902.

 Impressed or incised mark used on stoneware, 1827–1858.

 Rosette Mark impressed or printed on Doulton Ware and Lambeth Faience, 1880-1891.

(r.m. – rosette mark)

DOULTON
LAMBETH — Impressed or printed mark used on stoneware, with England added after 1891, 1858–1910.

H. DOULTON & CO. — Incised on panels and plaques by George Tinworth.

 Oval undated mark impressed on early Doulton Ware, 1869–1872.

(o.u.m. – oval undated mark)

DOULTON & SLATERS
PATENT — Doulton and Slater's Patent, 1885–1939.

(DSP – Doulton & Slater's Patent)

 Oval mark impressed and dated used on Doulton Ware, 1872–1876.

(o.m. – oval mark)

 Doulton Silicon Lambeth, with England added after 1891, 1880–1932.

(DSL – Doulton Silicon Lambeth)

Circular mark, impressed or printed, and sometimes dated in the centre, used on Lambeth Faience, 1873–1914.

(c.m. – circular mark)

 Rosette mark with England added, used on Doulton Ware and Lambeth Faience, 1891–1902.

(r.m. & e. – rosette mark and England)

 Impressed or printed mark, with England added after 1891, used on Lambeth Faience, 1873–1914.

DOULTON
LAMBETH
ENGLAND — Impressed or printed on small objects of Doulton Ware, 1891–1956.

Doulton Lambeth England, used on Doulton Ware and Lambeth Faience, 1891–1956.

(DLE – Doulton Lambeth England)

 Impressed or printed mark used on Crown Lambeth Ware, 1891–1905.

 Impressed or printed mark used on Impasto Ware, often dated in the centre and with England added after 1891, 1879–1914.

 Used on objects with a metallic coating, circa 1900.

 Printed mark used on Faience, with England added after 1891, 1880–1914.

 Printed on Morrisian Ware, 1901–1924.

 Impressed or printed on Marqueterie Ware, with England added after 1891, 1887–1906.

 Printed mark used on Brangwyn Ware.

 Impressed or printed on Marqueterie Ware, with England added after 1891, 1887–1906.

 Circle mark, lion and crown used on Doulton Lambeth and Burslem Ware, 1902–1956.

(c.m.l. & c. – circle mark, lion and crown)

 Impressed or printed on Marqueterie Ware, with England added after 1891, 1887–1906.

 Circle mark used on small objects of Doulton Lambeth and Burslem Ware, 1902–1956.

(RDE – Royal Doulton England)

 Impressed or printed on Marqueterie Ware, with England added after 1891, 1887–1906.

 Printed mark used on Royal Doulton Flambe, with 'Made in England' added from 1930, 1902–1930.

 Impressed or printed mark used on Carrara Ware, 1891–1924.

 Royal Doulton Flambe mark used on small pieces, 1904–1930.

Printed on Velluma Ware, 1911–1914.

Impressed or printed mark used on Persian Ware, 1920–1936.

Impressed or printed mark used on Doulton Ware, 1912–1956.

(s.c.m. – slip cast mark)

Printed mark used on Burslem stoneware, 1922–1927.

Printed mark used on Royal Doulton Titanian Ware, 1916–1929.

Circle mark and lion, impressed or printed on Doulton Ware, 1922–1956.

(c.m. & l. – circle mark and lion)

Printed mark used on Royal Doulton Titanian Ware, 1916–1929.

Printed mark used on Chang Ware with the monogram of H. Nixon, 1925–1940.

Printed mark used on hard-paste figures, 1918–1933.

Mark used mainly on wall plaques, 1925–1939.

Printed mark used on Chinese Jade, 1920–1940.

Printed mark used on Burslem earthenware, 1932 –present day.

Printed Flambe mark with Sung in script, 1920–1940.

Mark in current use, 1959–present day.

INDEX CHARACTER JUGS

INDEX OF FIGURES

INDEX

437

OTHER LYLE PUBLICATIONS

A Fortune in Your Attic   £16.95
86248-146-5

Advertising Antiques   £16.95
86248-147-3

Lyle Price Guide Art Nouveau & Deco   £14.95
86248-139-2

Lyle Price Guide China   £14.95
86248-140-6

Lyle Price Guide Clocks & Watches   £14.95
86248-149-X

Lyle Price Guide Dolls & Toys   £14.95
86248-141-4

Lyle Price Guide Furniture   £14.95
86248-150-3

Lyle Price Guide Militaria, Arms & Armour £14.95
86248-148-1

Lyle Price Guide Printed Collectables   £14.95
86248-156-2

1001 Antiques Worth a Fortune   £14.95
86248-118-X

Erotic Antiques   £14.95
86248-130-9